The Complete Works of
WASHINGTON
IRVING

Richard Dilworth Rust
General Editor

WOLFERT'S ROOST

Washington Irving

1851

WASHINGTON IRVING

WOLFERT'S ROOST

Edited by
Roberta Rosenberg

Twayne Publishers

Boston

1979

Published by Twayne Publishers

A Division of G. K. Hall & Co.

Copyright © 1979 by

G. K. Hall & Co.

All Rights Reserved

The Complete Works of Washington Irving

Volume XXVII

CENTER FOR EDITIONS OF
AMERICAN AUTHORS

AN APPROVED TEXT

MODERN LANGUAGE
ASSOCIATION OF AMERICA

®

Library of Congress Cataloging in Publication Data

Irving, Washington, 1783–1859.
Wolfert's Roost.

(The Complete works of Washington Irving ; v. 27)
I. Rosenberg, Roberta. II. Title.
PS2071.A1   1979   818′.2′07   79–4210
ISBN 0–8057–8519–1

Manufactured in the United States of America

ACKNOWLEDGMENTS

I am indebted to many persons and institutions. Particularly, I would like to express my thanks to Professor Lewis Leary and Professor Richard Rust of the University of North Carolina for their constant encouragement and guidance in the editing of this volume. I would also like to thank the many libraries which provided copies of the first edition and photocopies of the original manuscript. These libraries include The New York Public Library, the Henry E. Huntington Library, the University of Virginia Library, Knox College Library, the Redwood Library and Athenaeum, the Folger Shakespeare Library, the University of Pennsylvania Library, Yale University Library, and the University of North Carolina Library.

Among individuals, I am indebted to Professor Richard Beale Davis of the University of Tennessee and to Professor Ben Harris McClary of Wesleyan College for their preliminary work on *Wolfert's Roost.* Professor Joel Myerson of the University of South Carolina was also of great assistance in the final stages of the project.

I would also like to thank the Center for Editions of American Authors of the Modern Language Association which provided funds through its grant from the National Endowment for the Humanities. The University of North Carolina also provided me with student assistants who helped in the collation of the edition.

Finally, I owe a special thanks to Ronald Harlan Rosenberg for his untiring support throughout the project.

R. R.

Cleveland State University

CONTENTS

EDITORIAL APPENDIX

ILLUSTRATIONS

FRONTISPIECE

Washington Irving, 1851
An engraving by F. Halpin from
a sketch by Charles Martin

INTRODUCTION

In February, 1855, *Wolfert's Roost*, a collection of previously published sketches, appeared as Volume XV in Putnam's edition of *The Works of Washington Irving*. This book, "a hodge podge of his [Irving's] experiences from the age of eighteen to fifty-eight"[1] was actually a hastily sewn together patchwork quilt of pieces from the *Knickerbocker Magazine* and other popular periodicals. The two important periods in the development of this work were: (1) the years of 1832–1838, immediately preceding Irving's contributions to the *Knickerbocker,* and (2) the years of 1848–1854 before his decision to collect this periodical material into one volume. Both the pre-*Knickerbocker* era and the period in the late 1840's and early 1850's reveal Irving under financial, psychological, and literary pressures—his answer to all of these was to publish as quickly and as painlessly as possible.

References to the problems and solutions dating from the late 1830's are made in Irving's "Letter To the Editor of the *Knickerbocker,*" which was published in the issue of March, 1839. In it, Irving confesses that he is "tired of writing volumes; they do not afford exactly the relief I require; there is too much preparation, arrangement, and parade in this set form of coming before the public. I am growing too indolent and unambitious for anything that requires labor or display. I have thought, therefore, of securing to myself a snug corner in some periodical work, where I might, as it were, loll at my ease in my elbow chair, and chat sociably with the public, as with an old friend, on any chance subject that might pop into my brain."[2]

Irving's "indolence" provides only a partial explanation; finances forced his decision to accept a contract with Lewis Gaylord Clark and the *Knickerbocker Magazine*. Pierre Irving, his nephew and amanuensis, believed that the March letter had not conveyed "at what expense of feeling he [Irving] had just given up the task of 'writing volumes,' and bound himself to the irksome obligations of periodical labor. To have to draw upon a capricious fancy once a month for an article, was not a position he would have sought, but for the necessity pressing upon him for additional income."[3] The *Knickerbocker*'s offer of two thousand

1. Stanley T. Williams, *The Life of Washington Irving* (New York: Oxford University Press, 1935), II, 323 (hereafter cited as STW).

2. From the letter to the *Knickerbocker* editor, March, 1839, quoted in Pierre M. Irving, *The Life and Letters of Washington Irving* (New York: G. P. Putnam, 1864), III, 148 (hereafter cited as PMI).

3. PMI, IV, 149.

dollars a year was too great a sum for Irving to reject. So, for a period of three years, he wrote twenty-four tales and essays for Clark and the *Knickerbocker*.

Yet the reasons for Irving's decision in 1839 to rummage among his old trunks and their burden of "capricious fancy" cannot be explained by indolence and financial insecurity alone. The failure of all other literary projects precipitated his agreement with Clark. After seventeen years as a self-exiled American in Europe, Irving had returned home on May 21, 1832, with few literary prospects. The 1831 European financial crisis within the publishing field had abruptly ended his contract with Murray, his English publisher, and had forced him to look elsewhere. Depressed and insecure, he wrote to his brother Peter: "The restlessness and uncertainty in which I have been kept, have disordered my mind and feelings too much for imaginative writings. . . . The present state of things here completely discourages all idea of publication of any kind."[4]

Irving's repatriation into American life and literature was successful. In March, 1835, *A Tour on the Prairies* was published followed by *Astoria* (1836) and *Adventures of Captain Bonneville* (1837). However, during the late 1830's, his artistic and financial insecurities returned. "What has made me feel rather poor of late, and cautious as to extra expenses," he wrote to his sister, Mrs. Van Wart, "is the circumstances that for a long time past I have been unable to exercise my pen."[5]

In the fall of 1835, Irving took up an old project which he had long considered a challenging subject, a history of the conquest of Mexico. However, his plans were frustrated by William H. Prescott, the American historian, who had recently finished a history of Isabella and Ferdinand. Discovering that Prescott, to some extent, had anticipated him, Irving abandoned his work in January, 1839. In a letter to Prescott, the author expressed his disappointment at losing the opportunity to write on the conquest of Mexico: "Last autumn, after a fit of depression feeling the wont of something to arouse and exercise my mind, I again recurred to this subject. . . . In at once yielding up the theme to you, I feel that I am but doing my duty in leaving one of the most magnificent themes in American history to be treated by one who will build monuments in the literature of our country."[6] In 1844, Irving, then ambassador to Spain, again commented on the loss: "I doubt whether Mr. Prescott was aware of the sacrifice I made. This was a favorite subject, which had delighted my imagination ever since I was a boy."[7]

In the late 1830's Irving's sources for new books seemed to vanish.

4. From a letter to Peter Irving, November 6, 1831; PMI, II, 464.
5. From a letter to Mrs. Van Wart, December 1, 1838; PMI, III, 132.
6. From a letter to Wm. H. Prescott, January 18, 1839; PMI, III, 143.
7. From a letter to Pierre Irving, ca. 1844; PMI, III, 143.

But now the possibility of periodical publication in Clark's *Knickerbocker Magazine* enabled him to turn, as Stanley T. Williams has said, "the leaves of old notebooks" and to "write anything transmitable to cash."[8] Surely his decision to write for a magazine, after his unpleasant experience as editor of the *Analectic* from 1814–1815, demonstrates Irving's desperation at this time.

Although the *Knickerbocker* contract provided Irving with money and a medium for many of his half-written European and American sketches, he still hoped for some literary project which would "command a decent income independent of the irksome fagging of my pen."[9] The strain that had resulted from the *Knickerbocker* work is revealed in a letter to Mrs. Sarah Storrow, his niece, written two months after the expiration of the *Knickerbocker* contract: "I have written you two or three very uncomfortable letters lately, and am sorry for it; but I was discouraged by evils that seemed thickening around me, and felt doubtful whether I still retained the mental force and buoyancy sufficient to cope with them. Thank God, the very pressure of affairs had produced reaction."[10]

Irving's *Knickerbocker* commitment was both a physical and mental strain.[11] Because it was necessary to produce a new story every three weeks, he was no longer able to wait for mood or inspiration; he rummaged among his trunks for anything that could provide assistance with the result that unfinished and unpolished manuscripts were pulled out and submitted for publication. With the exception of the title story of "Wolfert's Roost," these old narratives were only superficially revised. Irving, who seemed to have viewed the *Knickerbocker* contract as the easiest way out of his difficulties, found it finally involving him in an arduous task. Even Longfellow, who once had admired him, now recognized that, "Washington Irving is writing away like fury in the

8. STW, II, 95.

9. From a letter to Mrs. Sarah Storrow, ca. December, 1841; PMI, III, 175.

10. *Ibid.*, p. 175.

11. The stories appeared in the *Knickerbocker Magazine* before they were published in *Wolfert's Roost*. The date immediately after the title designates the issue it appeared in: "Wolfert's Roost" (April, 1839), "The Birds of Spring" (May, 1839), "Mountjoy" (November and December, 1839), "The Bermudas" (January, 1840), "The Knight of Malta" (February, 1840), "A Time of Unexampled Prosperity" (April, 1840), "Sketches in Paris" (November and December, 1840), "Broek: or the Dutch Paradise" (January, 1841), "Guests from Gibbet Island" (October, 1839), "The Early Experiences of Ralph Ringwood" (August and September, 1840), "The Seminoles" (October, 1840), "The Count Van Horn" (March, 1840), "Don Juan—A Spectral Research" (March, 1841), "Legend of the Engulphed Convent" (March, 1840), "The Phantom Island" (July, 1839), and "Recollections of the Alhambra" (June, 1839).

Knickerbocker;—he had better not;—old remnants—odds and ends,—
Sleepy Hollow, and Granada. What a pity."[12]

The situation preceding the 1855 publication of *Wolfert's Roost* was
similar to the pre-1839 period. Financial and literary insecurity again
forced Irving to submit to a demanding contract with George Putnam
for the republication of his complete works and the supplying of other
new volumes, an undertaking for which he was ill prepared. His tenure
as ambassador to Spain, from 1842–1846, had left little opportunity
for writing. When in 1843, Carey, Lea, and Blanchard, his American
publishers of *Tales of a Traveller* and *A Tour on the Prairies,* ceased
publication of his works, Irving remarked that "everything behind me
seems to have turned to chaft and stubble."[13] As in his pre-*Knickerbocker*
period, he was depressed and alarmed; once again he turned to his
old trunk of literary bits and pieces for a means of support. Pierre
remembered that in April, 1847, his uncle had informed him of a new
literary project: "That you may not be frightened at my extravagance
and cut off supplies . . . I must tell you that I have lately been working
up some old stuff which had lain for years lumbering like rubbish in
one of my trunks, and which, I trust will pay . . . [my] expense."[14]

At this time Irving had also accepted a position in the law office of
his brother, John Treat Irving. This occupation was abruptly ended,
however, when George Putnam offered to republish Irving's collected
works, and on July 26, 1848, the contract was signed.[15] As in his contract
with Clark, Irving now began to publish at a harried pace; from 1849
to 1859, thirteen works were revised and four new works, or nine
volumes, were written. The printing and selling of approximately eight
hundred thousand books was proof enough of Irving's success. But by
the early 1850's, he was beginning to show the strain.

The *Life of Washington,* written and published almost simultaneously
with *Wolfert's Roost,* "had engrossed his [Irving's] mind to such a
degree, that, before he was aware, he had written himself into feeble-
ness of health."[16] Yet despite the book's detrimental effect upon its

12. Henry Wadsworth Longfellow, *The Letters of Henry Wadsworth Longfellow,*
ed. Andrew Hilen (Cambridge, Mass.: Harvard University Press, 1966), II, 163.
13. From a letter to Ebenezer Irving, ca. October, 1842; PMI, III, 229.
14. PMI, III, 401–2.
15. Irving was paid royalties on all books sold as well as a guaranteed income
for three years. The first year he received $1,000, the second $2,000, and the
third $3,000. It was also understood that new volumes would be published under
this arrangement.
16. PMI, IV, 321–22. Pierre is actually repeating the account given by Theodore
Tilton, the editor of the *New York Independent.* The words are, presumably,
Tilton's interpretation of a visit with the elderly Washington Irving at Sunnyside,
November 7, 1859.

author, Irving hurriedly commenced work on Volume II. The author confessed: "I live only in the Revolution . . . I have no other existence now—can think of nothing else."[17] The February, 1855, publication of *Wolfert's Roost* was seemingly bypassed in Irving's effort to complete the biography of George Washington. Sketches which had been hastily slapped together for the *Knickerbocker Magazine* were as speedily processed for inclusion in *Wolfert's Roost*. George Haven Putnam "had to entice the papers of that book from his [Irving's] drawers, for," he said, "I doubt whether he would have collected them himself."[18]

Ironically, when this volume of unrevised pieces appeared in 1855, it was thought by some to be an entirely new collection. Pierre believed that *Wolfert's Roost* seemed, "no doubt, to the majority of its readers, a new publication."[19] Critics on both sides of the ocean, heralded the book as a great addition to the Irving canon. Putnam noted that he saw Irving "affected actually to tears on reading some of the hearty and well-written personal tributes which the volume called forth."[20] The *Spectator* in London complimented the book despite some reservations about the originality of its material: "it is possible that *Wolfert's Roost* is a collection of fugitive pieces; or it may be revised selections from the author's papers while he has yet spirit to make them—a child, as it were, of his old age. . . . There is intended nothing new in it, either as respects subject, substance or style; but neither is there any falling off. . . . In some points perhaps there is even an improvement . . . greater mellowness . . . droll slyness."[21]

In New York, the *United States Magazine and Democratic Review* emphasized the lighter, romantic aspects of the work which earned for Irving the title of "official dowager of all . . . feminine literature of America."[22] This magazine complimented those, "inimitable stories which . . . form a most delightful melange, neither so long as to be considered tedious, nor too brief to arouse our interest. The stories possess the most diversified character, and are laid in every age and clime: we cordially recommend the book to the attention of all readers of standard romance as the most valuable contribution that has been made of late to the light literature of our day."[23]

17. PMI, IV, 196.
18. George Palmer Putnam, "Memories of Distinguished Authors," *Harper's Weekly* 27 (May, 1871), 496.
19. PMI, IV, 186.
20. Putnam, "Memories," p. 495.
21. Anon., "Washington Irving's *Chronicles of Wolfert's Roost*," *Littell's Living Age*, March 24, 1855, p. 723; first published in *The Spectator* 27 (January, 1855).
22. STW, II, 106.
23. Anonymous review of *Wolfert's Roost* by Washington Irving, in *United States Magazine and Democratic Review* 35 (March, 1855), 236.

Although Irving's sentimentalism seems to be moving against the currents made by such important nineteenth-century writers as Hawthorne and Emerson, in many respects, he is their precursor. His mixture of legend and history, fact and fiction, resembles Hawthorne's romances. Irving preferred to describe his writings as legends "rather than giving them the more pretending name of History or Chronicle. It enables me to indulge with less reserve or disquiet in those apocryphal details which are so improbable, yet so picturesque and romantic. Did I claim for these wild medleys of truth and fiction the dignity and credence of a history, I should throw discredit upon my regular historical works."[24]

A contemporary reviewer in the *Athenaeum* also discovered a link between the two writers. The critic remarked that it was "possible that 'Wolfert's Roost' . . . may have owned the same original as belonged to the 'house of seven gables,' peopled by Mr. Hawthorne with human beings so peculiar and pathetic."[25]

Neither Irving nor his publisher spent much time in editing or revising *Wolfert's Roost*. The two impressions of the first edition (1855) as well as the 1856, 1859, and 1861 impressions are replete with broken letters, misspellings, and dropped punctuation marks.[26] The alteration of the Putnam address on the title page was the only substantive revision.[27] Although *Wolfert's Roost* sketches had been reprinted throughout the century,[28] most of them have remained almost identical to the periodical stories published in the 1830's.[29]

24. STW, II, 106.

25. From a letter to Peter Irving, July 8, 1835; PMI, III, 74.

26. See discussion in the Textual Commentary for more information on this subject.

27. The only change that takes place is that in the "10 Park Place" printing, the word "flushed" (1A, 154.2–3) is moved to the next line instead of broken as "flush-ed" on lines 2–3, as in the "12 Park Place" printing. For this reason, every word on 1A, 154 in the "10 Park Place" imprint is moved up five spaces. Yet only the spacing and not the content is different.

28. The English edition published by Constable, *Chronicles of Wolfert's Roost, and Other Papers* (Edinburgh: T. Constable & Company, 1855) is the only authorized first English edition. It is not printed from the same plates as the Putnam American first edition and differs from the latter in a few substantives. Thus, it must be assumed that final setting copy for the American and English editions is not identical. The setting copy used for the printing of the Constable edition does not incorporate the last minute proof changes which Irving made for the American edition. The English first edition, therefore, is closer to the periodical in both accidentals and substantives. See the List of Rejected Substantives, pp. 315–18, for a list of the English variants.

29. One major change from periodical to first edition was the deletion of Geoffrey Crayon as the pseudonym for Irving. Although seventeen magazine stories designated Crayon as author, only two *Wolfert's Roost* tales retained Crayon.

HISTORY OF THE NORTH AMERICAN SKETCHES

After seventeen years in Europe, from 1815 to 1832, Irving, in an attempt to silence those American critics who considered him a European writer, decided to write on American subjects. However, after a few initial successes like *A Tour on the Prairies* (1835), he found himself, once more, without a workable American subject. Alarmed by this dearth of material, he rummaged among his American and European notebooks and unpublished fragments for inspiration. While the majority of the *Wolfert's Roost* North American tales are derived from native sources, a few sketches are adaptations of foreign material.

The sources for "The Creole Village," "Wolfert's Roost," "The Early Adventures of Ralph Ringwood," and "The Seminoles" are found in the frontier notebooks which Irving began in 1833. "Mountjoy" and "Guests from Gibbet Island," however, can be traced to the author's earlier travels in Europe. The plot and setting of "Mountjoy" were taken from the 1817 tour of Scotland while the theme of "Guests from Gibbet Island" was derived from a trip to Dresden, Germany in 1823.

"Wolfert's Roost"

This story, which receives its name from Irving's home near Tarrytown, Westchester County (which he later renamed "Sunnyside"), is divided into three "Chronicles." Chronicle I discusses Wolfert Acker, the original resident of the Irving residence, who was one of the "privy councillors" of Peter Stuyvesant. Chronicle II describes the period of Jacob Van Tassel during the "dark and troublous time of the revolutionary war,"[30] while Chronicle III, which first appears in the 1855 edition, relates the peaceful postwar era of Diedrich Knickerbocker.

Only two pages of manuscripts are extant, and these are only notes for the final version. This manuscript fragment gives the lineage of the Van Tassels in a form quite different from the finished story. It notes that the "First Van Tassel, or Van Texel, married a squaw named Plantasse. Had an imminent estate called Crab meadow on Long Island . . . the estate might have been recorded some time before the war; but he would not get the Van Tassels to acknowledge their descent from the Squaw."[31] When Irving introduces the Van Tassels in Chronicle II, he deletes the miscegenation and instead emphasizes "Jacob Van Tassel, a valiant Dutchman of the old stock of Van Tassels . . . as

30. *Wolfert's Roost* (New York: G. P. Putnam & Company, 1855), 15. All further references to the book (hereafter cited as WR) will be from this edition unless otherwise noted.
31. Miscellaneous holographs, in the Berg Collection of the New York Public Library.

originally written was Van Texel, being derived from the Texel in
Holland, which gave birth to that heroic line" (7.10–14).

The three Chronicles are from different sources. Chronicle I borrows
material from Samuel Purchas' *Purchas His Pilgrimes*.[32] The Purchas
legend, which Irving cites in a footnote and quotes from directly, is
found in "The Third Voyage of Master Henrie Hudson ... Written by
Robert Juet of Lime-House."[33] Juet, Hudson's first mate on a voyage
from Newfoundland to Cape Cod, describes a drinking party between
an Indian couple and the sailors. Although the punctuation and spelling
differ slightly, Irving quotes verbatim from Juet's description.

Chronicles II and III were derived from some of the same sources
as the *Knickerbocker History of New York*. A clue to the source of these
two chronicles is found in a letter which Irving wrote to Abel S. Thurston
about the author's long conversations with Van Tassel; Van Tassel is
described as "a type of the beligerent yeomanry of Westchester County,
who figured in the border feuds of Skinner and Cowboy in the time of
the Revolution."[34] Irving's allusion to "Skinner and Cowboy," a phrase
which is repeated in "Wolfert's Roost," suggests that some material
for the stories was received from Van Tassel.

Although the majority of tales in *Wolferts' Roost* were unrevised, the
title story underwent extensive alteration from its first appearance in
the April, 1839, issue of the *Knickerbocker Magazine* to the book edition
in 1855. Ostensibly there are four basic substantive differences between
the 1839 and 1855 versions: (1) the lack of Geoffrey Crayon as narrator
in the 1855; (2) the deletion of the introductory "letter to the editor"
which accompanied the 1839 story; (3) the addition of Chronicle
divisions in the 1855 text; and (4) the addition of a new third Chronicle
in the 1855 edition.

This new third Chronicle allows Irving to continue the saga of
Wolfert's Roost into future books. At the end of the story, the narrator
notes, "Reader, the Roost exists," and may "return ... in future pages"

32. Samuel Purchas, *Hakluytus Posthumus or Purchas His Pilgrimes* (Glasgow:
James MacLehose, 1906), XIII, 333–74.

33. *Ibid.*, p. 368. "And our Master and his Mate determined to trie some of
the chiefe men of the Countrey, whether they had any treacherie in them. So
they tooke them down into the Cabbin, and gave them so much Wine and Aque
vitae, that they were all merrie: and one of them had his wife with him, which
sate so modestly, as any of our Countrey women would doe in a strange place.
In the end one of them was drunke, which had beene aboard of our ship all
the time that we had been there; and that was strange to them, for they could
not tell how to take it."

34. From a letter to Abiel S. Thurston, December 11, 1855, quoted in
"Reminiscences of Washington Irving," ed. Lewis Gaylord Clark, *Knickerbocker
Magazine* 55 (January, 1860), 224.

(15.33, 31–32). Irving's decision not to continue the story can probably be explained by his advanced age and his preoccupation with other works.

Few critics commented on this tale or the essential differences between the 1839 and 1855 versions. Instead, most reviewers discussed the biographical parallels between Irving's residence at Sunnyside and this apparently fictitious Wolfert's Roost. One critic compared this tale with Hawthorne's *The House of the Seven Gables* and preferred Irving's "old fashioned stone mansion."[35]

"The Birds of Spring"

Although Irving made numerous notes about birds and scenery in his traveling journals, no manuscript exists of "The Birds of Spring." Until its first appearance in the May, 1839, issue of the *Knickerbocker Magazine,* little was known about this brief tale of birds, men, and morals. Unlike the extensively revised "Wolfert's Roost," this story was not substantively altered in 1855. Basically, the only major modifications were in the deletion of "Geoffrey Crayon, Gent." as narrator and in sentence arrangement. Irving switched and reversed phrases and clauses when he revised this tale for inclusion in *Wolfert's Roost.* In the *Wolfert's Roost* description of a phoebe, this "juggling" of sentence structure is especially evident: "he [phoebe] gradually gives up his elegant tastes and habits; doffs his poetical suit of black, assumes a russet dusty garb, and sinks to the gross enjoyments of common vulgar birds. His notes no longer vibrate on the ear..." (IA 36.1–4, T 20.33–35). The *Knickerbocker* version was altered but it retained the same ideas and tone: "his notes cease to vibrate on the ear. He gradually gives up his elegant tastes and habits; doffs his poetical and professional suit of black, assumes a russet or rather dusty garb, and enters into the gross enjoyments of common, vulgar birds" (KnM 437.3–6). With the exception of a few word changes ("sinks" for "enters") the only revisions are structural.

"The Birds of Spring" belongs to the conservative, sentimentalist literature popular in the ladies' magazines of the nineteenth century. Irving's two choices of poetic inspiration and allusion in this sketch are Alexander Wilson (1766–1813) and John Logan (1748–1788) who share Irving's love of moralized nature. Although Irving's treatment of the phoebe has been compared to Shelley's depiction of the skylark,[36] it

35. Anonymous review of *Wolfert's Roost, Athenaeum,* February 17, 1855, p. 192.

36. Here I must disagree with Edward Wagenknecht's interpretation of this sketch: "He [Irving] praised the skylark before Shelley made it fashionable to do so, and there is one paper in *Wolfert's Roost* ('The Birds of Spring') in which he may be said to have anticipated John Burroughs" (*Washington Irving: Moderation Displayed* [New York: Oxford University Press, 1962], 42).

must be noted that this sketch opens with the narrator's confession that, while in his "quiet residence in the country, aloof from fashion, politics, and the money market," he was left "rather at a loss for important occupation" and thus driven "to the study of nature and other low pursuits" (17.2–4). Since this tale was "extracted into almost every paper in the Union,"[37] it must have been well received by those nineteenth-century readers who looked to nature for ethical instruction.

"The Creole Village"

Upon his return from Europe in 1832, Irving set upon various frontier expeditions which took him to Kentucky, the Carolinas, and Virginia. In 1835, he published *A Tour on the Prairies*. Possibly "The Creole Village" was intended for insertion in this volume but was withdrawn and published two years later in Henry Herbert's annual, *The Magnolia* (New York: Monson Bancroft, 1837).

Irving's first mention of the story is found in a letter to the editor of the *New York American*.

> Sir: I perceive a prolonged and angry discussion in the papers, with which my name has been strangely mingled. The manner in which I have become implicated is this: In a trifling sketch of a French Creole village, inserted in one of the latest annuals, I observed, incidentally, that the Virginians retain peculiarities characteristic of the times of Queen Elizabeth and Sir Walter Raleigh. By this remark I have drawn upon me some very ungracious language from a writer of North Carolina, who charges me with a gross violation of the truth of history.... If I am wrong in this idea, I plead ignorance rather than submit to the imputation of wilfully misstating facts; but I believe that the most accurate researches will establish the correctness of the casual remark which has brought upon me so much ire.[38]

Yet Irving's letter reveals much about his attitude toward his tale. One may infer from Irving's ironical tone, that "The Creole Village," a "trifling tale," is not important enough to fight about.

After writing this letter to the editor, Irving soon forgot his sketch. Even when it was to be included in *Wolfert's Roost*, he spent little time on either its revision or correction. Thus the 1855 version, with the

---

37. PMI, IV, 148.

38. From a letter to the editor of the *New York American*, January 4, 1837; PMI, III, 100–101.

exception of some minor changes,[39] is substantially the same. Once again Geoffrey Crayon is dropped as the narrator of the tale. Other alterations are basically made for conciseness. In addition, he switches the order of independent and dependent clauses as he did in both "Wolfert's Roost" and "The Birds of Spring." The only major addition to the 1855 edition is a footnote at the end of the story, in which Irving explains that since the time of the sketch's first appearance, the expression "almighty dollar' has "passed into current circulation" (27.28). He adds that he means no disrespect for religion by this statement; in fact, he wishes to show disrespect for those who treat money as if it were God and thus "an object of worship" (27.41–42). Aside from this footnote, however, "The Creole Village" was left unrevised from the 1830's to 1855.

"Mountjoy"

The story of Mountjoy and his youthful follies is actually one section of a novel which Irving began during his tour of Scotland in 1817.[40] Many of Irving's friends had urged him to write a novel-length work, and on their advice and as a personal experiment, the artist of the short tale commenced a work entitled *Rosalie*.[41]

The details of Irving's first novelistic endeavor are not clear,[42] but the fragmentary notes for *Rosalie* show an important resemblance to passages of "Mountjoy." Basically, the story of Rosalie has many of the same character types, situations, and thematic concerns. Stanley T. Williams notes that "The plot of the story of Rosalie, so far as it may be reconstructed is concerned with the love of a philosophical and mildly asinine young man for the volatile Rosy. She is rescued, apparently from the Richmond fire. The lover meets Rosy unexpectedly in society in Philadelphia. There is a quarrel and a reconciliation. We see the hero at home with his father and sisters. Rosy goes to Kentucky.

39. All revisions of substantives in the copy-text are noted in the List of Emendations. This list includes every one of Irving's alterations throughout the composition of *Wolfert's Roost*.

40. I am indebted to Stanley T. Williams' edition of a *Tour in Scotland 1817* (New Haven: Yale University Press, 1925). Mr. Williams annotated the notebooks and also compared passages of "Mountjoy" with the novel fragment "Rosalie."

41. The story of "Rosalie" suggests Irving's desire to write a novel. Williams notes that "the creator of 'Buckthorne and His Friends' and 'Mountjoy' was not altogether a writer of essays and short stories" (*ibid.*, 93, n.).

42. Williams observes that "This collection of puzzling notes is apparently the rough draft of a novel . . . the whole scheme of Irving's projected story remains obscure" (*ibid.*, p. 17).

Another scene, presumably the last, shows the lover and Rosy happy together in the mountains, and the children about them."[43]

However, Williams does not mention the most obvious and conclusive proof that Mountjoy is indeed a part of Rosalie. On the last page of the Mountjoy manuscript (MSa, 93.18, T, 61.1), the name of "Rosalie" is crossed out and is replaced through interlining by the name of Mountjoy's lover, "Julia." Other parallels between the two stories are found in specific details. Rosalie's lover speaks of "His idea of settling in the wilderness with Glencoe for a companion."[44] Similarly, Mountjoy will live in a "perfect fairy bower, buried among sweets and roses. . . . Glencoe, too, shall no more be the solitary being that he now appears. He shall have a home with us" (40.2–6). After a careful comparison of the two texts, it is clear that the unfinished novel supplied some of the material for the "Mountjoy" short story.

While *Rosalie* is the primary source for this story, other fragments from the manuscript of the *Tour of Scotland*, such as "Personalia: Reading, Writing, and Miscellaneous notes," supply many of the details for "Mountjoy." In his Scottish journal of January 1, 1818, Irving reminisced that, "my father dubbed me the Philosopher from my lonely & abstracted habits—but I was the least of a philosopher as a boy Robinson Cruesoe [*sic*]."[45] Mountjoy also discusses his mental condition when he sees the footprint in the woods: "This was sufficient for an imagination like mine. Robinson Crusoe himself, when he discovered the print of a savage foot on the beach of his lonely island, could not have been more suddenly assailed with thick-coming fancies" (36.8–11).

Irving's reasons for abandoning both *Rosalie* and his Scottish material, sometime between 1817 and 1819, are explained by numerous stories. At first Irving intended to use the Scottish material in the *Sketch Book* which he was preparing for publication in 1819–1820. However, he abandoned Rosalie when the story received a poor reception from his friends. An explanation of the circumstances surrounding this decision is given by Lewis Gaylord Clark:

And speaking of "The Sketch-Book," we may mention here a circumstance connected with the story of "Mountjoy," which afterward appeared among the "Crayon Papers" in the *Knickerbocker*. One evening three or four eminent friends, among them the great artist *Washington Allston* and *Leslie*, happened to meet at *Mr. Irving's* lodgings in London; and as he was about at that time to submit to a prominent London publisher the manuscript of "The Sketch-

43. *Ibid.*, p. 95.
44. *Ibid.*, p. 96.
45. *Ibid.*, p. 103.

Book," he proposed to read two or three of the papers for the entertainment of his friends. "I then," said *Mr. Irving*, "took up 'Mountjoy,' and had read several pages, when happening to look up, I *thought* I saw signs of flagging interest in the countenance of *Allston*. I presently closed the manuscript, with a remark to the effect that 'if they were not tired of listening, I confessed to some fatigue in reading so long.' This incident decided me: I did not finish the sketch, but laid it in my trunk, and never even glanced at it again for seventeen years."[46]

Clark then brings the manuscript of "Mountjoy" up to the date of its insertion in the *Knickerbocker* by describing the events around its publication. "The neat, uninterlined and unerased manuscript, uniform with that of all the other articles which appeared at the time in the 'Sketch-Book' was as fresh as yesterday, when it was placed in our hands for insertion in the *Knickerbocker*."[47]

Although the extant manuscript of "Mountjoy" is not in the condition of which Clark speaks, it is the first tale of North America for which a manuscript exists. The revisions in the manuscript suggest that Irving's original intention was not serial publication—the final form it took in the November and December, 1839, issues of *Knickerbocker Magazine*. Since the manuscript was written as one continuous story, Irving had to paste a printed title page into the original manuscript on page 48 (T, 42), and had to write a new introduction to section two, which stated, "After the mortifying occurences, mentioned in the last number."[48]

Because many of the manuscript revisions were made by excising parts of pages and pasting in revisions, it is difficult to assess the extent to which Irving modified the original story for periodical publication. Generally, the visible alterations were minor.

Another problem arises when analyzing revisions between manuscript and first magazine publication. The author's handwritten manuscript is not extant for MSa, 56–77 (44.23–56.5) and MSa, 91–92 (60.1–60.33). A later printed version of the story replaces the missing manuscript. Therefore, it is difficult to estimate the amount of revision that the original version underwent before it was published in *Knickerbocker*.

The 1855 version of "Mountjoy" is not the first book publication. In 1845, Lewis Gaylord Clark included some of the more popular *Knickerbocker* stories in a collection entitled *The Knickerbocker Sketch-Book* (New York: Burgess, Stringer & Co.). Little is known about Irving's

46. Clark, "Reminiscences of Irving," p. 224.
47. *Ibid.*, p. 224.
48. The original manuscript of "Mountjoy" is in the Manuscript Division of the New York Public Library.

authorial control of this version, and thus it has little authority in the establishment of the 1855 edition. Irving's first mention of "Mountjoy," after its publication in 1839, was in April 27, 1849, when, in a letter to Clark, he wrote, "I will thank you to send me the two numbers of the Knickerbocker which contain the story of Mountjoy."[49] The date of this letter is important because it followed Putnam's offer to publish Irving's entire work. Irving had retained republication rights on the *Knickerbocker* stories and was probably contemplating the collection which would become *Wolfert's Roost* six years later. More importantly, one can infer from this letter that Irving used periodical and manuscript as the basis for the 1855 edition. The similarities in both substantives and accidentals in periodical and 1855 versions suggest that this assumption is verifiable.[50] The only major substantive change from *Knickerbocker* to *Wolfert's Roost* is the deletion of Geoffrey Crayon as Irving's pseudonym.

Even in the most positive of reviews, "Mountjoy" is praised only as "a drawing-room tale of the best annual quality."[51] Such reactions partially explain the story's unfinished, unrevised condition. One internal proof of Irving's insecurity about the sketch is found in the last paragraph which states, "How far I succeeded in adopting the plan, how I fared in the farther pursuit of knowledge, and how I succeeded in my suit of Julia Somerville, may afford matter for a farther communication to the public, if this simple record of my early life is fortunate enough to excite any curiosity" (60.43–61.4). Since the periodical ends with a "To Be Continued" it is probable that Irving wished encouragement before he would proceed with the story. One may assume, therefore, that either the tale failed to "excite any curiosity" or Irving, himself, lost interest. In any case, his enthusiasm was not particularly great in 1855, for he did not even revise the last paragraph in order to create the illusion of a finished piece. Whether he still retained some hope that his story would finally be recognized is unknown.

"The Bermudas: A Shakespearian Research"

Although "The Bermudas" purports to be a "Shakespearian Research" into the source materials for *The Tempest*, it is actually a collection of

49. From a letter to Lewis Gaylord Clark, April 27, 1849; the manuscript is presently owned by Herbert Kleinfield.

50. The parallels in both accidentals and substantives will be discussed in the textual history. However, this letter suggests that in the absence of manuscript, periodical, not first edition, should serve as copy-text.

51. Anonymous review of *Wolfert's Roost*, *Athenaeum*, February 17, 1855, p. 193.

pre- and post-Shakespearian shipwreck stories.[52] Irvin's interest in the legendary and mythical power of shipwreck was first seen in the story entitled "The Voyage" published in *The Sketch Book*.[53] When a ghost ship is spyed in the distance, the narrator of "The Voyage" mentions that "the sight of this wreck, as usual, gave rise to many dismal anecdotes,"[54] which may, in the future, "fill a volume with the reveries of a sea-voyage."[55]

The text of "The Bermudas"[56] is divided into two sections. The first section entitled "A Shakespearian Research," is an historical analysis of material available to Shakespeare at the time of *The Tempest*. It serves as a prologue to the tale of adventure that follows. The travel narrative, entitled "The Three Kings of Bermuda," takes its inspiration from Samuel Purchas' *His Pilgrimes*, but is essentially an original creation.

One of the main sources for the first historical section is Silvester Jourdain's *A Discovery of the Barmudas, Otherwise called the Ile of Divels. By Sir Thomas Gates, Sir George Somers, and Captayne Newport, with divers others* (London, 1610). This is the first published account of the voyage of the *Sea Venture* and eight other ships to Virginia. Sir Thomas Gates, and his men were going to the colony when their ship went off course and was wrecked off the coast of Bermuda. Presumably, an island of devils and strange occurrences, Bermuda turned out to be a habitable place in which the men survived. Jourdain's account of this shipwreck appeared in both 1610 and again anonymously in 1613 under the title, *A Plaine Description of the Barmudas, Now Called Sommer Islands*.[57] It is this 1613 version that Irving read and quoted in the opening pages of "The Bermudas."

In the sketch, Irving quotes almost verbatim from *A Plaine Description*. The Jourdain text notes that, "the Ilands of the Barmudas, as every man knoweth that hath heard or read of them, were never inhabited by any Christian or heathen people, but ever esteemed, and reputed, a most

52. Williams notes that Irving based many of his stories on early experiences. " 'The Bermudas' recalls *The Sketch Book* (cf. 'The Voyage,' pp. 19–27)" (STW, II, 325).

53. *The Sketch Book* (New York: G. P. Putnam & Company, 1865).

54. *Ibid.*, p. 24.

55. *Ibid.*, pp. 27–28.

56. The manuscript for this story suggests that it was written or rewritten at two different times. "The Bermudas: A Shakespearian Research" is written in an even, neat, almost vertical script, while "The Three Kings of Bermuda and their Treasure of Ambergris" is composed in a slanted, almost illegible hand. The two manuscripts are in different locations at present: "The Bermudas" is in the Folger Shakespeare Library; "The Three Kings" is in the Berg Collection of the New York Public Library.

57. Silvester Jourdain, *A Discovery of the Barmudas* (1610; reprinted, New York: Scholars' Facsimiles, 1940).

prodigious and inchanted place, affoording nothing but gusts stormes, and foule weather; which made every Navigator and Mariner avoide them, as Scylla and Charibdis; or as they would shunne the Devil him-selfe."[58] In "The Bermudas" Irving states that, " 'the islands of the Bermudas,' says the old narrative of this voyage, 'as every man knoweth that hath heard or read of them were never inhabited by any christian or heathen people, but were ever esteemed and reputed a most prodigious and inchanted place, affording nothing but gusts, stormes, and foul weather, which made every navigator and mariner to avoide them as Scylla and Charybdis, or as they would shun the divell himself' " (64.41–65.4).

The inspiration for the second manuscript about "The Three Kings of Bermuda," originated in the historical Bermuda narratives, but the events of the story were largely imaginative. The background for the three king's tale of ambergris was probably suggested by Jourdain's description of the treasures of Bermuda which included a "great store of pearle, and some of them very faire, round and orientall. . . . There hath beene like-wise found some good quantity of Amber Greece, and that of the best sort."[59]

The structure of the story was also provided by another source which Irving had made use of in "Wolfert's Roost." Chapter XVII of Purchas' *His Pilgrimes*[60] deals with the "Relations of Summer Ilands, taken out of M. Richard Norwood, his Map and Notes added thereto printed 1622."[61] The author of this Bermuda history describes the tale of three men who did not return to Virginia with the other members of the Somer's crew but instead, "staied voluntarily . . . [and] found in Sommerset Iland, which is a part of Sandys Tribe, a verie great treasure of Ambergreece to the valew of nine or ten thousand pound sterling . . . this new discovery of the Sommer Ilands, being thus made knowne in England, to the Virginia Company, by these men which returned, they sold it to some hundred and twentie persons of the same Company."[62] In Chapter XVI, "English Voyages to the Summer Iland," Purchas gives the names of the

58. *Ibid.*, pp. 8–9.

59. *Ibid.*, pp. 16–17.

60. It should also be noted that Jourdain's narrative was incorporated into Volume IX, Chapter XVI of Purchas *His Pilgrimes*: "Let us now heare the Relation sent from an English Colonie planted there under the governor of Master Richard Moore. This following Discourse hath been printed, and was added to a Tractate of Master Silvester Jordan" (p. 173).

61. In fact, Volume XIX of Purchas *His Pilgrimes* generally discusses "English Plantations, Discoveries, Acts and Occurrents in Virginia and Summer Islands" (p. xxii).

62. *Ibid.*, XIX, 179.

three men who stayed behind as Carter, Water, and Chard, the same names as Irving's "three kings" of Bermuda.

Purchas also provides other details which will reappear in the Irving adventure story: "For Amber-greece and Pearle wee have not had leasure; in so few daies since our arrivall to give lookes out for the one, or to fish for the other; but the three men which were left there, have found of them both."[63] When adapting the Purchas narrative, Irving emphasizes only the "ambergreece" and adds much of his own humor and satire. Neither Jourdain nor Purchas mention the "royal" nature of Carter, Water, and Chard; obviously this is Irving's attempt to re-create a *Tempest* of his own. The influence of both Jourdain and Purchas is unmistakable, however. In the "Bermudas" manuscript, "ambergris" is spelled in the older form found in both Jourdain and Purchas. During a revision of the manuscript, Irving excised "ambergreece" and inserted the modernized version, "ambergris."

One allusion within the story provides an approximate date of composition for this tale. When describing the idyllic environment of the island, Irving speaks of Fletcher's picture of the "halcyon lot of the fisher man" (63.26). This quotation, which is found in the author's journals[64] for the years 1819–1823, suggests that Irving was reworking the manuscript at the same time.

In any case, sometime before 1840, Irving decided to revise this two-part manuscript and to submit it for publication in the January, 1840, issue of *Knickerbocker Magazine*. Like most *Knickerbocker* stories, "The Bermudas" was virtually unrevised. In fact, one mistake in the magazine version demonstrates Irving's lack of care in revising or reading proofs. The manuscript designates the ship which carried the Somers' crew as the "Sea-Venture" (64.16). When the *Knickerbocker* printed the story, it called the vessel the "Sea-Vulture" (KnM, 19). This rather important difference, which was overlooked by Irving in reading proof for both periodical and 1855 editions, is indicative of the author's haphazard publishing procedure. The only major alteration in the 1855 *Wolfert's Roost* is the deletion of "By the Author of the Sketch-Book" after the story title.

"The Bermudas" is one of Irving's more successful attempts to combine history and legend, fact and fiction. One contemporary reviewer captures the essence of his talent for uniting the historical and fictional: "Here are scraps of history, mingling with pieces of fiction—the real and the unreal relieving each other in a manner that is very agreeable."[65]

63. *Ibid.*, p. 176.
64. In *Journals and Notebooks, Volume III, 1819–1827*, ed. Walter A. Reichart (Madison: University of Wisconsin Press, 1970), p. 580.
65. Anon., "Washington Irving," *The Eclectic Magazine* 34 (April, 1855), 548; first published in the *Dublin University Magazine* 45 (March, 1855), 370–78.

"Guests From Gibbet Island"

"Guests" is typical of Irving's American tales, for it is an adaptation of a
foreign story[66] into an American environment. Irving takes an anecdote
written by Jakob Grimm in *Deutsche Sagen* (Berlin, 1818), and expands
it into a sketch of American men and manners. As early as 1823, he
notes in his journal, that he is reading Grimm: "just arrived in Paris—
Have a long chat about Dresden—Airey stops at Hotel Richelieu read
in German work of Grimms."[67] However, the adaptation of foreign
material was a difficult, time-consuming task for Irving. He confesses
in a letter to his brother Peter that, "It will take me a little time to get
hold of them [the German subjects] properly, as I must read a little and
digest the plan and nature of them in my mind. There are such quantities of these legendary and romantic tales now littering from the press
both in England and Germany, that one must take care not to fall into
the commonplace of the day. . . . I must strike out some way of my
own, suited to my own way of thinking and writing."[68] This search for
originality at least partially explains why the first mention of his interest
in Grimm in 1823 and the publication of the story in 1839 are so far
apart. In addition, an analysis of the incomplete, extant manuscript of
"Guests" suggests the author's difficulties in composition. The pagination
in the upper-right-hand corner has been crossed out and renumbered as
many as three times. Obviously, the finished story was heavily re-
structured and rewritten.

The final transformation of the Grimm story, however, is an original
work. Walter Reichart, in a critique on Irving and Germany, describes
the Grimm story and compares Irving's version: "a drunken innkeeper
jocosely invites three men hanged on the gallows, whom he notices on
his way home, to sup with him. Arriving at home he finds them awaiting
him in his room. He collapses and three days later is dead. Irving expanded this anecdote of less than a page into a routine Knickerbocker
story with pirates, hidden booty, a Dutch innkeeper and his shrewish
wife, and the gallows guests who cause his death and haunt his house."[69]

---

66. Henry A. Pochmann in his article "Irving's German Tour and His Tales,"
Proceedings of the Modern Language Association 45 (1930), 1150–87 discusses
the method of transforming German tales into Irvingesque sketches. Walter A.
Reichart, *Washington Irving and Germany* (Ann Arbor: University of Michigan
Press, 1957) has an expanded study of Irving's use of German material.

67. From a journal entry dated December 24, 1823; published in the *Journal of
Washington Irving 1823–1824*, ed. Stanley T. Williams (Cambridge, Mass.: Harvard
University Press, 1931), p. 92.

68. From a letter to Peter Irving; quoted in *Washington Irving and Germany*,
p. 138.

69. *Ibid.*, p. 156.

Irving "Americanizes" the German tale through the creation of a fictional author, the Barent Van Schaick. In the October, 1839, issue of the *Knickerbocker Magazine*, "Guests from Gibbet Island" appears with a fictional "Letter to the Editor" from Van Schaick. Van Schaick, who has forgotten Jakob Grimm, the German originator of the story, provides the "source" of the tale:

> Sir: I observed in your last month's periodical, a communication from a Mr. *Vanderdonk*, giving some information concerning Communipaw. I herewith send you, Mr. Editor, a legend connected with that place; and am much surprised it should have escaped the researches of your very authentic correspondent, as it relates to an edifice scarcely less fated than the House of the Four Chimneys. I give you the legend in its crude and simple state, as I heard it related; it is capable, however of being deleted, inflated, and dressed up into very imposing shape and dimensions. Should any of your ingenious contributors in this line feel inclined to take it in hand they will find ample materials, collaterial and illustration, among the papers of the late Reinier Skaats, many years since crier of the court, and keeper of the City Hall, in the city of the Manhattoes; or in the library of that important and utterly renown functionary, Mr. Jacob Hays, long time high Constable, who, in the course of his valuable facts, to be rivalled only by that great historical collection, "The Newgate Calendar." (KnM, 342)

In adapting the story to a Dutch-American environment, he felt the need to negate its European roots.

Although few reviewers select this tale for special recognition, it must have been one of the more popular *Knickerbocker* stories, for Lewis Gaylord Clark included it in his *Knickerbocker Sketch-Book* (New York, 1845). The next book publication of "Guests" is an interesting one since it contains a puzzling passage, not included in any other version. In 1849, Putnam published *A Book of the Hudson*, a collection of Irving's essays. Although the *Hudson* version is almost identical, it contains one additional passage: "It is an old Spanish proverb worthy of all acceptions, that 'where God denies sons the devil sends nephews.' and such was the case in the present instance."[70] Although Irving claimed to have read proof for the Putnam volumes, this questionable passage cannot be accepted or rejected with certainty, since it was not included in any other edition of the story. The problem is made even more complex

70. *The Book of the Hudson* (New York: G. P. Putnam, 1849), pp. 15–16.

because the 1855 *Wolfert's Roost* does not retain the proverb either and the manuscript for this portion of the story is not extant.[71]

One major change found in the *Knickerbocker Sketch-Book*, *The Book of the Hudson*, and *Wolfert's Roost* versions of "Guests" is the elimination of the "letter" by Barent Van Schaick which appeared in *Knickerbocker Magazine*. "Guests" is now only a "Legend of Communipaw Found Among the Papers at Wolfert's Roost." However, this alteration is the only important one from 1839 to 1855. The substantive modifications in the *Wolfert's Roost* edition generally follow a pattern of revision seen in other stories. Words are reversed and modifiers are deleted, but the plot and tone are not altered significantly.

Despite the numerous publications of "Guests from Gibbet Island," there are relatively few critiques. Although the adventures of Vanderscamp are similar in nature to those in the "Legend of Sleepy Hollow," few reviewers saw any parallel. One contemporary analysis gave a favorable mention, however, when it noted that "Guests" had "all the freshness of fancy which we found in the *Sketch-Book*, all the sly, pleasant and most racy humor of 'Knickerbocker.' "[72]

"The Early Experiences of Ralph Ringwood"

This tale of "Ralph Ringwood" is a biographical account of William P. Duval (1784–1854), governor of Florida. Irving met Duval in Philadelphia in 1833 and amassed various bits and pieces of information in a notebook entitled, "Notes of Conversations with Wm. P. Duvall the original of Ralph Ringwood."[73] In "The Early Experiences of Ralph Ringwood," as well as in "The Seminoles," he gleans from these notes, "some anecdotes of his [Duval's] early and eccentric career in, as nearly as I can recollect, the very words in which he related them" (157.35). The events and situations described in "Ralph Ringwood" are unembellished because Irving found them, "so strikingly characteristic

71. Extant manuscript is "Guests from Gibbet Island," in the University of Virginia Library. The anecdote about the appearance of nephews (pp. 15–16) is only found in the *Hudson* edition and is not reprinted in any later version of the story; it can be assumed, therefore, that *Hudson* was not used as the basis for the 1855 edition of *Wolfert's Roost*.

72. "Washington Irving," *The Eclectic Magazine*, p. 547.

73. The manuscript of "Notes of Conversations with Wm. P. Duvall the original of Ralph Ringwood" is in the Berg Collection of the New York Public Library. Pierre M. Irving helps to date the composition of this story: "I pass over the first portion of this year 1833 which was spent in the bosom of the domestic circle at No. 3 Bridge Street, the residence of his brother Ebenezer, with the exception of a flying visit to Philadelphia, in the course of which he picked up his material for Ralph Ringwood" (PMI, III, 59).

of the individual, and of the scenes and society into which his peculiar humors carried him" (157.37–38).

Although there is no extant manuscript of the completed text, a rough draft is preserved.[74] This draft from the library of Pierre M. Irving, contains not only the events in chronological order, but also a prose style similar to the finished story.

Irving abandoned his notebook on Duval in 1833 and did not resume work on it until he decided to use the notes as the basis for a biographical sketch of the governor in the August and September, 1840, issues of *Knickerbocker*. The reasons why "Ralph Ringwood" was left in the trunks for approximately seven years are open to speculation. In a letter to Peter, his brother, on January 8, 1835, Irving explained that he had been delayed in publishing new work because of "the expectation manifested that I would publish something about this country." He felt that he was unable to prepare "anything, under whip and spur, that would satisfy" himself.[75]

Little is known about the reception of the *Knickerbocker* version of "Ralph Ringwood"; yet it certainly must have been popular because Clark included it in the *Knickerbocker Sketch-Book* (1845). Except for the missing biographical footnote about Duval, this version is virtually identical with that which appeared in the *Knickerbocker Magazine*. When "Ralph Ringwood" was included in *Wolfert's Roost*, it was equally unrevised. A few phrases were altered, but the story was similar in content.

"Ralph Ringwood" is at once typically American and typically Irvingesque, for it incorporates the classic initiation rite of the boy in the wilderness with the author's penchant for a sentimental sketch of men and manners. The young man who goes into the wilderness in search of fortune is rewarded with a stolen kiss from a future wife. Although Irving begins his tale as an initiation rite, it is an initiation into the drawing room, not the wilderness. One of Irving's contemporaries discussed the essential attraction of Irving's sentimentalized romantic style which is "indeed charming, so far as it goes. That is not, possibly, very far, as at least very deep."[76]

74. The original manuscript draft with notes of "The Early Experiences of Ralph Ringwood" is in the Huntington Library.

75. From a letter to Peter Irving, January 8, 1835; PMI, III, 65.

76. An anonymous review of Irving's collected works entitled "American Authorship" appeared in *Littell's Living Age*, June 7, 1853, p. 646; the piece was first published in the *New Monthly Magazine*.

"The Seminoles"

Like "The Adventures of Ralph Ringwood," the subject of "The Seminoles" is also William P. Duval. While "Ralph Ringwood" deals with the early boyhood of Duval, the three sketches which comprise "Seminoles" discuss the governor's two mature achievements: the peaceable removal of the Seminole Indians to Southern Florida,[77] and mass education for the Indian tribes.

The first sketch, entitled "The Seminoles," serves as an introduction to the other two,[78] and is an analysis of the customs and manners of the Indian tribe. Its source is William Bartram's *Travels Through North and South Carolina, Georgia, East and West Florida*,[79] which Irving, in some sections, quotes almost entirely, adding only a few connective phrases. Although Irving cites Bartram as the source of the material, his debt to the American naturalist is not fully revealed. One example of Irving's unstated reliance on Bartram can be found in a description of Florida:

Bartram, who travelled through Florida in the latter part of the last century, speaks of passing through a great extent of ancient Indian fields, now silent and deserted, over grown with forests, orange groves and rank vegetation, the site of the ancient Alachua, the capital of a famous and powerful tribe, who in days of old could assemble thousands at ball-play and other athletic exercises "over these then happy fields and green plains." "Almost every step we take," adds he, "over these fertile heights, discovers the remains and traces of ancient human habitations and cultivation." (182.17–22)

Irving's system of quotation is misleading, since he seems to be indebted to Bartram for only the words within quotation marks. When one studies the Bartram text, however, Irving's dependence upon the *Travels* is seen to be more extensive:

77. For William Pope Duval (1784–1854), see the *Dictionary of American Biography*, ed. Allen Johnson and Dumas Malone (New York: Scribner's, 1930), III, 557.
78. The other two tales are "Origin of the White, the Red, and the Black Men," and "The Conspiracy of Neamathla." Since they are completely different, it is necessary to treat them separately.
79. William Bartram, *Travels Through North and South Carolina, Georgia, East and West Florida* (1792; reprinted Savannah: The Beehive Press, 1973). All further references to Bartram are from this edition. In *Wolfert's Roost*, Irving gives the title as *Travels in North America*.

Passing through a great extent of ancient Indian fields, now grown over with forests of stately trees, Orange groves, and luxuriant herbage, the old trader, my associate, informed me it was the ancient Alachua, the capital of that famous and powerful tribe, who peopled the hills surrounding the Savanna, when, in days of old, they could assemble by thousands at ball play and other juvenile diversions and athletic exercises, over those, then happy, fields and green plains. And there is no reason to doubt of his account being true, as almost every step we take over those fertile heights, discovers remains and traces of ancient human habitations and cultivations.[80]

Every paragraph includes material with or without quotation marks which is taken directly from the pages of Bartram's narrative.[81] While the first and last paragraphs of the sketch are Irving's, the rest of "The Seminoles" is virtually copied from the *Travels*.

The sources for the second "Seminole" sketch entitled, "Origin of the White, the Red, and the Black Men," are historical rather than literary. Like "Ralph Ringwood," this tale is based on the "Conversations with Governor Duval" manuscript. As in the first sketch, Irving writes an introductory paragraph which gives the setting and time of the tale; the rest of the essay is interspersed with quotations from the "Conversations with Governor Duval."

The source for the third story, "The Conspiracy of Neamathla," is found in a separate manuscript about Duval entitled "Notes for the Conspiracy of Neamathla." This manuscript is actually a rough draft of the finished tale. Unlike the fragmented descriptions in the "Conversations with Governor Duval," the "Conspiracy" draft is written in complete sentences and paragraphs. The story of Duval's Indian pacification is retold in this manuscript.

The printer's manuscripts for two of the three stories in "The Seminoles" are extant. Only the notes of "Origin" are unrecovered.[82] Both manuscripts, written sometime between 1834 and 1840, show few revisions or additions but do provide some information about Irving's original intentions for these sketches. A "#4" is marked above the title of "The Seminoles" manuscript; underneath the title is a deleted heading which reads, "anecdotes of the Seminoles." If, in fact, this is

80. Bartram, p. 196.

81. The Bartram and Irving texts have similar passages on the following pages (pages of *Wolfert's Roost* [1855] are followed by pages from *Travels* [1792]): pp. 290 (209); 291 (209–19, 243); 292 (242); 293 (243).

82. Irving's notes for "Origin of the White, the Red, and the Black Men" as well as for "The Conspiracy of Neamathla" are now in the Huntington Library.

the fourth anecdote, then it is possible that the author wished to prepare a whole series of Seminole tales which would eventually be collected in book form. His plans for this larger work were probably abandoned, and in October, 1840, after the August and September installments of "The Experiences of Ralph Ringwood," Irving published these three Indian stories in the *Knickerbocker Magazine* as one sketch entitled "The Seminoles." The popularity of "The Seminoles" is evident by its numerous republications. "The Conspiracy of Neamathla" was a particular favorite and was reprinted in both *The New Yorker* (October 17, 1840) and *The Evergreen* (November, 1840). Both reprints of the story are duplicates of the *Knickerbocker* tale and are not important for the first book publication in the 1855 edition.

HISTORY OF THE EUROPEAN SKETCHES

On his first trip to Europe in 1804, Irving filled his traveling notebooks and journals with character sketches and descriptive passages of foreign surroundings. During his subsequent trips through England, France, and Germany, Irving, like Cooper, found a wealth of information unattainable in an America without a past or a tradition. In a letter to Henry Brevoort on November 6, 1816, Irving explains why he chose to visit Europe: "At the hotel where we put up we had a most singular whimsical assemblage of beings. I don't know whether you were ever at an English watering place, but if you have not been, you have missed the best opportunity at studying English oddities; both moral and physical.—I no longer wonder at the English being such excellent caricaturists, they have such an inexhaustible number and variety of subjects to study from."[83] Irving's interest in European caricature can be seen in stories like "The Contented Man," "Sketches in Paris," and "Broek." Each one depicts the individualistic and amusing European for a curious American audience. In many respects, Irving was the original innocent abroad, desiring to absorb as much of a foreign culture as possible.

Yet Irving was not only intrigued by the carefree and humorous national characteristics. Europe possessed somber legends and historical nightmares which would be likewise communicated to Americans: "I have just returned from the prison of Marie Antoinette. Under the palace of Justice is a range of cavernous dungeons, called the Conciergerie, the last prison in which criminals are so confined previous to execution.... My flesh crept on my bones as I passed through the regions of despair,

83. From a letter to Brevoort, November 6, 1816; quoted in *Letters of Washington Irving to Henry Brevoort*, ed. George S. Hellman (New York: G. P. Putnams' Sons, 1918), pp. 194–95.

and fancied these dens peopled with their wretched inhabitants. . . .
What a place for a queen, and such a queen! one brought up so delicately,
fostered, admired, adored.'[84]

In another letter to Brevoort, Irving defends his decision to remain
in Europe and to write on essentially "foreign" themes:

> You urge me to return to New York and say, nay ask whether I
> mean to renounce my country. For this last question I have no
> reply to make, and yet I will make a reply. As far as my precarious
> and imperfect abilities enable me, I am endeavouring to serve my
> country. Whatever I have written has been written with the
> feelings and published as the writings of an American . . . as to
> coming home, I should at this moment be abandoning my literary
> plans, such as they are. I should lose my labor in various literary
> materials which I have in hand, and to work up which I must be
> among the scenes where they were conceived.[85]

During the seventeen years that Irving remained in Europe, from
1815 to 1832, he gathered tales, sketches, and legends which would
eventually be published in books like *Tales of a Traveller* and *The
Sketch Book.* Others not published in the early 1830's would be
retained for future use; some of these discarded sketches were inserted
in periodicals and were published in *Wolfert's Roost* in 1855.

"A Time of Unexampled Prosperity"

In 1836, Irving speculated on Western lands and lost much needed
capital. In 1840, he confessed to Pierre that both he (Irving) and the
American public were, "gradually getting through this 'valley of
the shadow of death,' which the whole busy world has had some
years past to traverse, and I am in hopes that the severe lessons received this time will be held in remembrance, and have a wholesome
effect for the residue of our existence."[86]

For personal reasons, however, Irving chose not to depict the
Western land swindle of 1836. Instead he illustrated present-day
follies with a tale of past stupidities—the Mississippi Bubble affair
of early eighteenth-century France. During this financial scandal,
speculation on paper currency led to economic bankruptcy for France
and the disgrace of her political ministers. Pierre noted the connection
between Irving's "historical" tale and financial failures: "He [Irving]

---

84. From a sketch of Conciergerie, December 23, 1821; PMI, III, 34–35.
85. From a letter to Henry Brevoort, March 10, 1821; *Letters to Brevoort*,
pp. 353–54.
86. From a letter to Pierre Irving, April, 1841; PMI, III, 152–53.

had written feelingly on the subject, for he himself was now suffering the embarrassment arising from investments made in just such a time of fictitious prosperity and unreal fortunes."[87]

The sources which Irving consulted while researching this financial scandal are mentioned in Clark's "Editor's Tale," for April, 1840, and include MacPherson's *Annals of Commerce,* Saint Simon's *Memoires,* Dulaure's *History of Paris,* Villan's *Memoires,* Voltaire's *History of Parliament,* and Lacretelle's *History of France.*[88] However, when Irving finally wrote the essay, he ignored the histories and characterized the Mississippi Bubble as "a matter that has passed into a proverb, and become a phrase in every one's mouth, yet of which not one merchant in ten has probably a distinct idea" (97.1–3). He mentioned neither the sources cited by Clark nor the contemporary books in English which dealt with the scandal; his underestimation of his audience's knowledge would eventually hurt the chances for the story's success.

Although no manuscript is extant, it is possible to calculate the approximate date of composition through internal and external evidence. The narrator notes that the Americans "are suffering under the effects of a severe access of the credit system, and just recovering from one of its ruinous delusions" (97.5–7). This "ruinous delusion" was the previously mentioned Western land speculation of 1836. It is probable that the research for the story was done during Irving's trip to France in the mid–1820's and the final draft and introduction were written over ten years later in an effort to update the tale.

After its publication in *Knickerbocker Magazine* in April, 1840, "A Time of Unexampled Prosperity" was not reprinted again until the *Wolfert's Roost* edition. Like the American tales, "A Time" is largely unrevised. Only two substantive changes of any note are found: the deletion of "The Author of the Sketch-Book" as creator of the tale, and the alteration of the phrase "from the slow accumulations of industry" (118.43–119.1; KnM, 190)[89] to "from the safe pursuits of industry."

The essay received mixed criticism. Despite the fact that Irving showed "Geoffrey Crayon in a new light—that of the sound political economist," one reviewer was quick to add that the story was "skilfully done . . . yet the facts are well known, and they have no peculiarity beyond excellent workmanship."[90]

87. PMI, III, 152.

88. Lewis Gaylord Clark, "Editor's Table," *Knickerbocker Magazine* 15 (April, 1840), 350–51.

89. For the symbol KnM see the List of Abbreviations, p. 243.

90. "Washington Irving's Chronicles of *Wolfert's Roost,*" *Littell's Living Age,* p. 723.

"Count Van Horn"

In his April, 1840, *Knickerbocker* "Editor's Table," while discussing the "Time of Unexampled Prosperity," Clark mentioned another previously published short sketch of the same period. "The Count Van Horn," said Clark, "was but an episode in the veritable history. It was of the shares of *Law's* famous bank, it will be remembered, that the Count and his companions robbed the Jewish broker. Large quantities of this stock were borne about the persons of more than two thousands of the citizens of Paris; and the thirst for gain which this spurious wealth engendered, undermined the morals of half the community."[91] Clark also introduces an unpublished manuscript which, he contends, should have been included with "The Count Van Horn." The unpublished manuscript is an important introduction to "The Count Van Horn" because it describes the prerevolutionary lack of morals or reason in France. An unfortunate abbé, who leaves the dinner table to view a wagon load of prisoners going to the guillotine, waves to a friend in the cart. The abbé is unceremoniously thrown into the wagon and whisked away to his death. The senseless brutality of Parisian life is illustrated by the last few lines of the anecdote: "One chair, however, remained vacant; and after a while, the question began to be asked. 'Where is Monsieur the abbé? What has become of the abbé? Alas! by this time, the poor abbé was headless!'"[92]

This little moral tale, like "The Count Van Horn," warns those living in volatile times that the defenseless become unwilling victims of the strong, greedy, and irrational. In the "Count Van Horn" a similar incident is related: "About this time, the famous Mississippi scheme of Law, was at its height; or rather it began to threaten that disastrous catastrophy which convulsed the whole financial world. Every effort was making to keep the bubble inflated. The vagrant population of France was swept off from the streets at night, and conveyed to Harve de Grace, to be shipped to the projected colonies" (194.33–38). One night the helpless Count Van Horn, himself, is almost "swept" from the streets of Paris into the boat. Although he escapes with his life this time, like the abbé of the anecdote, he falls victim to general ruthlessness and irrationality. The many parallel incidents in "A Time of Unexampled Prosperity," and "The Count Van Horn," suggest that these two stories are companion pieces, originally composed in the 1820's in France and revised for publication in 1836–1837.

91. Clark, "Editor's Table," p. 350.
92. Barbara Damon Simpson, "A Footnote to Washington Irving," *The Yale University Gazette* 40 (April, 1966), 195–96.

The almost complete manuscript[93] reveals few substantive changes from original to *Knickerbocker Magazine* publication in March, 1840. The only major addition, which begins in the periodical and is carried through to the 1855 edition, is a passage concerning the malevolence of fate: "A circumstance which occurs in this part of the Count's story, seems to point him out as a fated man. His mother, and his brother, the Prince Van Horn, had received intelligence some time before at Baussigny, of the dissolute life the Count was leading at Paris. . . . They despatched a gentleman of the prince's household to Paris, to pay the debts. . . . the gentleman did not arrive at Paris until the day after the murder" (195.34–42). The sense of the helpless individual at the mercy of fate is a theme that was probably added during the period of 1836–1837, when Irving was revising the manuscript for publication in *Knickerbocker*.

With the exception of this rather important addition, Irving spent little time in revising the "Count Van Horn." Ironically, this lack of revision plays an important role in the formation of the final version. The rather stark, unkind portraits of the French aristocracy and system of justice are the opinions of the young Irving. Stanley Williams may have had "The Count Van Horn" in mind when he characterized the *Wolfert's Roost* narratives as "unrevised for the most part they breathe forth on many pages, unlike *Mahomet*, the spirit of Irving's youth."[94]

"Broek: Or The Dutch Paradise"

While stories like "A Time of Unexampled Prosperity" and "The Count Van Horn' deal with the unpleasant realities of human cruelty and greed, the sketch entitled "Broek: Or the Dutch Paradise" is an escapist satire. Although Irving gently chides the overly fastidious members of this imaginary village, he simultaneously approves of and delights in their fantasy world.

Irving probably researched the information on Broek during his European travels in the 1820's.[95] In reality, Broek is "a toy-village four

93. In the Manuscript Division, New York Public Library. Fourteen pages of "The Count Van Horn" manuscript are in the Manuscript Division. One page is in the Manuscript Department, University of Virginia Library. One page is also in the Beinecke Library, Yale University Library. One page is in the Redwood Library and Athenaeum, Newport, Rhode Island, and another page is at Knox College, Galesburg, Illinois. The unrecovered pages include manuscript pages 14–16, 19, and 23 to the end of the tale.

94. STW, II, 226.

95. Stanley Williams states that this story "may be traced to Irving's renewed interest in 1838 in Dutch-American history" (STW, II, 324). The manuscript fragment for this story is extant in the University of Virginia Library.

miles from Amsterdam ... like a whimsical bit from China glazed down in the midst of Holland."[96]

Although the sketch appeared in the January, 1841, issue of *Knickerbocker Magazine,* the two pages of extant manuscript suggest that Irving had intended it for another volume. The title is largely printed on top of the front page, and almost as an afterthought, the words "Crayon Papers" are scribbled in the upper-left-hand corner in a darker ink. A comparison among manuscript, *Knickerbocker* and *Wolfert's Roost* versions reveals that Irving altered little when he adapted the sketch for magazine and book. When "Broek" was inserted in *Wolfert's Roost,* it was not altered beyond the changing of a few accidentals and the deletion of "Geoffrey Crayon, Gent." as Irving's pseudonym.

This extremely short and equally light story was immensely popular. While more complex tales such as "Ralph Ringwood" were apparently ignored, nearly every reviewer selected "Broek" for special praise. The *Athenaeum* especially enjoyed the "whimsical"[97] nature of the sketch. One reason for this English periodical's notice is more evident when one analyzes the condescending tone of the *Athenaeum*'s review. The critic remarks that "quiet readers can 'see no harm' in a pure style, especially from a new country like America, which has a literature yet to establish."[98] While the *Athenaeum* selects "Broek" as an example of proper American writing, it is simultaneously critical of the more serious, transcendentalist literature of the day: "It is better, we think, for a man to tell his story as Mr. Irving, Mr. Hawthorne, or Mr. Longfellow does, than to adopt the style Emersonian—in which thoughts may be buried so deep that common seekers shall be unable to find them."[99]

It is not at all surprising that "Broek" and "The Birds of Spring" were the two most popular tales in *Wolfert's Roost.* Both of these moral satires appealed to a gentler, less complicated world than the one that existed in the Emersonian universe. Another devotee of stories like "Broek" sums up the general attitude toward the sketch: "It is marked by the delicate purity of style, the quiet humor, the beautiful imagination, the lucid narrative, and the spiritual description.... It is delightful, among the crowd of 'popular' works—the undistinguished throng of books with

96. Anonymous review of *Wolfert's Roost* in the *Athenaeum,* February 7, 1855, p. 193.
97. *Ibid.*
98. *Ibid.,* p. 192.
99. *Ibid.*

less character and less merit—which appear, to recognize this work of a master."[100]

"Sketches in Paris in 1825"

"The Sketches in Paris" reveal the erratic composition of the *Wolfert's Roost* stories. The seven brief tales, which comprise this piece, were composed and revised in the late teens and early 1820's.[101] However, they were left unpublished from 1816 until 1840 while Irving attempted to expand some of them for a new *Sketch Book*. When rewriting "French and English animosity" he informed Murray that he "should have two volumes of the 'Sketch Book' ready for him in the spring."[102] Plans for a new *Sketch Book* were abandoned and the "Sketches in Paris" was apparently stored for future use.

These brief tales "from the travelling note-books of Geoffrey Crayon, Gent." (WR, 192) contains bits and pieces of information about Paris found in the journals of the 1820's. The beginnings of the first sketch about "A Parisian Hotel," are found in a journal entry for January 22, 1824: "Miss Airey told me of several old families quartered in apartments of the Chateau of Versailles—fine quarters but poor living—poverty of some of the old families."[103] In general, the month of December, 1823, is the height of Irving's interest in and work on the Parisian sketches. On December 18, 1823, Irving notes: "Copy & correct sketch of old Frenchman."[104] One day later, the entry states, "Rewrite & enlarge sketch about Tulleries."[105] The journal for December 24 mentions: "After a night of broken rest and scanty sleep rise at 8. After breakfast rewrite and enlarge sketch of Eng & French Character—write to Livius— rewrite & correct sketch of Eng. Absentee."[106]

Although most of the journal entries are nothing more than notations about current work, Irving occasionally elaborated upon an incident that would eventually be incorporated into a sketch. "The Field of Waterloo" probably took its inspiration from a discussion that Irving

100. Anonymous review of *Wolfert's Roost* in *Putnam's Monthly* 28 (April, 1855), p. 444.
101. Williams notes that the "Sketches in Paris in 1824" was begun in the winter of 1823–1824. Yet the original source for these anecdotes can be found in the notebooks of the late teens. See Williams' *Notes While Preparing Sketch Book & c 1817* (New Haven: Yale University Press, 1927).
102. From a letter to Murray, December 22, 1823; PMI, II, 178–79.
103. In *Journals and Notebooks, Volume III*, p. 276.
104. *Ibid.*, p. 259.
105. *Ibid.*
106. *Ibid.*, p. 262.

had with a Mr. Drummond and Dr. Robert Alexander Chirmside while in Paris; Irving described this conversation in his journal:

> He & Drummond gave many particulars of the battle of Waterloo where they were both present. Drummond says there never was an occasion when so many Gentlemen run away. The Officers & men were quitting the ground continually.... Speaks of the Splendid appearance of the french Curiassirs as they advanced when the sun was out & gleaming on their amour.... Vivacity of the french charges—It soon subsided however when it came in stubborn conflict with the steadiness of the English—The artillery did most execution ripping up the masses of french—horsemen who strewed the field—French office of horse always advanced in front of their men—The french require it to spirit them on tho it is exceedingly dangerous to the officers—[107]

Other journal entries demonstrate that Irving received many of his perceptions and opinions about Paris and the Parisians from acquaintances and friends like Francois Joseph Talma, the French actor: "We talked of French character. He says the french are kind & hospitable—Difference between English & french... Eng. are a noble people—but the french more aimable & agreeable to live among—I spoke of the kindness of the french among themselves—the ties of neighborhood are next to those of relationship & the name of neighbor has something of kindred in it.... Talma full of warmth—nature & frankness."[108] When one compares Talma's views of French hospitality to Irving's description in "French and English Character," the similarities are striking: "The Frenchman's habitation like himself, is open, cheerful, bustling, and noisy.... Any body has access to himself and his apartments; his very bed-room is open to visitors, whatever may be its state of confusion; and all this not from any peculiarly hospitable feeling, but from that communicative habit which predominates over his character" (127.3–12).

Talma also provides much of the information for Irving's sketch on "Paris at the Restoration." Irving's journal for April 25, 1821, notes that Talma "remarked that Paris was very much changed; thinks the French character greatly changed; more grave. You see the young men from the colleges, said he; how grave they are; they walk together, conversing incessantly on politics and other grave subjects; says the nation

107. *Ibid.*, pp. 290–91.
108. *Ibid.*, p. 248.

has become as grave as the English."[109] Such opinions influenced Irving's statement in "Paris at the Restoration" that "The events of the last thirty years have rendered the French a more reflecting people. . . . It is only old Frenchmen, now-a-days, that are gay and trivial; the young are very serious personages" (135.10–22).

Although many of the ideas for the "Sketches" can be traced to the journals of 1823, Irving was still at work on "English and French Characters" in August, 1824. What is perhaps more unusual is the fact that he was still revising in August, 1833: "The day turned out fine. Wrote a little on French and English Characteristics."[110] Irving's sporadic attention to this sketch is indicative of his treatment of "Sketches in Paris" and of *Wolfert's Roost* in general. Time lapses between writing and revision could be as short as a month, as long as ten years.

Three of the seven author's manuscripts for "Sketches in Paris" are extant and several[111] provide a clue to the genesis of the work as a whole. Above the title of "English and French Character" is a larger heading which reads "Parisian Sketches in 1825." Thus it can be assumed that Irving's original intention was to publish these Parisian anecdotes in some collected form. Likewise, it should be noted that a few sketches were originally intended for publication in another collection. The title for "Tuilleries and Windsor Castle" is "National Edifices #8" which was later crossed out. The "Tuilleries" is the only surviving sketch under this thematic heading.

109. Journal entry for April 25, 1821; quoted in PMI, II, 41. In addition, the postscript to "Paris at the Restoration" can be traced directly to a personal observation of Irving's, recorded in his journal of August 16, 1825: "Walking down the Rue de las Paix I met the Duke of Wellington just coming from Place Vandome—column of Napoleon—He was strolling along in blue frock & white trousers—Umbrella under his arm—English & french—& soldiers passing him unconscious that it was the great Wellington they were elbowing.—He sauntered along with air of nonchalance—gazing at print shops & c—looks pale—face thin—cheeks fallen in—hair very grey" (*Journal and Notebooks, Volume III*, pp. 509–10). The Irving short story is almost a verbatim account: He [Wellington] was alone, simply attired in a blue frock; with an umbrella under his arm, and his hat down over his eyes, sauntering across the Place Vendome, close by the Column of Napoleon. He gave a glance up at the column as he passed, and continued his loitering way up the Rue de la Paix; stopping occasionally to gaze in at the shop-windows; elbowed now and then by other gazers . . ." (135.25–30).
110. *Journal and Notebooks, Volume III*, p. 384.
111. There are extant manuscripts for the following sketches: "English and French Character," University of Virginia Library; "The Tuilleries and Windsor Castle," Huntington Library; and "Paris at the Restoration," University of Virginia Library. Also of interest is the pagination. There is no attempt by Irving to order the manuscript pages consecutively for periodical publication. Each story is numbered separately.

This complex history of composition suggests numerous thwarted publishing schemes and plans,[112] and partially explains the long delay in the stories' appearances from their inception in the 1820's to the first periodical printing in November and December, 1840, issues of *Knicker-bocker Magazine*. Another "Letter to the Editor," which appears in the December issue, explains the significant time lapse. "Geoffrey Crayon" begs the audience's indulgence concerning this unrevised collection of stories:

> Sir: I send you a few more extracts from my travelling note-books. They are the first sketchings of a series of essays, narrative, descriptive, and characteristic, which I intended to improve and extend at my leisure, but which I have suffered for years to lie neglected among my papers, until the subjects of which they treat are almost out of date. Such as they are, I trust them to the indulgence of your readers.[113]

Crayon's literary confession is close to the truth. There is almost no revision from manuscript to periodical; furthermore, the 1855 edition is equally unchanged. Irving turns a phrase or reverses a sentence; yet the sketches are ostensibly the same.

Geoffrey Crayon need not have made his *Knickerbocker* apology to the public for "Sketches in Paris" was a popular collection. Its success is attested to by the fact that *The New-Yorker* republished four of the seven sketches in its December 26, 1840, issue.[114] Those critics who praised *Wolfert's Roost* for its contribution to sentimental literature selected "Sketches" for special commendation. The *Dublin Magazine* called the work "Almost the pleasantest papers, by the way, in the volume—which is admirably correct as a piece of descriptive writing."[115] However "out-of-date" these tales of Parisian life seemed to Geoffrey

112. Stanley Williams underestimates the time spent on the Parisian tales. He states that "The 'Sketches in Paris' ... commenced in the winter of 1823–24, and the other French tales were probably of the same litter" (STW, II, 325). In fact, the composition began in the late teens and continued into the 1830's.

113. *Knickerbocker Magazine* 16 (December, 1840), 519. This story was divided into two parts: November, 1840, pp. 425–30 and December, 1840, pp. 519–30.

114. *The New-Yorker* published "English and French Character," "Tuilleries and Windsor Castle," "Field of Waterloo," and "Paris at the Restoration." It republished only the second half of the "Sketches in Paris," or the December *Knickerbocker* installment. Whether this was a critical decision on the literary value of the first three stories is unknown, since *The New-Yorker* gave no explanation for its selections. The only other substantive changes that they made were the deletion of the Geoffrey Crayon pseudonym and the "Letter to the Editor of the Knickerbocker."

115. Anon., "Washington Irving," *The Eclectic Magazine*, p. 550.

Crayon, they contained the beautiful prose which ingratiated Irving to his audience.

"A Contented Man"

Like the majority of Irving's sketches of European men and manners, the source for "A Contented Man" is found in the early notebooks. The original contented man appeared in *Notes While Preparing Sketch Book* (1817) as a "Frenchman. fiddler at the English theatre plays away until bell rings for curtain to rise. lays down fiddle stick. takes a long pinch of snuff—pulls out cold cott hkf.—blows nose—gives one look of contempt at the stage & dives thro the low door. no idea of seeing such trumpery."[116]

Although the exact date of the extant manuscript[117] is unknown, one can assume that the above character sketch remained untouched until 1826 or 1827 when Irving wrote the story for publication in Alaric A. Watts' *The Literary Souvenir; or, Cabinet of Poetry and Romance* (London, 1827). This first periodical version differs little from the manuscript. Likewise, the first American magazine printing, in the *New York American* for December 22, 1826, is quite close to the manuscript as well. Since the *New York American* often reprinted pieces it found in British journals, this version is probably a copy of the English version which appeared in late 1826 as a gift annual. The piece was reprinted once again in America in *The Casket* for March, 1827.

When the sketch reappeared in *Wolfert's Roost*, it was almost identical to previous versions; only the deletion of the Geoffrey Crayon pseudonym was substantively different. The sketch received some positive notices from one reviewer who remarked that both "A Contented Man" and "Sketches in Paris" demonstrate "Washington Irving's just but good natured appreciation of the character and manners of Europe."[118] Although Americans suspected Irving's fascination with European affairs, they could not dispute the fact that he was America's translator of the old world.

---

116. In a footnote to *Notes While Preparing Sketch Book*, Stanley Williams comments that "Perhaps the original of the French fiddler in 'A Contented Man,' is found in the sketch given above" (p. 85, n.).

117. The manuscript of "A Contented Man" is in the University of Virginia Library. About ninety percent of the manuscript is extant.

118. Anon., "Washington Irving's *Chronicles of Wolfert's Roost*," *Littell's Living Age*, March 24, 1855, p. 723; first published in *The Spectator*, January 27, 1855, pp. 114–15.

"The Knight of Malta"

In this tale, a narrator describes his travels in Sicily and Catania and then recounts a ghost story related to him by a Chevalier L_____. Most of the details in this story are autobiographical and can be found in Irving's European journals of 1804–1805. A journal entry for February 12, 1805, mentions Pietro Landolini, to whom Irving "had brought Letters of introduction from his [Landolini's] Brother who is antiquarian to the King of Naples at Syracuse."[119] He remarks that Landolini is "a Knight of Malta ... and has politely offered to be our cicerone in shewing us the curiosities of the place."[120] Although many of the details of the tale are noted in the journals, the ghost story, entitled "The Grand Prior of Minorca," is derived from an unnamed and unrecovered "French memoir" which Irving cited in a footnote (94.24–26).

While many of the characters and places described are found in the 1805 journals, an analysis of the extant manuscript reveals that the final draft was not written until 1839. The title for the first section about Sicily and Chavalier Landolini reads, "The Knight of Malta./To the Editor of the Knickerbocker." Thus it can be assumed that nearly thirty-five years had passed before the story was completed for publication in the *Knickerbocker Magazine*. There is also manuscript evidence that the second part of the tale, "The Grand Prior of Minorca/A Veritable Ghost Story," was also written sometime after October, 1839. Page 21–22 of the "Grand Prior" are actually two opened envelopes which Irving pasted together. Since the envelopes are postmarked February 17 and October 9, 1939, the manuscript[121] was written or revised after October, 1839, when Irving was in the process of rummaging among old notebooks and trunks for *Knickerbocker* stories. Thus "The Knight of Malta" presents a typical composition history for *Wolfert's Roost*; fifty years of sporadic writing and rewriting, from 1805 to 1855, went into this twenty-page tale.

When Irving prepared the manuscript for publication in the February, 1840, *Knickerbocker*, his only substantive changes were in diction. Few modifications were made in the next periodical publication in *The Evergreen* (March, 1840) which is actually a reprint of the *Knickerbocker* text. *The Evergreen* reprint even retains the story's introduction "To the Editor of the Knickerbocker."

119. *Journals and Notebooks, Volume I, 1803–1806*, ed. Nathalia Wright (Madison: University of Wisconsin Press, 1969), p. 201.

120. *Ibid.*

121. This is actually a common characteristic of the Irving manuscripts and is quite helpful in dating the composition. The entire manuscript is extant in the Berg Collection of the New York Public Library.

When Irving decided to include "The Knight of Malta" in *Wolfert's Roost*, he revised it, once again, in a superficial way. Obvious references to the *Knickerbocker*, as well as the "Letter by Geoffrey Crayon, Gent." were eliminated. About the only noteworthy alteration was the regularization of titles for fictional characters. In the 1855 edition, Irving was more scrupulous in assigning titles of nobility which would reflect national usage. All Frenchmen are referred to as "chevaliers" while their Spanish counterparts are designated as "cavaliers."

"The Knight of Malta" was one of the more popular stories in the book. A reviewer for *The Spectator* commented that the tale "introduces the reader to European ghost stories, told with the writer's wonted cleverness."[122] Another critic compared the ghost story to the celebrated legendary narratives in *Tales of a Traveller*. Although hastily conceived and revised, "The Knight of Malta" met with the kind of success that Irving's more carefully written stories had received previously.

HISTORY OF THE SPANISH SKETCHES

Since *Wolfert's Roost* is a grab-bag collection of Irving's unpublished manuscripts, it is only logical that one section be devoted to his Spanish tales. "The Widow's Ordeal," "Don Juan," "Legend of the Engulphed Convent," "The Phantom Island," and "Recollections of Alhambra" can all be traced to Irving's residence in Spain from 1826 to 1829.[123] Although Irving served as ambassador to Spain from 1842 to 1846, little literary work was accomplished because he was preoccupied with political and diplomatic matters and was unable to capture the magic of Alhambra that he had felt twelve years before.[124]

Irving's initial interest in Spain began in childhood and is reflected in his later writings.[125] Yet his continental travels did not take him to Spain until 1826 when he went in order to translate Fernan des de Navarrete's *Coleccion de los visages y descubrimientos que hicieron por mar los espinoles desde fines del siglo XV* for his friend Alexander

122. "Washington Irving's *Chronicles of Wolfert's Roost*," *Littell's Living Age*, p. 723.

123. For a fuller, more detailed account, see Stanley T. Williams, *The Spanish Background of American Literature* (New Haven: Yale University Press, 1955), II, 3–45.

124. Williams notes that "When in 1846, he finally returned to America, his journals were blank" (*Spanish Background*, II, 7). Although this is an exaggeration, Irving's late 1840's letters are full of lamentations about his inability to write creatively during this period.

125. Williams discusses the books Irving read in childhood which were on Spanish subjects. He also maintains that certain passages in *The Alhambra* are autobiographical. See *Spanish Background*, II, 9–10.

Everett. Although Irving was to be paid fifteen hundred dollars, he soon lost interest in the scholarly project and decided to write a history of Christopher Columbus based on the information in Navarrete and other historical manuscripts.[126] This history, which eventually was published as *The Life and Voyages of Christopher Columbus*, was followed by *The Conquest of Granada* (1828) and *The Alhambra* (1832).

While working in the library of Spanish literature and history in Madrid owned by Obadiah Rich, American consul to Spain, Irving came upon tales of Spanish men, manners, and legendary heroes. It is here that he discovered new materials for the numerous short sketches which were included in *Wolfert's Roost*. Irving now turned to the *articulo de costumbres* of Fernan Caballero for the Spanish counterpart to his French, German, and English tales of men and manners.[127]

Although Irving was artistically inspired in his work on Spanish legends, there is also another important reason for his new interest; Spanish literature provided, "an enchanted garden for the antiquarian lover of legends, for the dreamer destined to find it more beautiful than his dreams—and for a writer in search of fresh material.... Here might be unearthed something for an American public a little tired of Geoffrey Crayon."[128]

During his first stay in Spain, Irving collected notebooks on the legends, myths, and tragic and comic aspects of Spain; pieces that were not included in *Columbus*, *Granada* or *Alhambra*, were filed under "miscellanea ... sufficient to last him for the remainder of his life."[129] Much of this miscellanea would be utilized in the 1830's when Irving, rummaged through old notebooks for the *Knickerbocker Magazine*. Half-written tales of the life of Don Roderick the Goth, along with reminiscences of Alhambra were quickly revised in an attempt to fulfill the contract with Lewis Gaylord Clark in 1839[130] and later with George Putnam in 1855.

"The Widow's Ordeal"

In this tale of trial by combat, Irving relates a story of "the youthful, and, as yet, glorious days, of Roderick the Goth; who subsequently

126. Irving has been accused of plagiarism in his use of Navarrete's material. See the *Southern Literary Messenger* 7 (March, 1841), 231–39, and Putnam's defense of Irving in "Memories of Distinguished Authors," p. 494.

127. Williams, *Spanish Background*, II, 9.

128. *Ibid.*, p. 19.

129. *Ibid.*, p. 24.

130. Williams judges the Spanish *Knickerbocker* stories in approximately the same way. He believed that "*Wolfert's Roost*, too, with its spoils from still other Spanish notebooks kept these memories of Spain fair" (*Spanish Background*, II, 37).

tarnished his fame at home by his misdeeds, and, finally, lost his kingdom and his life on the banks of the Guadalete, in that disastrous battle,
which gave up Spain a conquest to the Moors" (72.36–40). Although
the tale may have Spanish background,[131] it can be traced to Irving's
journals from Dresden, which as Henry Pochmann noted, Irving
had "long saved 'against another fit of story-telling' . . . of a 'couple who
prayed continuously for children but in spite of their prayers they never
got any, which was thot very remarkable.' "[132] This tale of unfulfilled
prayer was "many years later . . . [revised] to advantage in 'The Widow's
Ordeal,' " and made "the pivotal point of the story."[133]

This blending of German legend and Spanish environment is typical
of the Spanish stories which appear in *Wolfert's Roost*. In an effort to
escape the milieu of Geoffrey Crayon, Irving used the exotic scenery of
Spain and its domination by the Moors, in order to add novelty and
ambience to an old German tale. This ability to combine different
traditions demonstrates "how Irving would seize upon this or that
scrap of lore that [he] ran across in his literary rambles, and how he
would turn it to literary use."[134]

Although Irving had amassed material for "The Widow's Ordeal" on
his trip to Dresden in 1822–1823, he did not use it until 1837. Like many
of the Spanish tales, it sat in a trunk for years, until publication in the
late 1830's. The reasons for the delay are not clear, and since no manuscript for the original sketch is extant, it is difficult to estimate the
amount of revision the tale underwent before it appeared in *The
Magnolia* (1837).[135]

The version of "The Widow's Ordeal" found in *The Magnolia* differs
substantially from the 1855 Putnam edition. Irving no longer uses "The
Author of the Sketch-Book," or Geoffrey Crayon, as his pseudonym. Generally the modifications in word choice show Irving's conscious effort at
conciseness.

Although Irving expended a great deal of effort in revision, "The
Widow's Ordeal" is not among the most highly praised of his tales. It
has, however, been considered one of the few short stories in the
volume.[136] A critic for the *New Monthly Magazine* described the tale

131. For more information, see Henry Pochmann, "Irving's German Tour and
His Tales," *Proceedings of the Modern Language Association* 45 (1930), 1150–87.
    132. *Ibid.*, p. 1183.
    133. *Ibid.*
    134. *Ibid.*
    135. "The Widow's Ordeal," in *Magnolia* (New York: Monson Bancroft, 1837),
pp. 257–74.
    136. For further information on the four kinds of Irvingesque short stories, see
Pochmann, "Irving's German Tour and His Tales."

as "in the vein of *Tales of a Traveller* . . . for the entertainment of a youthful circle round the Christmas fire."[137]

"Don Juan—A Spectral Research"

Like "The Widow's Ordeal," this tale is also indebted to a German story for its source. Irving probably read Friedrich Gottschalck's "The Miraculous Fish" in translation in *The German Novelists* (1826) by Thomas Roscoe.[138] The Gottschalck tale presents a Don Juan figure named Count Isang who unknowingly rapes his sister while sacking a nunnery. Irving's debt to both Gottschalck and Roscoe is seen in a comparison of the Roscoe and Irving Don Juan figures. Count Isang is "the last heir of this old and noble family who was a young lord blessed with great personal advantages, but wild and dissolute to a degree."[139] Don Manuel de Manara, Irving's own Don, is "a gay young fellow . . . who having come to a great estate by the death of his father, gave the reins to his passions, and plunged into all kinds of dissipation" (205.20–23).

Both Count Isang and Don Manuel are threats to the order of virtue and purity in their respective towns. Isang "soon became the dread of the surrounding district. As he rode through the peaceful hamlet the maidens flew from his sight as from that of a sorcerer. Husbands barred their doors to protect their wives, and fathers their daughters."[140] Don Manuel's reign of terror is equally as reprehensible; he "was the cause of doors being barred and windows grated. . . . his very name was a word of terror to all the jealous husbands and cautious fathers of Seville" (205.25–29).

There are essential differences between the Gottschalck original and the Irving adaptation however. Because Americans would never tolerate the theme of incest, the attempt at sacking the nunnery is foiled in the Irving version.[141] He also avoids the somber didacticism of the German

137. Anon., "Wolfert's Roost," *Littell's Living Age*, August 11, 1855, p. 354; first published in the *New Monthly Magazine* 104 (July, 1855), 297–99.

138. Pochmann points out that "Irving may easily have known this collection since Thomas Roscoe was the son of William Roscoe to whom Irving devoted a laudatory sketch of nine pages in *The Sketch Book*" ("Irving's German Tour and His Tales," p. 1182).

139. Friedrich Gottschalck, "The Miraculous Fish," in *The German Novelists*, ed. Thomas Roscoe (London: Henry Colburn, 1826), II, 159.

140. *Ibid.*, p. 158.

141. In "Irving's German Tour and His Tales" Pochmann notes that while "this tale of Gottschalck's served as a suggestion for Irving's tale, it is very likely that Irving avoided the theme of incest for moral reasons. America in the early years of the nineteenth century would not have welcomed such a tale" (p. 1183).

source by allowing a frivolous narrator to relate the tale, which is supposedly derived from "a Spanish friend, a curious investigator of the popular traditions and other good-for-nothing lore of the city . . . who was kind enough to imagine he had met, in me, with a congenial spirit" (202.30–32).

Since Irving was familiar with the Gottschalck story as early as 1826, his reasons for delaying publication of his adaptation until the March, 1841, issue of *Knickerbocker Magazine* are unknown. After its publication, however, Irving ignored the story until he decided to include it among the *Wolfert's Roost* papers. At that point, he made some substantive changes which are quite similar to the additions and deletions found in the other tales. "Geoffrey Crayon" is removed as the author of the story and unnecessary modifiers are deleted for conciseness.

"Don Juan—A Spectral Research," more than any other tale in *Wolfert's Roost*, emphasizes Irving's inability to deal with the grandiose theme. He uses the story of the mysterious Don Juan as an analogy to a lesser-known figure of moral legend and anecdote. The sentimentalism which pervades the Irving version is especially evident in the concluding paragraph: "Since that time, I never fail to attend the theatre whenever the story of Don Juan is represented, whether in pantomime or opera. In the sepulchral scene, I feel myself quite at home; and when the statue makes his appearance, I greet him as an old acquaintance" (209.1–4). Generally, Irving was a master at extracting the sentimental from a myth or tale and was more at ease with feeling and inspiration than with serious literary or philosophical ideas. He, himself, confessed to a certain lack of scholarly perceptiveness when he stated that he was "prone to receive greater pleasure without nicely analyzing the source, and sometimes apt to clap his hands when grave critics shake their heads."[142]

"Legend of the Engulphed Convent"

In 1847, Irving wrote to Pierre and explained why he had not published more of his Spanish material: "When I was in Madrid, in 1826–'27, just after I had finished Columbus, I commenced a series of Chronicles illustrative of the wars between the Spaniards and the Moors. . . . The Chronicle of the Conquest of Granada was not so immediately successful as I had anticipated, though it has held its way better than many other of my works which were more taking at first. I am apt to get out of conceit of anything I do; and I suffered the manuscript of those Chronicles to lie in my trunks like waste paper."[143] One chronicle,

142. From a letter to James H. Hacket, April 17, 1849; PMI, IV, 40.
143. From a letter to Pierre Irving, April 14, 1847; PMI, IV, 14–15.

which probably had been discarded for many years, was "Legend of the Engulphed Convent." According to evidence in the extant manuscript,[144] this tale about the invasion of Spain by the Moors was the second in a series of Spanish sketches which Irving had planned for publication under the *Conquest of Granada* theme. Above the title in the manuscript, there is a "#2" which may indicate that the legend was one of a group dealing with this subject.

Although the "Legend of the Engulphed Convent" was begun in 1826–1827, it did not appear until the March, 1840, issue of *Knickerbocker*. Depressed over the disappointing reception to the earlier *Conquest of Granada,* Irving abandoned his project on Spanish subjects altogether. However, the demands of the *Knickerbocker* caused him to open his traveling notebooks and to salvage what he could from his collection of Spanish papers.

Few substantive changes were made until the 1855 version, which is generally more concise. Other revisions included the elimination of "Geoffrey Crayon, Gent." as the "author" of the tale.

Spanish tales such as the "Legend of the Engulphed Convent" were consistently praised by the critics. One contemporary reviewer in the *New Monthly Magazine* noted that "The pen that wrote tales of the Alhambra, and records of Spanish and Moorish life, in times of chivalry and high emprise, also furnishes us in the present volume with kindred morceaux of legendary lore."[145]

"The Phantom Island"

Although the quest of St. Brandan for a perfect island was known in most languages and countries, Irving gave the legend a Spanish flavor by setting it "at the time of the conquest of Spain, in the eighth century, when the blessed cross was cast down, and the crescent erected in its place" (216.24–25). The heroes in this tale are seven bishops who "had fled from the peninsula, and embarked in quest of some ocean island, or distant land, where they might found seven Christian cities, and enjoy their faith unmolested" (216.27–30).

Lewis Gaylord Clark has provided further information about Irving's "enchanted islands":

the reader must not infer that the story of the "Enchanted Island" from the pen of *Mr. Irving,* in preceding pages, is altogether a sketch of the imagination ... there were certain Portuguese, of the island of Palma and Teneriffe, who affirmed that, being driven about

144. The manuscript is in the Berg Collection of the New York Public Library.
145. "Wolfert's Roost," *Littell's Living Age,* p. 354.

by a tempest, they had come suddenly upon the island of Saint
Brandan.... Some confounded it with the fabled island of the
Seven Cities, where seven Spanish bishops, with their flocks, took
refuge, on the Conquest of Spain by the Moors ... there can be no
doubt, that the popular legend of the "Island of the Seven Cities,"
so current during the time of Columbus, may be as implicitly relied
upon, as the incontrovertible tradition respecting the island of
Saint Brandan.[146]

Clark also directs the reader to the "Appendix" in Irving's *Life and
Voyages of Christopher Columbus,* which contains "from divers old
Spanish and Portuguese authorities, many extremely curious and amusing facts, relative to this subject."[147] Thus it is obvious that both the introduction to the tale entitled "The Phantom Island"[148] and the legend of
"The Adalantado of the Seven Cities" are Irving's adaptations of myth
and superstition.

During his stay in Madrid from 1826 to 1829, Irving apparently had
discovered the tale of St. Brandan while in desultory reading for *Granada*
and *Columbus.* Stanley T. Williams describes the genesis of "The Phantom Island" as "one happy day in Rich's library when he [Irving] threw
aside both the *Columbus* and the *Granada* and copied from an old
chronicle the exquisite story of St. Brandan."[149] Obadiah Rich's library,
which contained a variety of old tracts and historical documents, no
doubt possessed some versions of the St. Brandan legend. In his research
for other volumes, Irving probably came upon the legend, and, realizing
the potential of such a tale, added it to his notebook. Since the author's
manuscript is not extant, however, it is difficult to reconstruct the composition process. One can only speculate that the notes for the story were

146. Lewis Gaylord Clark, "Editor's Table," *Knickerbocker Magazine* 16 (July,
1839), 92–93.
147. The "Appendix" to the *Life and Voyages of Christopher Columbus* (New
York: Lovell, Coryell & Company, 188?) gives a complete history of the legend:
"The Island of the Seven Cities was identified with the island mentioned by
Aristotle as haveing been discovered by the Carthaginians, and was put down
in the early maps, about the time of Columbus, under the name of Antilla. At
the time of the discovery of New Spain, reports were brought to Hispaniola
of the civilization of the country: that the people wore clothing: that their houses
and temples were solid, spacious, and often magnificent; and that crosses were
occasionally found among them.... For a time the old tradition of the Seven
Cities was revived, and many thought that they were to be found in the same
part of New Spain" (p. 709).
148. For some reason, Irving decided to change the title of the essay from "The
Enchanted Island" in the *Knickerbocker* to "The Phantom Island" in *Wolfert's Roost.*
149. STW, II, 325.

taken between 1826 and 1827 and that a final draft was written before the *Knickerbocker* publication in July, 1839.

"The Enchanted Island" was reprinted in the London periodical entitled *The Romancist* (1839). The English version is similar to the *Knickerbocker* piece, with the exception of one additional passage which is deleted in the American magazine. It can therefore be assumed that the reprint in *The Romancist* did not include the last minute changes which Irving made in the proof sheets of the *Knickerbocker* version.

When he revised "The Phantom Island" for publication in *Wolfert's Roost*, he altered nearly ninety-five percent of the story. "The Author of The Sketch-Book" was dropped from the title. Furthermore, the 1855 edition is noticeably more concise, Irving having condensed some of the lengthy descriptions and eliminated unnecessary details which cluttered the plot action. The deletion of literary and historical allusions helped to shorten the tale as well. One example is the modification of the description of "the Fortunate Islands of the ancients; which, according to some ingenious and speculative minds, are mere wrecks and remnants of the vast island of Atlantis, mentioned by Plato, as having been swallowed up by the ocean" (KnM, 26), which was rewritten as: "Those who have read the history of the Canaries, the Fortunate Islands of the ancients, may remember the wonders told of this enigmatical island" (214.16–18).

Yet, when Irving removed material from one paragraph, he often inserted it in another. Thus most of the "revisions" were mere jugglings. In one instance he deleted the phrase "sun-gilt peaks and long, shadowy promontories" from the *Wolfert's Roost* version (214.22), and then added it to a succeeding paragraph on the same page.

When *Wolfert's Roost* was published, "The Phantom Island" was selected by many critics for special mention. Frederic Cozzens, in his novel *The Sparrowgrass Papers*, describes the enthusiasm which his children showed for this story: "As for our eldest, the reading to him of 'The Adalantado of the Seven Cities'... has filled his head with ships, sails, anchors and salt water."[150]

"Recollections of the Alhambra"

Like the other Spanish stories, "Recollections of the Alhambra" is divided into a prologue and a narrative tale about the chivalric period of Christian and Moor. The introduction discusses "a dreamy sojourn... [in] the silent and deserted halls of the Alhambra, surrounded with the

150. Frederic E. Cozzens, *The Sparrowgrass Papers or Living in the Country* (Philadelphia: J. B. Lippincott & Company, 1865), p. 65.

insignia of regal sway, and the vivid, though dilapidated traces of Oriental luxury... (230.3–10). The second section of "Recollections," entitled "The Abencerrage," is a paraphrase of Montemayor's *Diana*[151] and relates the "illustrious line of the Abencerrages, who in the proud days of Moslem domination were the soul of every thing noble and chivalric" (230.23–25). In both sections, Irving conveys the romance and mystery that he had experienced on his first trip to Spain.

In a May, 1829, letter to Henry Brevoort, Irving describes Granada as "one of the most remarkable romantic and delicious spots in the world. ... when I am not occupied with my pen, I lounge with my book about these oriental apartments. ... It absolutely appears to me like a dream; or as if I am spell bound in some fairy palace."[152]

This stay at the Alhambra was more than a time of relaxation however. Irving used it for writing and revising many of the stories and books he had worked on while in Spain: "During my sojourn in the Alhambra," he wrote to Brevoort, "I shall have leisure and quiet to look over my manuscripts, and to get them in order so as to present some other work to the public before long."[153] One of the sketches he "looked-over" was the tale of "The Abencerrage." Yet it remained unpublished until he combined it with an autobiographical reminiscence of the Alhambra for the June, 1839, *Knickerbocker Magazine*.

"Recollections of the Alhambra" was reprinted in *The Romancist* (1839). The English version is similar to the version which appeared in the *Knickerbocker*, with the exception of one deleted passage. It can therefore be assumed that Irving decided to add some additional material when he revised the proof sheets for the *Knickerbocker*.

As in other Spanish sketches, the differences between the periodical and 1855 version are numerous. Generally the *Wolfert's Roost* edition is more concise and detailed, although the attempt at conciseness is often a juggling of sentences and phrases. *Knickerbocker* opens with a reminiscence by Geoffrey Crayon about "the beautiful hall of the Abencerrages, beside the fountain celebrated in the tragic story of that devoted race" (KnM, 485.5-7). He then relates the entire history of thirty-six cavaliers who are sacrificed in a bloody battle. At first glance,

---

151. Twice in the story, Irving directs the reader to not only Montemayor, but also to Conde's *History of the Domination of the Arabs* from which he took the basic outline for this tale. Stanley Williams notes that "Irving's version of the *Diana* is a fairly free translation ... of *La Diana de Jorge de Montemayor* (Barcelona, 1886), p. 146f: 'En tiempo del valeroso infante don Fernando' " (STW, II, 325).

152. From a letter to Henry Brevoort, May 23, 1829; quoted in *Letters of Washington Irving to Henry Brevoort*, pp. 425–26.

153. *Ibid.*, p. 428.

this somber history seems to have been deleted in the 1855 version, but it actually reappears three pages later. The only other substantive revision is the elimination after the title of "The Author of the Sketch-Book" or "Geoffrey Crayon" as the creator of the tale.

Few critics have commented on either the introduction to the "Recollections" or on Irving's free translation of the Montemayor tale. When this story is mentioned, it is usually spoken of in connection with the other Spanish tales. "Don Juan," "Legend of the Engulphed Convent," "The Phantom Island," and "Recollections of the Alhambra" all contain prologues which announce the narrator, and provide a fictional source for the story to follow. The second part is a free translation from either a well-known writer (as in the case of Montemayor) or an unknown author (as Fray Antonio de Sancta Maria). Possibly Irving best sums up the value and content of these Spanish tales when he defends them in a letter to his nephew Pierre: "These old Morisco Spanish subjects have a charm that makes me content to write about them at half price. They have so much that is high-minded and chivalrous and quaint and picturesque and adventurous, and at times half comic about them."[154]

154. From a letter to Pierre Irving, April 15, 1847; PMI, IV, 17.

WOLFERT'S ROOST

WOLFERT'S ROOST

About five-and-twenty miles from the ancient and renowned city of
Manhattan, formerly called New-Amsterdam, and vulgarly called New-
York, on the eastern bank of that expansion of the Hudson, known
among Dutch mariners of yore, as the Tappan Zee, being in fact the
great Mediterranean Sea of the New-Netherlands, stands a little old-
fashioned stone mansion, all made up of gable-ends, and as full of
angles and corners, as an old cocked hat. It is said, in fact, to have
been modelled after the cocked hat of Peter the Headstrong, as the
Escurial was modelled after the gridiron of the blessed St. Lawrence.
Though but of small dimensions, yet, like many small people, it is of
mighty spirit, and values itself greatly on its antiquity, being one of
the oldest edifices, for its size, in the whole country. It claims to be
an ancient seat of empire, I may rather say an empire in itself, and
like all empires, great and small, has had its grand historical epochs.
In speaking of this doughty and valorous little pile, I shall call it by
its usual appellation of "The Roost;" though that is a name given to it
in modern days, since it became the abode of the white man.

Its origin, in truth, dates far back in that remote region commonly
called the fabulous age, in which vulgar fact becomes mystified, and
tinted up with delectable fiction. The eastern shore of the Tappan
Sea was inhabited in those days by an unsophisticated race, existing
is all the simplicity of nature; that is to say, they lived by hunting
and fishing, and recreated themselves occasionally with a little toma-
hawking and scalping. Each stream that flows down from the hills
into the Hudson, had its petty sachem, who ruled over a hand's breadth
of forest on either side, and had his seat of government at its mouth.
The chieftain who ruled at the Roost, was not merely a great warrior,
but a medicine-man, or prophet, or conjurer, for they all mean the
same thing, in Indian parlance. Of his fighting propensities, evidences
still remain, in various arrow-heads of flint, and stone battle-axes,
occasionally digged up about the Roost: of his wizard powers, we
have a token in a spring which wells up at the foot of the bank, on
the very margin of the river, which, it is said, was gifted by him with
rejuvenating powers, something like the renowned Fountain of Youth
in the Floridas, so anxiously but vainly sought after by the veteran
Ponce de Leon. This story, however, is stoutly contradicted by an
old Dutch matter-of-fact tradition, which declares that the spring in

3

question was smuggled over from Holland in a churn, by Femmetie Van Blarcom, wife of Goosen Garret Van Blarcom, one of the first settlers, and that she took it up by night, unknown to her husband, from beside their farm-house near Rotterdam; being sure she should find no water equal to it in the new country—and she was right.

The wizard sachem had a great passion for discussing territorial questions, and settling boundary lines, in other words, he had the spirit of annexation; this kept him in continual feud with the neighboring sachems, each of whom stood up stoutly for his hand-breadth of territory; so that there is not a petty stream nor rugged hill in the neighborhood, that has not been the subject of long talks and hard battles. The sachem, however, as has been observed, was a medicine-man, as well as warrior, and vindicated his claims by arts as well as arms; so that, by dint of a little hard fighting here, and hocus-pocus (or diplomacy) there, he managed to extend his boundary-line from field to field and stream to stream, until it brought him into collision with the powerful sachem of Sing Sing.* Many were the sharp conflicts between these rival chieftains for the sovereignty of a winding valley, a favorite hunting ground watered by a beautiful stream called the Pocantico. Many were the ambuscades, surprisals, and deadly onslaughts, that took place among its fastnesses, of which it grieves me much that I cannot furnish the details, for the gratification of those gentle but bloody-minded readers, of both sexes, who delight in the romance of the tomahawk and scalping-knife. Suffice it to say, that the wizard chieftain was at length victorious, though his victory is attributed, in Indian tradition, to a great medicine, or charm, by which he laid the sachem of Sing-Sing and his warriors asleep, among the rocks and recesses of the valley, where they remain asleep to the present day, with their bows and war-clubs beside them. This was the origin of that potent and drowsy spell, which still prevails over the valley of the Pocantico, and which has gained it the well-merited appellation of Sleepy Hollow. Often, in secluded and quiet parts of that valley, where the stream is overhung by dark woods and rocks, the ploughman, on some calm and sunny day, as he shouts to his oxen, is surprised at hearing faint shouts from the hill sides in reply; being, it is said, the spell-bound warriors, who half start from their rocky couches and grasp their weapons, but sink to sleep again.

The conquest of the Pocantico was the last triumph of the wizard

* A corruption of the Old Indian name, O-sin-sing. Some have rendered it, O-sin-song, or O-sing-song; in token of its being a great market town; where any thing may be had for a mere song. Its present melodious alteration to Sing Sing is said to have been made in compliment to a Yankee singing-master, who taught the inhabitants the art of singing through the nose.

sachem. Notwithstanding all his medicine and charms, he fell in battle, in attempting to extend his boundary line to the east, so as to take in the little wild valley of the Sprain, and his grave is still shown, near the banks of that pastoral stream. He left, however, a great empire to his successors, extending along the Tappan Sea, from Yonkers quite to Sleepy Hollow, and known in old records and maps by the Indian name of Wicquaes-Keck.

The wizard Sachem was succeeded by a line of chiefs, of whom nothing remarkable remains on record. One of them was the very individual on whom master Robert Juet, made that sage experiment, gravely recorded by the latter, in the narrative of the discovery.

"Our master and his mate determined to try some of the cheefe men of the country, whether they took them down into the cabin, and gave them so much wine and aqua vitæ, that they were all very merrie; one of them had his wife with him, which sate so modestly as any of our countrywomen would do in a strange place. In the end, one of them was drunke; and that was strange to them, for they could not tell how far to take it.*

How far master Hendrick Hudson and his worthy mate carried their experiment with the sachem's wife, is not recorded, neither does the curious Robert Juet make any mention of the after consequences of this grand moral test; tradition, however, affirms that the sachem, on landing, gave his modest spouse a hearty rib-roasting, according to the connubial discipline of the aboriginals; it further affirms, that he remained a hard drinker to the day of his death; trading away all his lands, acre by acre, for aqua vitæ; by which means the Roost and all its domains, from Yonkers to Sleepy Hollow, came, in the regular course of trade, and by right of purchase, into the possession of the Dutchmen.

The worthy government of the New Netherlands was not suffered to enjoy this grand acquisition unmolested. In the year 1654, the losel Yankees of Connecticut, those swapping, bargaining, squatting enemies of the Manhattoes, made a daring inroad into this neighborhood, and founded a colony called Westchester, or, as the ancient Dutch records term it, Vest Dorp, in the right of one Thomas Pell, who pretended to have purchased the whole surrounding country of the Indians; and stood ready to argue their claims before any tribunal of christendom.

This happened during the chivalrous reign of Peter Stuyvesant, and roused the ire of that gunpowder old hero. Without waiting to discuss claims and titles, he pounced at once upon the nest of nefarious squatters, carried off twenty-five of them in chains to the Manhattoes,

* See Juet's Journal, Purchas Pilgrim.

nor did he stay his hand, nor give rest to his wooden leg, until he had driven every Yankee back into Connecticut, or obliged him to acknowledge allegiance to their High Mightinesses. In revenge, however, they introduced the plague of witchcraft into the province. This doleful malady broke out at Vest Dorp, and would have spread throughout the country had not the Dutch farmers nailed horse-shoes to the doors of their houses and barns, sure protections against witchcraft, many of which remain to the present day.

The seat of empire of the wizard sachem now came into the possession of Wolfert Acker, one of the privy counsellors of Peter Stuyvesant. He was a worthy, but ill-starred man, whose aim through life had been to live in peace and quiet. For this he had emigrated from Holland, driven abroad by family feuds and wrangling neighbors. He had warred for quiet through the fidgetting reign of William the Testy, and the fighting reign of Peter the Headstrong, sharing in every brawl and rib-roasting, in his eagerness to keep the peace and promote public tranquillity. It was his doom, in fact, to meet a head wind at every turn, and be kept in a constant fume and fret by the perverseness of mankind. Had he served on a modern jury he would have been sure to have eleven unreasonable men opposed to him.

At the time when the province of the New Netherlands was wrested from the domination of their High Mightinesses by the combined forces of Old and New England, Wolfert retired in high dudgeon to this fastness in the wilderness, with the bitter determination to bury himself from the world, and live here for the rest of his days in peace and quiet. In token of that fixed purpose he inscribed over his door (his teeth clenched at the time) his favorite Dutch motto, "Lust in Rust," (pleasure in quiet). The mansion was thence called Wolfert's Rust—(Wolfert's Rest), but by the uneducated, who did not understand Dutch, Wolfert's Roost; probably from its quaint cock-loft look, and from its having a weather-cock perched on every gable.

Wolfert's luck followed him into retirement. He had shut himself up from the world, but he had brought with him a wife, and it soon passed into a proverb throughout the neighborhood that the cock of the Roost was the most henpecked bird in the country. His house too was reputed to be harassed by Yankee witchcraft. When the weather was quiet every where else, the wind, it was said, would howl and whistle about the gables; witches and warlocks would whirl about upon the weather-cocks, and scream down the chimneys; nay it was even hinted that Wolfert's wife was in league with the enemy, and used to ride on a broomstick to a witches' sabbath in Sleepy Hollow. This, however, was all mere scandal, founded perhaps on her occasionally flourishing a broomstick in the course of a curtain lecture, or raising a storm within doors, as termagant wives are apt to do, and against which sorcery horse shoes are of no avail.

Wolfert Acker died and was buried, but found no quiet even in the grave: for if popular gossip be true, his ghost has occasionally been seen walking by moonlight among the old gray moss-grown trees of his apple orchard.

CHRONICLE II

The next period at which we find this venerable and eventful pile rising into importance, was during the dark and troublous time of the revolutionary war. It was the keep or stronghold of Jacob Van Tassel, a valiant Dutchman of the old stock of Van Tassels, who abound in Westchester County. The name, as originally written, was Van Texel, being derived from the Texel in Holland, which gave birth to that heroic line.

The Roost stood in the very heart of what at that time was called the debatable ground, lying between the British and American lines. The British held possession of the city and island of New York; while the Americans drew up towards the Highlands, holding their head-quarters at Peekskill. The intervening country from Croton River to Spiting Devil Creek was the debatable ground in question, liable to be harried by friend and foe, like the Scottish borders of yore.

It is a rugged region; full of fastnesses. A line of rocky hills extends through it like a backbone, sending out ribs on either side; but these rude hills are for the most part richly wooded, and inclose little fresh pastoral valleys watered by the Neperan, the Pocantico,* and other beautiful streams, along which the Indians built their wigwams in the olden time.

In the fastnesses of these hills, and along these valleys existed, in the time of which I am treating, and indeed exist to the present day, a race of hard-headed, hard-handed, stout-hearted yeomen, descendants of the primitive Nederlanders. Men obstinately attached to the soil,

---

* The Neperan, vulgarly called the Saw-Mill River, winds for many miles through a lovely valley, shrouded by groves, and dotted by Dutch farm-houses, and empties itself into the Hudson, at the ancient Dorp of Yonkers. The Pocantico, rising among woody hills, winds in many a wizard maze, through the sequestered haunts of Sleepy Hollow. We owe it to the indefatigable researches of MR. KNICKERBOCKER, that those beautiful streams are rescued from modern common-place, and reinvested with their ancient Indian names. The correctness of the venerable historian may be ascertained by reference to the records of the original Indian grants to the Herr Frederick Philipsen, preserved in the county clerk's office, at White Plains.

and neither to be fought nor bought out of their paternal acres. Most of them were strong Whigs throughout the war; some, however, were Tories, or adherents to the old kingly rule; who considered the revolution a mere rebellion, soon to be put down by his majesty's forces. A number of these took refuge within the British lines, joined the military bands of refugees, and became pioneers or leaders to foraging parties sent out from New York to scour the country and sweep off supplies for the British army.

In a little while the debatable ground became infested by roving bands, claiming from either side, and all pretending to redress wrongs and punish political offences; but all prone in the exercise of their high functions, to sack hen-roosts, drive off cattle, and lay farm-houses under contribution: such was the origin of two great orders of border chivalry, the Skinners and the Cow Boys, famous in revolutionary story; the former fought, or rather marauded under the American, the latter under the British banner. In the zeal of service, both were apt to make blunders, and confound the property of friend and foe. Neither of them in the heat and hurry of a foray had time to ascertain the politics of a horse or cow, which they were driving off into captivity; nor, when they wrung the neck of a rooster, did they trouble their heads whether he crowed for Congress or King George.

To check these enormities, a confederacy was formed among the yeomanry who had suffered from these maraudings. It was composed for the most part of farmers' sons, bold, hard-riding lads, well armed, and well mounted, and undertook to clear the country round of Skinner and Cow Boy, and all other border vermin; as the Holy Brotherhood in old times cleared Spain of the banditti which infested her highways.

Wolfert's Roost was one of the rallying places of this confederacy, and Jacob Van Tassel one of its members. He was eminently fitted for the service: stout of frame, bold of heart, and like his predecessor, the warrior sachem of yore, delighting in daring enterprises. He had an Indian's sagacity in discovering when the enemy was on the maraud, and in hearing the distant tramp of cattle. It seemed as if he had a scout on every hill, and an ear as quick as that of Fine Ear in the fairy tale.

The foraging parties of tories and refugees had now to be secret and sudden in their forays into Westchester County; to make a hasty maraud among the farms, sweep the cattle into a drove, and hurry down to the lines along the river road, or the valley of the Neperan. Before they were half way down, Jacob Van Tassel, with the holy brotherhood of Tarrytown, Petticoat Lane, and Sleepy Hollow, would be clattering at their heels. And now there would be a general scamper for King's Bridge, the pass over Spiting Devil Creek into the British lines. Sometimes the moss-troopers would be overtaken, and eased of part of their booty. Sometimes the whole cavalgada would urge its headlong course across the bridge with thundering tramp and dusty whirl-wind. At such times their pursuers would rein up their steeds, survey that perilous pass with wary eye and, wheeling about, indemnify themselves by foraging the refugee region of Morrisania.

While the debatable land was liable to be thus harried, the great Tappan Sea, along which it extends, was likewise domineered over by the foe. British ships of war were anchored here and there in the wide expanses of the river, mere floating castles to hold it in subjection. Stout galleys armed with eighteen pounders, and navigated with sails and oars, cruised about like hawks; while row-boats made descents upon the land, and foraged the country along shore.

It was a sore grievance to the yeomanry along the Tappan Sea to behold that little Mediterranean ploughed by hostile prows, and the noble river of which they were so proud, reduced to a state of thraldom. Councils of war were held by captains of market-boats and other river craft, to devise ways and means of dislodging the enemy. Here and there on a point of land extending into the Tappan Sea, a mud work would be thrown up, and an old field-piece mounted, with which a knot of rustic artillerymen would fire away for a long summer's day at some frigate dozing at anchor far out of reach; and reliques of such works may still be seen overgrown with weeds and brambles, with per-adventure the half-buried fragment of a cannon which may have burst.

Jacob Van Tassel was a prominent man in these belligerent opera-tions; but he was prone moreover, to carry on a petty warfare of his own for his individual recreation and refreshment. On a row of hooks above the fireplace of the Roost, reposed his great piece of ordnance; a duck, or rather goose gun of unparalleled longitude, with which it was said he could kill a wild goose half way across the Tappan Sea. Indeed there are as many wonders told of this renowned gun, as of the enchanted weapons of classic story. When the belligerent feeling was strong upon Jacob, he would take down his gun, sally forth alone, and prowl along shore, dodging behind rocks and trees, watching for hours together any ship or galley at anchor or becalmed; as a valorous mouser will watch a rat hole. So sure as a boat approached the shore, bang! went the great goose gun, sending on board a shower of slugs and buck shot; and away scuttled Jacob Van Tassel through some woody ravine. As the Roost stood in a lonely situation, and might be attacked, he guarded against surprise by making loop-holes in the stone walls, through which to fire upon an assailant. His wife was stout-hearted as himself, and could load as fast as he could fire, and his sister, Nochie Van Wurmer, a redoubtable widow, was a match,

as he said, for the stoutest man in the country. Thus garrisoned, his
little castle was fitted to stand a siege, and Jacob was the man to
defend it to the last charge of powder.

In the process of time the Roost became one of the secret stations,
or lurking places, of the Water Guard. This was an aquatic corps in
the pay of government, organized to range the waters of the Hudson,
and keep watch upon the movements of the enemy. It was composed
of nautical men of the river and hardy youngsters of the adjacent
country, expert at pulling an oar or handling a musket. They were
provided with whale-boats, long and sharp, shaped like canoes, and
formed to lie lightly on the water, and be rowed with great rapidity.
In these they would lurk out of sight by day, in nooks and bays, and
behind points of land; keeping a sharp look-out upon the British ships,
and giving intelligence to head quarters of any extraordinary movement.
At night they rowed about in pairs, pulling quietly along with muffled
oars, under shadow of the land, or gliding like spectres about frigates
and guard ships to cut off any boat that might be sent to shore. In this
way they were a source of constant uneasiness and alarm to the enemy.

The Roost, as has been observed, was one of their lurking places;
having a cove in front where their whale-boats could be drawn up out
of sight, and Jacob Van Tassel being a vigilant ally ready to take a
part in any "scout or scrummage" by land or water. At this little
warrior nest the hard-riding lads from the hills would hold consultations with the chivalry of the river, and here were concerted divers
of those daring enterprises which resounded from Spiting Devil Creek
even unto Anthony's Nose. Here was concocted the midnight invasion
of New-York Island, and the conflagration of Delancy's Tory mansion,
which makes such a blaze in revolutionary history. Nay more, if the
traditions of the Roost may be credited, here was meditated by Jacob
Van Tassel and his compeers, a nocturnal foray into New York itself,
to surprise and carry off the British commanders Howe and Clinton,
and put a triumphant close to the war!

There is no knowing whether this notable scheme might not have
been carried into effect, had not one of Jacob Van Tassel's egregious
exploits along shore with his goose-gun, with which he thought himself
a match for any thing, brought vengeance on his house.

It so happened, that in the course of one of his solitary prowls he
descried a British transport aground; the stern swung toward shore
within point-blank shot. The temptation was too great to be resisted.
Bang! went the great goose-gun from the covert of the trees, shivering
the cabin windows and driving all hands forward. Bang! bang! the
shots were repeated. The reports brought other of Jacob's fellow bush-
fighters to the spot. Before the transport could bring a gun to bear,

or land a boat to take revenge, she was soundly peppered, and the coast evacuated.

This was the last of Jacob's triumphs. He fared like some heroic spider that has unwittingly ensnared a hornet to the utter ruin of his web. It was not long after the above exploit that he fell into the hands of the enemy in the course of one of his forays, and was carried away prisoner to New York. The Roost itself, as a pestilent rebel nest, was marked out for signal punishment. The cock of the Roost being captive, there was none to garrison it but his stout-hearted spouse, his redoubtable sister, Nochie Van Wurmer, and Dinah, a strapping negro wench. An armed vessel came to anchor in front; a boat full of men pulled to shore. The garrison flew to arms, that is to say, to mops, broom-sticks, shovels, tongs, and all kinds of domestic weapons; for unluckily, the great piece of ordnance, the goose-gun, was absent with its owner. Above all, a vigorous defence was made with that most potent of female weapons, the tongue. Never did invaded hen-roost make a more vociferous outcry. It was all in vain. The house was sacked and plundered, fire was set to each corner, and in a few moments its blaze shed a baleful light far over the Tappan Sea. The invaders then pounced upon the blooming Laney Van Tassel, the beauty of the Roost, and endeavored to bear her off to the boat. But here was the real tug of war. The mother, the aunt, and the strapping negro wench, all flew to the rescue. The struggle continued down to the very water's edge; when a voice from the armed vessel at anchor, ordered the spoilers to desist; they relinquished their prize, jumped into their boats, and pulled off, and the heroine of the Roost escaped with a mere rumpling of the feathers.

As to the stout Jacob himself, he was detained a prisoner in New-York for the greater part of the war; in the mean time the Roost remained a melancholy ruin, its stone walls and brick chimneys alone standing, the resorts of bats and owls. Superstitious notions prevailed about it. None of the country people would venture alone at night down the rambling lane which led to it, overhung with trees and crossed here and there by a wild wandering brook. The story went that one of the victims of Jacob Van Tassel's great goose-gun had been buried there in unconsecrated ground.

Even the Tappan Sea in front was said to be haunted. Often in the still twilight of a summer evening, when the Sea would be as glass, and the opposite hills would throw their purple shadows half across it, a low sound would be heard as of the steady vigorous pull of oars, though not a boat was to be descried. Some might have supposed that a boat was rowed along unseen under the deep shadows of the opposite shores; but the ancient traditionists of the neighborhood knew better.

Some said it was one of the whale-boats of the old water-guard, sunk by the British ships during the war, but now permitted to haunt its old cruising grounds; but the prevalent opinion connected it with the awful fate of Rumbout Van Dam of graceless memory. He was a roystering Dutchman of Spiting Devil, who in times long past had navigated his boat alone one Saturday the whole length of the Tappan Sea, to attend a quilting frolic at Kakiat, on the western shore. Here he had danced, and drunk, until midnight, when he entered his boat to return home. He was warned that he was on the verge of Sunday morning; but he pulled off nevertheless, swearing he would not land until he reached Spiting Devil, if it took him a month of Sundays. He was never seen afterwards; but may be heard plying his oars, as above mentioned, being the Flying Dutchman of the Tappan Sea, doomed to ply between Kakiat and Spiting Devil until the day of judgment.

CHRONICLE III

The revolutionary war was over. The debatable ground had once more become a quiet agricultural region; the border chivalry had turned their swords into ploughshares, and their spears into pruning hooks, and hung up their guns, only to be taken down occasionally in a campaign against wild pigeons on the hills, or wild ducks upon the Hudson. Jacob Van Tassel, whilome carried captive to New York, a flagitious rebel, had come forth from captivity a "hero of seventy-six." In a little while he sought the scenes of his former triumphs and mishaps, rebuilt the Roost, restored his goose-gun to the hooks over the fireplace, and reared once more on high the glittering weathercocks.

Years and years passed over the time-honored little mansion. The honeysuckle and the sweetbrier crept up its walls; the wren and the phœbe bird built under the eaves; it gradually became almost hidden among trees, through which it looked forth, as with half-shut eyes, upon the Tappan Sea. The Indian spring, famous in the days of the wizard sachem, still welled up at the bottom of the green bank; and the wild brook, wild as ever, came babbling down the ravine, and threw itself into the little cove where of yore the water-guard harbored their whaleboats.

Such was the state of the Roost many years since, at the time when Diedrich Knickerbocker came into this neighborhood, in the course of his researches among the Dutch families for materials for his immortal history. The exterior of the eventful little pile seemed to him full of promise. The crow-step gables were of the primitive architecture of the province. The weathercocks which surmounted them had crowed in the glorious days of the New Netherlands. The one above the porch had actually glittered of yore on the great Vander Heyden palace at Albany!

The interior of the mansion fulfilled its external promise. Here were records of old times; documents of the Dutch dynasty, rescued from the profane hands of the English, by Wolfert Acker, when he retreated from New Amsterdam. Here he had treasured them up like buried gold, and here they had been miraculously preserved by St. Nicholas, at the time of the conflagration of the Roost.

Here then did old Diedrich Knickerbocker take up his abode for a time, and set to work with antiquarian zeal to decipher these precious documents, which, like the lost books of Livy, had baffled the research of former historians; and it is the facts drawn from these sources which give his work the preference, in point of accuracy, over every other history.

It was during his sojourn in this eventful neighborhood, that the historian is supposed to have picked up many of those legends, which have since been given by him to the world, or found among his papers. Such was the legend connected with the old Dutch church of Sleepy Hollow. The church itself was a monument of bygone days. It had been built in the early times of the province. A tablet over the portal bore the names of its founders: Frederick Filipson, a mighty man of yore, patroon of Yonkers, and his wife Katrina Van Courtland, of the Van Courtlands of Croton; a powerful family connexion, with one foot resting on Spiting Devil Creek, and the other on the Croton River.

Two weathercocks, with the initials of these illustrious personages, graced each end of the church, one perched over the belfry, the other over the chancel. As usual with ecclesiastical weathercocks, each pointed a different way; and there was a perpetual contradiction between them on all points of windy doctrine; emblematic, alas! of the Christian propensity to schism and controversy.

In the burying-ground adjacent to the church, reposed the earliest fathers of a wide rural neighborhood. Here families were garnered together, side by side, in long platoons, in this last gathering place of kindred. With pious hand would Diedrich Knickerbocker turn down the weeds and brambles which had overgrown the tombstones, to decipher inscriptions in Dutch and English, of the names and virtues of succeeding generations of Van Tassels, Van Warts, and other historical worthies, with their portraitures faithfully carved, all bearing the family likeness to cherubs.

The congregation in those days was of a truly rural character. City fashions had not as yet stole up to Sleepy Hollow. Dutch sun-bonnets and honest homespun still prevailed. Every thing was in primitive style, even to the bucket of water and tin cup near the door in summer, to assuage the thirst caused by the heat of the weather or the drouth of the sermon.

The pulpit, with its wide-spreading sounding board, and the communion table, curiously carved, had each come from Holland in the olden time, before the arts had sufficiently advanced in the colony for such achievements. Around these on Sundays would be gathered the elders of the church, gray-headed men who led the psalmody, and in whom it would be difficult to recognize the hard-riding lads of yore, who scoured the debatable land in the time of the revolution.

The drowsy influence of Sleepy Hollow was apt to breathe into this sacred edifice; and now and then an elder might be seen with his handkerchief over his face to keep off the flies, and apparently listening to the dominie; but really sunk into a summer slumber, lulled by the sultry notes of the locust from neighboring trees.

And now a word or two about Sleepy Hollow, which many have rashly deemed a fanciful creation, like the Lubberland of mariners. It was probably the mystic and dreamy sound of the name which first tempted the historian of the Manhattoes into its spellbound mazes. As he entered, all nature seemed for the moment to awake from its slumbers and break forth into gratulations. The quail whistled a welcome from the corn field; the loquacious cat-bird flew from bush to bush with restless wing proclaiming his approach, or perked inquisitively into his face, as if to get a knowledge of his physiognomy. The woodpecker tapped a tattoo on the hollow apple tree, and then peered round the trunk, as if asking how he relished the salutation; while the squirrel scampered along the fence, whisking his tail over his head by way of a huzza.

Here reigned the golden mean extolled by poets, in which no gold was to be found and very little silver. The inhabitants of the Hollow were of the primitive stock, and had intermarried and bred in and in, from the earliest time of the province, never swarming far from the parent hive, but dividing and subdividing their paternal acres as they swarmed.

Here were small farms, each having its little portion of meadow and corn field; its orchard of gnarled and sprawling apple trees; its garden in which the rose, the marigold and hollyhock, grew sociably with the cabbage, the pea, and the pumpkin; each had its low-eaved mansion redundant with white-headed children; with an old hat nailed against the wall for the housekeeping wren; the coop on the grass-plot, where the motherly hen clucked round with her vagrant brood: each had its stone well, with a moss-covered bucket suspended to the long

balancing pole, acording to antediluvian hydraulics; while within doors
resounded the eternal hum of the spinning wheel.

Many were the great historical facts which the worthy Diedrich
collected in these lowly mansions, and patiently would he sit by the
old Dutch housewives with a child on his knee, or a purring grimalkin
on his lap, listing to endless ghost stories spun forth to the humming
accompaniment of the wheel.

The delighted historian pursued his explorations far into the foldings
of the hills where the Pocantico winds its wizard stream among the
mazes of its old Indian haunts; sometimes running darkly in pieces of
woodland beneath balancing sprays of beech and chestnut: sometimes
sparkling between grassy borders in fresh green intervals; here and
there receiving the tributes of silver rills which came whimpering down
the hill sides from their parent springs.

In a remote part of the Hollow, where the Pocantico forced its way
down rugged rocks, stood Carl's mill, the haunted house of the neighborhood. It was indeed a goblin-looking pile; shattered and time-worn;
dismal with clanking wheels and rushing streams, and all kinds of
uncouth noises. A horse shoe nailed to the door to keep off witches,
seemed to have lost its power; for as Diedrich approached, an old
negro thrust his head all dabbled with flour, out of a hole above the
water wheel, and grinned and rolled his eyes, and appeared to be the
very hobgoblin of the place. Yet this proved to be the great historic
genius of the Hollow, abounding in that valuable information never to
be acquired from books. Diedrich Knickerbocker soon discovered his
merit. They had long talks together seated on a broken millstone, heedless of the water and the clatter of the mill; and to his conference with
that African sage, many attribute the surprising, though true story of
Ichabod Crane, and the Headless Horseman of Sleepy Hollow. We
refrain, however, from giving farther researches of the historian of
the Manhattoes, during his sojourn at the Roost; but may return to
them in future pages.

Reader, the Roost still exists. Time, which changes all things, is slow
in its operations on a Dutchman's dwelling. The stout Jacob Van Tassel,
it is true, sleeps with his fathers; and his great goose-gun with him:
yet his strong-hold still bears the impress of its Dutch origin. Odd rumors
have gathered about it, as they are apt to do about old mansions, like
moss and weather stains. The shade of Wolfert Acker still walks his
unquiet rounds at night in the orchard; and a white figure has now and
then been seen seated at a window and gazing at the moon, from a room
in which a young lady is said to have died of love and green apples.

Mementoes of the sojourn of Diedrich Knickerbocker are still cherished at the Roost. His elbow chair and antique writing-desk maintain their place in the room he occupied, and his old cocked hat still hangs on a peg against the wall.

THE BIRDS OF SPRING

My quiet residence in the country, aloof from fashion, politics, and the money market, leaves me rather at a loss for occupation, and drives me occasionally to the study of nature, and other low pursuits. Having few neighbors, also, on whom to keep a watch, and exercise my habits of observation, I am fain to amuse myself with prying into the domestic concerns and peculiarities of the animals around me; and, during the present season, have derived considerable entertainment from certain sociable little birds, almost the only visiters we have, during this early part of the year.

Those who have passed the winter in the country, are sensible of the delightful influences that accompany the earliest indications of spring; and of these, none are more delightful than the first notes of the birds. There is one modest little sad-colored bird, much resembling a wren, which came about the house just on the skirts of winter, when not a blade of grass was to be seen, and when a few prematurely warm days had given a flattering foretaste of soft weather. He sang early in the dawning, long before sunrise, and late in the evening, just before the closing in of night, his matin and his vesper hymns. It is true, he sang occasionally throughout the day; but at these still hours, his song was more remarked. He sat on a leafless tree, just before the window, and warbled forth his notes, few and simple, but singularly sweet, with something of a plaintive tone that heightened their effect.

The first morning that he was heard, was a joyous one among the young folks of my household. The long, death-like sleep of winter was at an end; nature was once more awakening; they now promised themselves the immediate appearance of buds and blossoms. I was reminded of the tempest-tossed crew of Columbus, when, after their long dubious voyage, the field birds came singing round the ship, though still far at sea, rejoicing them with the belief of the immediate proximity of land. A sharp return of winter almost silenced my little songster, and dashed the hilarity of the household; yet still he poured forth, now and then, a few plaintive notes, between the frosty pipings of the breeze, like gleams of sunshine between wintry clouds.

I have consulted my book of ornithology in vain, to find out the name of this kindly little bird, who certainly deserves honor and favor far beyond his modest pretensions. He comes like the lowly violet, the most unpretending, but welcomest of flowers, breathing the sweet promise of the early year.

17

Another of our feathered visiters, who follow close upon the steps of winter, is the Pe-wit, or Pe-wee, or Phœbe-bird; for he is called by each of these names, from a fancied resemblance to the sound of his monotonous note. He is a sociable little being, and seeks the habitation of man. A pair of them have built beneath my porch, and have reared several broods there, for two years past, their nest being never disturbed. They arrive early in the spring, just when the crocus and the snow-drop begin to peep forth. Their first chirp spreads gladness through the house. "The Phœbe-birds have come!" is heard on all sides; they are welcomed back like members of the family; and speculations are made upon where they have been, and what countries they have seen, during their long absence. Their arrival is the more cheering, as it is pronounced, by the old weather-wise people of the country, the sure sign that the severe frosts are at an end, and that the gardener may resume his labors with confidence.

About this time, too, arrives the blue-bird, so poetically yet truly described by Wilson. His appearance gladdens the whole landscape. You hear his soft warble in every field. He sociably approaches your habitation, and takes up his residence in your vicinity. But why should I attempt to describe him, when I have Wilson's own graphic verses, to place him before the reader?

WHEN winter's cold tempests and snows are no more,
    Green meadows and brown furrowed fields reäppearing,
The fishermen hauling their shad to the shore,
    And cloud-cleaving geese to the lakes are a-steering;
When first the lone butterfly flits on the wing,
    When red glow the maples, so fresh and so pleasing,
O then comes the blue-bird, the herald of spring,
    And hails with his warblings the charms of the season.

The loud-piping frogs make the marshes to ring;
    Then warm glows the sunshine, and warm grows the weather;
The blue woodland flowers just beginning to spring,
    And spice-wood and sassafras budding together;
O then to your gardens, ye housewives, repair,
    Your walks border up, sow and plant at your leisure;
The blue-bird will chant from his box such an air,
    That all your hard toils will seem truly a pleasure!

He flits through the orchard, he visits each tree,
    The red flowering peach, and the apple's sweet blossoms;
He snaps up destroyers, wherever they be,
    And seizes the caitiffs that lurk in their bosoms;

He drags the vile grub from the corn it devours,
  The worms from the webs where they riot and welter;
His song and his services freely are ours,
  And all that he asks is, in summer a shelter.

The ploughman is pleased when he gleans in his train,
  Now searching the furrows, now mounting to cheer him;
The gard'ner delights in his sweet simple strain,
  And leans on his spade to survey and to hear him.
The slow lingering school-boys forget they'll be chid,
  While gazing intent, as he warbles before them,
In mantle of sky-blue, and bosom so red,
  That each little loiterer seems to adore him.

The happiest bird of our spring, however, and one that rivals the European lark, in my estimation, is the Boblincon, or Boblink, as he is commonly called. He arrives at that choice portion of our year, which, in this latitude, answers to the description of the month of May, so often given by the poets. With us, it begins about the middle of May, and lasts until nearly the middle of June. Earlier than this, winter is apt to return on its traces, and to blight the opening beauties of the year; and later than this, begin the parching, and panting, and dissolving heats of summer. But in this genial interval, nature is in all her freshness and fragrance: 'the rains are over and gone, the flowers appear upon the earth, the time of the singing of birds is come, and the voice of the turtle is heard in the land.' The trees are now in their fullest foliage and brightest verdure; the woods are gay with the clustered flowers of the laurel; the air is perfumed by the sweet-briar and the wild rose; the meadows are enamelled with clover-blossoms; while the young apple, the peach, and the plum, begin to swell, and the cherry to glow, among the green leaves.

This is the chosen season of revelry of the Boblink. He comes amidst the pomp and fragrance of the season; his life seems all sensibility and enjoyment, all song and sunshine. He is to be found in the soft bosoms of the freshest and sweetest meadows; and is most in song, when the clover is in blossom. He perches on the topmost twig of a tree, or on some long flaunting weed, and as he rises and sinks with the breeze, pours forth a succession of rich tinkling notes; crowding one upon another, like the outpouring melody of the skylark, and possessing the same rapturous character. Sometimes he pitches from the summit of a tree, begins his song as soon as he gets upon the wing, and flutters tremulously down to the earth, as if overcome with ecstacy at his own music. Sometimes he is in pursuit of his paramour; always in full song, as if he would win her by his melody; and always with the same appearance of intoxication and delight.

Of all the birds of our groves and meadows, the Boblink was the envy of my boyhood. He crossed my path in the sweetest weather, and the sweetest season of the year, when all nature called to the fields and the rural feeling throbbed in every bosom; but when I, luckless urchin! was doomed to be mewed up, during the livelong day, in that purgatory of boyhood, a school-room. It seemed as if the little varlet mocked at me, as he flew by in full song, and sought to taunt me with his happier lot. Oh, how I envied him! No lessons, no tasks, no hateful school; nothing but holiday, frolic, green fields, and fine weather. Had I been then more versed in poetry, I might have addressed him in the words of Logan to the cuckoo:

> Sweet bird! thy bower is ever green,
>   Thy sky is ever clear;
> Thou hast no sorrow in thy note,
>   No winter in thy year.
>
> Oh! could I fly, I'd fly with thee;
>   We'd make, on joyful wing,
> Our annual visit round the globe,
>   Companions of the spring!

Farther observation and experience have given me a different idea of this little feathered voluptuary, which I will venture to impart, for the benefit of my school-boy readers, who may regard him with the same unqualified envy and admiration which I once indulged. I have shown him only as I saw him at first, in what I may call the poetical part of his career, when he in a manner devoted himself to elegant pursuits and enjoyments, and was a bird of music, and song, and taste, and sensibility, and refinement. While this lasted, he was sacred from injury; the very school-boy would not fling a stone at him, and the merest rustic would pause to listen to his strain. But mark the difference. As the year advances, as the clover-blossoms disappear and the spring fades into summer, he gradually gives up his elegant tastes and habits; doffs his poetical suit of black, assumes a russet dusty garb, and sinks to the gross enjoyments of common vulgar birds. His notes no longer vibrate on the ear; he is stuffing himself with the seeds of the tall weeds on which he lately swung and chanted so melodiously. He has become a "bon vivant," a "gourmand;" with him now there is nothing like the "joys of the table." In a little while he grows tired of plain homely fare, and is off on a gastronomical tour in quest of foreign luxuries. We next hear of him with myriads of his kind, banqueting among the reeds of the Delaware; and grown corpulent with good feeding. He has changed his name in travelling. Boblincon no more— he is the *Reed-bird* now, the much sought for titbit of Pennsylvania epicures; the rival in unlucky fame of the ortolan! Wherever he goes, pop! pop! pop! every rusty firelock in the country is blazing away. He sees his companions falling by thousands around him.

Does he take warning and reform?—Alas not he! Incorrigible epicure! again he wings his flight. The rice swamps of the south invite him. He gorges himself among them almost to bursting; he can scarcely fly for corpulency. He has once more changed his name, and is now the famous *Rice-bird* of the Carolinas.

Last stage of his career; behold him spitted with dozens of his corpulent companions, and served up, a vaunted dish, on the table of some Southern gastronome.

Such is the story of the Boblink; once spiritual, musical, admired, the joy of the meadows, and the favorite bird of spring; finally, a gross little sensualist who expiates his sensuality in the larder. His story contains a moral, worthy the attention of all little birds and little boys; warning them to keep to those refined and intellectual pursuits, which raised him to so high a pitch of popularity, during the early part of his career; but to eschew all tendency to that gross and dissipated indulgence, which brought this mistaken little bird to an untimely end.

Which is all at present, from the well-wisher of little boys and little birds,

GEOFFREY CRAYON.

THE CREOLE VILLAGE

A SKETCH FROM A STEAMBOAT

First published in 1837

In traveling about our motley country, I am often reminded of Ariosto's account of the moon, in which the good paladin Astolpho found every thing garnered up, that had been lost on earth. So I am apt to imagine, that many things lost in the old world, are treasured up in the new; having been handed down from generation to generation, since the early days of the colonies. A European antiquary, therefore, curious in his researches after the ancient and almost obliterated customs and usages of his country, would do well to put himself upon the track of some early band of emigrants, follow them across the Atlantic, and rummage among their descendants on our shores.

In the phraseology of New England might be found many an old English provincial phrase, long since obsolete in the parent country, with some quaint relics of the roundheads; while Virginia cherishes peculiarities characteristic of the days of Elizabeth and Sir Walter Raleigh.

In the same way, the sturdy yeomanry of New Jersey and Pennsylvania keep up many usages fading away in ancient Germany; while many an honest, broad-bottomed custom, nearly extinct in venerable Holland, may be found flourishing in pristine vigor and luxuriance in Dutch villages, on the banks of the Mohawk and the Hudson.

In no other part of our country, however, are the customs and peculiarities, imported from the old world by the earlier settlers, kept up with more fidelity than in the little, poverty-stricken villages of Spanish and French origin, which border the rivers of ancient Louisiana. Their population is generally made up of the descendants of those nations, married and interwoven together, and occasionally crossed with a slight dash of the Indian. The French character, however, floats on top, as, from its buoyant qualities, it is sure to do, whenever it forms a particle, however small, of an intermixture.

In those serene and dilapidated villages, art and nature seem to stand still, and the world forgets to turn round. The revolutions that distract other parts of this mutable planet, reach not here, or pass over without leaving any trace. The fortunate inhabitants have none of that public spirit which extends its cares beyond its horizon, and imports trouble and perplexity from all quarters in newspapers. In fact, newspapers are almost unknown in these villages, and as French is the current language, the inhabitants have little community of opinion with their republican neighbors. They retain, therefore, their old habits of passive obedience to the decrees of government, as though they still lived under the absolute sway of colonial commandments, instead of being part and parcel of the sovereign people, and having a voice in public legislation.

A few aged men, who have grown gray on their hereditary acres, and are of the good old colonial stock, exert a patriarchal sway in all matters of public and private import; their opinions are considered oracular, and their word is law.

The inhabitants, moreover, have none of that eagerness for gain, and rage for improvement, which keep our people continually on the move, and our country towns incessantly in a state of transition. There the magic phrases, "town lots," "water privileges," "railroads," and other comprehensive and soul-stirring words, from the speculator's vocabulary, are never heard. The residents dwell in the houses built by their fore-fathers, without thinking of enlarging or modernising them, or pulling them down and turning them into granite stores. The trees, under which they have been born, and have played in infancy, flourish un-disturbed; though, by cutting them down, they might open new streets, and put money in their pockets. In a word, the almighty dollar, that great object of universal devotion throughout our land, seems to have no genuine devotees in these peculiar villages; and unless some of its missionaries penetrate there, and erect banking houses and other pious shrines, there is no knowing how long the inhabitants may remain in their present state of contented poverty.

In descending one of our great western rivers in a steamboat, I met with two worthies from one of these villages, who had been on a distant excursion, the longest they had ever made, as they seldom ventured far from home. One was the great man, or Grand Signior of the village; not that he enjoyed any legal privileges or power there, every thing of the kind having been done away when the province was ceded by France to the United States. His sway over his neighbors was merely one of custom and convention, out of deference to his family. Beside, he was worth full fifty thousand dollars, an amount almost equal, in the imaginations of the villagers, to the treasures of king Solomon.

This very substantial old gentleman, though of the fourth or fifth generation in this country, retained the true Gallic feature and deport-ment, and reminded me of one of those provincial potentates, that are to be met in the remote parts of France. He was of a large frame, a ginger-bread complexion, strong features, eyes that stood out like

glass knobs, and a prominent nose, which he frequently regaled from
a gold snuff-box, and occasionally blew with a colored handkerchief,
until it sounded like a trumpet.

He was attended by an old negro, as black as ebony, with a huge
mouth, in a continual grin; evidently a privileged and favorite servant,
who had grown up and grown old with him. He was dressed in creole
style—with white jacket and trowsers, a stiff shirt collar, that threatened
to cut off his ears, a bright madrass handkerchief tied round his head,
and large gold ear-rings. He was the politest negro I met with in a western
tour; and that is saying a great deal, for, excepting the Indians, the
negroes are the most gentlemanlike personages to be met with in those
parts. It is true, they differ from the Indians in being a little extra
polite and complimentary. He was also one of the merriest; and here,
too, the negroes, however we may deplore their unhappy condition,
have the advantage of their masters. The whites are, in general, too
free and prosperous to be merry. The cares of maintaining their rights
and liberties, adding to their wealth, and making presidents, engross
all their thoughts, and dry up all the moisture of their souls. If you
hear a broad, hearty, devil-may-care laugh, be assured it is a negro's.

Beside this African domestic, the signior of the village had another
no less cherished and privileged attendant. This was a huge dog, of
the mastiff breed, with a deep, hanging mouth, and a look of surly
gravity. He walked about the cabin with the air of a dog perfectly
at home, and who had paid for his passage. At dinner time he took
his seat beside his master, giving him a glance now and then out of a
corner of his eye, which bespoke perfect confidence that he would not
be forgotten. Nor was he—every now and then a huge morsel would
be thrown to him, peradventure the half-picked leg of a fowl, which
he would receive with a snap like the springing of a steel-trap—one
gulp, and all was down; and a glance of the eye told his master that
he was ready for another consignment.

The other village worthy, traveling in company with this signior, was
of a totally different stamp. Small, thin, and weazen-faced, as Frenchmen are apt to be represented in caricature, with a bright, squirrel-like
eye, and a gold ring in his ear. His dress was flimsy, and sat loosely
on his frame, and he had altogether the look of one with but little
coin in his pocket. Yet, though one of the poorest, I was assured he
was one of the merriest and most popular personages in his native village.

Compere Martin, as he was commonly called, was the factotum of
the place—sportsman, schoolmaster, and land-surveyor. He could sing,
dance, and, above all, play on the fiddle, an invaluable accomplishment
in an old French creole village, for the inhabitants have a hereditary

love for balls and fêtes; if they work but little, they dance a great deal, and a fiddle is the joy of their heart.

What had sent Compere Martin traveling with the Grand Signior I could not learn; he evidently looked up to him with great deference, and was assiduous in rendering him petty attentions; from which I concluded that he lived at home upon the crumbs which fell from his table. He was gayest when out of his sight; and had his song and his joke when forward, among the deck passengers; but altogether Compere Martin was out of his element on board of a steamboat. He was quite another being, I am told, when at home, in his own village.

Like his opulent fellow traveler, he too had his canine follower and retainer—and one suited to his different fortunes—one of the civilest, most unoffending little dogs in the world. Unlike the lordly mastiff, he seemed to think he had no right on board of the steamboat; if you did but look hard at him, he would throw himself upon his back, and lift up his legs, as if imploring mercy.

At table he took his seat a little distance from his master; not with the bluff, confident air of the mastiff, but quietly and diffidently; his head on one side, with one ear dubiously slouched, the other hopefully cocked up; his under teeth projecting beyond his black nose, and his eye wistfully following each morsel that went into his master's mouth.

If Compere Martin now and then should venture to abstract a morsel from his plate, to give to his humble companion, it was edifying to see with what diffidence the exemplary little animal would take hold of it, with the very tip of his teeth, as if he would almost rather not, or was fearful of taking too great a liberty. And then with what decorum would he eat it! How many efforts would he make in swallowing it, as if it stuck in his throat; with what daintiness would he lick his lips; and then with what an air of thankfulness would he resume his seat, with his teeth once more projecting beyond his nose, and an eye of humble expectation fixed upon his master.

It was late in the afternoon when the steamboat stopped at the village which was the residence of these worthies. It stood on the high bank of the river, and bore traces of having been a frontier trading post. There were the remains of stockades that once protected it from the Indians, and the houses were in the ancient Spanish and French colonial taste, the place having been successively under the domination of both those nations prior to the cession of Louisiana to the United States.

The arrival of the signior of fifty thousand dollars, and his humble companion, Compere Martin, had evidently been looked forward to as an event in the village. Numbers of men, women, and children, white, yellow, and black, were collected on the river bank; most of

them clad in old-fashioned French garments, and their heads decorated
with colored handkerchiefs, or white nightcaps. The moment the steamboat came within sight and hearing, there was a waving of handkerchiefs,
and a screaming and bawling of salutations, and felicitations, that baffle
all description.

The old gentleman of fifty thousand dollars was received by a train
of relatives, and friends, and children, and grandchildren, whom he
kissed on each cheek, and who formed a procession in his rear, with a
legion of domestics, of all ages, following him to a large, old-fashioned
French house, that domineered over the village.

His black valet de chambre, in white jacket and trowsers, and gold
ear-rings, was met on the shore by a boon, though rustic companion,
a tall negro fellow, with a long, good-humored face, and the profile
of a horse, which stood out from beneath a narrow-rimmed straw hat,
stuck on the back of his head. The explosions of laughter of these two
varlets on meeting and exchanging compliments, were enough to electrify
the country round.

The most hearty reception, however, was that given to Compere
Martin. Every body, young and old, hailed him before he got to land.
Every body had a joke for Compere Martin, and Compere Martin had
a joke for every body. Even his little dog appeared, to partake of his
popularity, and to be caressed by every hand. Indeed, he was quite a
different animal the moment he touched the land. Here he was at
home; here he was of consequence. He barked, he leaped, he frisked
about his old friends, and then would skim round the place in a wide
circle, as if mad.

I traced Compere Martin and his little dog to their home. It was
an old ruinous Spanish house, of large dimensions, with verandas
overshadowed by ancient elms. The house had probably been the
residence, in old times, of the Spanish commandant. In one wing of
this crazy, but aristocratical abode, was nestled the family of my
fellow traveler; for poor devils are apt to be magnificently clad and
lodged, in the cast-off clothes and abandoned palaces of the great
and wealthy.

The arrival of Compere Martin was welcomed by a legion of women,
children, and mongrel curs; and, as poverty and gayety generally go
hand in hand among the French and their descendants, the crazy
mansion soon resounded with loud gossip and lighthearted laughter.

As the steamboat paused a short time at the village, I took occasion
to stroll about the place. Most of the houses were in the French taste,
with casements and rickety verandas, but most of them in flimsy and
ruinous condition. All the wagons, ploughs, and other utensils about
the place were of ancient and inconvenient Gallic construction, such

as had been brought from France in the primitive days of the colony. The very looks of the people reminded me of the villages of France.

From one of the houses came the hum of a spinning wheel, accompanied by a scrap of an old French chanson, which I have heard many a time among the peasantry of Languedoc, doubtless a traditional song, brought over by the first French emigrants, and handed down from generation to generation.

Half a dozen young lasses emerged from the adjacent dwellings, reminding me, by their light step and gay costume, of scenes in ancient France, where taste in dress comes natural to every class of females. The trim bodice and colored petticoat, and little apron, with its pockets to receive the hands when in an attitude for conversation; the colored kerchief wound tastefully round the head, with a coquettish knot perking above one ear; and the neat slipper and tight drawn stocking, with its braid of narrow ribbon embracing the ankle where it peeps from its mysterious curtain. It is from this ambush that Cupid sends his most inciting arrows.

While I was musing upon the recollections thus accidentally summoned up, I heard the sound of a fiddle from the mansion of Compere Martin, the signal, no doubt, for a joyous gathering. I was disposed to turn my steps thither, and witness the festivities of one of the very few villages I had met with in my wide tour, that was yet poor enough to be merry; but the bell of the steamboat summoned me to re-embark.

As we swept away from the shore, I cast back a wistful eye upon the moss-grown roofs and ancient elms of the village, and prayed that the inhabitants might long retain their happy ignorance, their absence of all enterprise and improvement, their respect for the fiddle, and their contempt for the almighty dollar.* I fear, however, my prayer is doomed to be of no avail. In a little while, the steamboat whirled me to an American town, just springing into bustling and prosperous existence.

The surrounding forest had been laid out in town lots; frames of wooden buildings were rising from among stumps and burnt trees. The place already boasted a court-house, a jail, and two banks, all built of pine boards, on the model of Grecian temples. There were rival hotels, rival churches, and rival newspapers; together with the usual number of judges, and generals, and governors; not to speak of doctors by the dozen, and lawyers by the score.

* This phrase used for the first time, in this sketch, has since passed into current circulation, and by some has been questioned as savoring of irreverence. The author, therefore, owes it to his orthodoxy to declare that no irreverence was intended even to the dollar itself; which he is aware is daily becoming more and more an object of worship.

The place, I was told, was in an astonishing career of improvement, with a canal and two railroads in embryo. Lots doubled in price every week; every body was speculating in land; every body was rich; and every body was growing richer. The community, however, was torn to pieces by new doctrines in religion and in political economy; there were camp meetings, and agrarian meetings; and an election was at hand which, it was expected, would throw the whole country into a paroxysm.

Alas! with such an enterprising neighbor, what is to become of the poor little creole village!

MOUNTJOY:

OF SOME PASSAGES OUT OF THE LIFE OF A CASTLE-BUILDER

I was born among romantic scenery, in one of the wildest parts of the Hudson; which at that time was not so thickly settled as at present. My father was descended from one of the old Huguenot families, that came over to this country on the revocation of the edict of Nantz. He lived in a style of easy, rural independence, on a patrimonial estate that had been for two or three generations in the family. He was an indolent, good-natured man, took the world as it went, and had a kind of laughing philosophy, that parried all rubs and mishaps, and served him in place of wisdom. This was the part of his character least to my taste, for I was of an enthusiastic, excitable temperament, prone to kindle up with new schemes and projects; and he was apt to dash my sallying enthusiasm by some unlucky joke; so that, whenever I was in a glow with any sudden excitement, I stood in mortal dread of his good humor.

Yet he indulged me in every vagary; for I was an only son, and of course a personage of importance in the household. I had two sisters, older than myself, and one younger. The former were educated at New-York, under the eye of a maiden aunt; the latter remained at home, and was my cherished play-mate, the companion of all my thoughts. We were two imaginative little beings, of quick susceptibility, and prone to see wonders and mysteries in every thing around us. Scarce had we learned to read, when our mother made us holiday presents of all the nursery literature of the day; which at that time consisted of little books covered with gilt paper, adorned with "cuts," and filled with tales of fairies, giants, and enchanters.

What draughts of delightful fiction did we then inhale! My sister Sophy was of a soft and tender nature. She would weep over the woes of the Children in the Wood; or quake at the dark romance of Blue-Beard, and the terrible mysteries of the blue chamber, but I was all for enterprize and adventure. I burned to emulate the deeds of that heroic prince, who delivered the white cat from her enchantment; or he of no less royal blood, and doughty emprize, who broke the charmed slumber of the Beauty in the Wood!

The house in which we lived, was just the kind of place to foster such propensities. It was a venerable mansion, half villa, half farm-house. The oldest part was of stone, with loop-holes for musketry, having served as a family fortress in the time of the Indians. To this there

had been made various additions, some of brick, some of wood, according
to the exegencies of the moment; so that it was full of nooks and crooks,
and chambers of all sorts and sizes. It was buried among willows, elms,
and cherry trees, and surrounded with roses and holly-hocks, white
honey suckle and sweet-briar clambering about every window! A brood
of hereditary pigeons sunned themselves upon the roof; hereditary
swallows and martins built about the eaves and chimnies; and hereditary
bees hummed about the flower-beds.

Under the influence of our story-books, every object around us now
assumed a new character, and a charmed interest.

The wild flowers were no longer the mere ornaments of the fields,
or the resorts of the toilful bee; they were the lurking places of fairies.
We would watch the humming-bird, as it hovered around the trumpet
creeper at our porch, and the butterfly as it flitted up into the blue
air, above the sunny tree tops, and fancy them some of the tiny beings
from fairy land. I would call to mind all that I had read of Robin
Goodfellow, and his power of transformation. Oh how I envied him
that power! How I longed to be able to compress my form into utter
littleness; to ride the bold dragon-fly; swing on the tall bearded grass;
follow the ant into his subterraneous habitation, or dive into the
cavernous depths of the honeysuckle!

While I was yet a mere child, I was sent to a daily school, about
two miles distant. The school-house was on the edge of a wood; close
by a brook overhung with birches, alders, and dwarf willows. We of
the school who lived at some distance, came with our dinners put up
in little baskets. In the intervals of school hours, we would gather round
a spring under a tuft of hazel bushes, and have a kind of pic nic; inter-
changing the rustic dainties with which our provident mothers had
fitted us out. Then, when our joyous repast was over, and my companions were disposed for play, I would draw forth one of my
cherished story-books, stretch myself on the green sward, and soon
lose myself in its bewitching contents.

I became an oracle among my school-mates, on account of my
superior erudition, and soon imparted to them the contagion of my
infected fancy. Often in the evening, after school hours, we would
sit on the trunk of some fallen tree in the woods, and vie with each
other in telling extravagant stories, until the whip-poor-will began his
nightly moaning, and the fire-flies sparkled in the gloom. Then came
the perilous journey homeward. What delight we would take in getting
up wanton panics, in some dusky part of the wood; scampering like
frightened deer; pausing to take breath; renewing the panic, and
scampering off again, wild with fictitious terror!

Our greatest trial was to pass a dark, lonely pool, covered with pond-lillies, peopled with bull-frogs and water-snakes, and haunted by two white cranes. Oh! the terrors of that pond! How our little hearts would beat, as we approached it; what fearful glances we would throw around! and if by chance a plash of a wild duck, or the guttural twang of a bull-frog struck our ears, as we stole quietly by away we sped, nor paused until completely out of the woods. Then, when I reached home, what a world of adventures, and imaginary terrors, would I have to relate to my sister Sophy!

As I advanced in years, this turn of mind increased upon me, and became more confirmed. I abandoned myself to the impulses of a romantic imagination, which controled my studies, and gave a bias to all my habits. My father observed me continually with a book in my hand, and satisfied himself that I was a profound student; but what were my studies? Works of fiction; tales of chivalry; voyages of discovery; travels in the East; every thing, in short, that partook of adventure and romance. I well remember with what zest I entered upon that part of my studies, which treated of the heathen mythology and particularly of the sylvan dieties. Then indeed my school-books became dear to me. The neighborhood was well calculated to foster the reveries of a mind like mine. It abounded with solitary retreats, wild streams, solemn forests, and silent valleys. I would ramble about for a whole day, with a volume of Ovid's Metamorphoses in my pocket, and work myself into a kind of self delusion, so as to identify the surrounding scenes with those of which I had just been reading. I would loiter about a brook that glided through the shadowy depths of the forest, picturing it to myself the haunt of Naiades. I would steal round some bushy copse that opened upon a glade, as if I expected to come suddenly upon Diana and her nymphs; or to behold Pan and his satyrs bounding, with whoop and halloo, through the woodland. I would throw myself, during the panting heats of a summer noon, under the shade of some wide-spreading tree, and muse and dream away the hours, in a state of mental intoxication. I drank in the very light of day as nectar, and my soul seemed to bathe with extacy in the deep blue of a summer sky.

In these wanderings, nothing occurred to jar my feelings, or bring me back to the realities of life. There is a repose in our mighty forests, that gives full scope to the imagination. Now and then I would hear the distant sound of the wood-cutter's axe, or the crash of some tree which he had laid low; but these noises, echoing along the quiet landscape, could easily be wrought by fancy into harmony with its illusions. In general, however, the woody recesses of the neighborhood were peculiarly wild and unfrequented. I could ramble for a whole day, without coming upon any traces of cultivation. The partridge of

the wood scarcely seemed to shun my path, and the squirrel, from
his nut-tree, would gaze at me for an instant, with sparkling eye, as
if wondering at the unwonted intrusion.

I cannot help dwelling on this delicious period of my life; when as
yet I had known no sorrow, nor experienced any worldly care. I have
since studied much, both of books and men, and of course have grown
too wise to be so easily pleased; yet with all my wisdom, I must confess
I look back with a secret feeling of regret to the days of happy
ignorance, before I had begun to be a philosopher.

———————

It must be evident that I was in a hopeful training, for one who was
to descend into the arena of life, and wrestle with the world. The
tutor, also, who superintended my studies, in the more advanced stage
of my education, was just fitted to complete the *fata morgana*, which
was forming in my mind. His name was Glencoe. He was a pale,
melancholy-looking man, about forty years of age; a native of Scotland,
liberally educated, and who had devoted himself to the instruction
of youth, taste, rather than necessity: for, as he said, he loved the
human heart, and delighted to study it in its earlier impulses. My two
elder sisters, having returned home from a city boarding-school, were
likewise placed under his care, to direct their reading in history and
belles-lettres.

We all soon became attached to Glencoe. It is true, we were at first
somewhat prepossessed against him. His meagre, pallid countenance,
his broad pronunciation; his inattention to the little forms of society;
and an awkward and embarrassed manner, on first acquaintance, were
much against him; but we soon discovered that, under this unpromising
exterior, existed the kindest urbanity; the warmest sympathies; the
most enthusiastic benevolence. His mind was ingenious and acute. His
reading had been various, but more abstruse than profound, his memory
was stored, on all subjects, with facts, theories, and quotations, and
crowded with crude materials for thinking. Then, in a moment of
excitement, would be, as it were, melted down, and poured forth in
the lava of a heated imagination. At such moments, the change in the
whole man was wonderful. His meagre form would acquire a dignity
and grace; his long, pale visage would flash with a hectic glow; his
eyes would beam with intense speculation, and there would be pathetic
tones and deep modulations, in his voice, that delighted the ear, and
spoke movingly to the heart.

But what most endeared him to us, was the kindness and sympathy
with which he entered into all our interests and wishes. Instead of

curbing and checking our young imaginations with the reins of sober reason, he was a little too apt to catch the impulse, and be hurried away with us. He could not withstand the excitement of any sally of feeling or fancy; and was prone to lend heightening tints to the illusive colouring of youthful anticipation.

Under his guidance, my sisters and myself soon entered upon a more extended range of studies; but while they wandered, with delighted minds, through the wide field of history and belles-lettres, a nobler walk was opened to my superior intellect.

The mind of Glencoe presented a singular mixture of philosophy and poetry. He was fond of metaphysics, and prone to indulge in abstract speculations, though his metaphysics were somewhat fine spun, and fanciful, and his speculations were apt to partake of what my father most irreverently termed "humbug." For my part, I delighted in them, and the more especially, because they set my father to sleep, and completely confounded my sisters. I entered, with my accustomed eagerness into this new branch of study. Metaphysics were now my passion. My sisters attempted to accompany me, but they they soon faltered, and gave out before they had got half way through Smith's Theory of Moral Sentiments. I, however, went on, exalting in my strength. Glencoe supplied me with books, and I devoured them with appetite, if not digestion. We walked and talked together under the trees before the house; or sat apart, like Milton's angels, and held high converse upon themes beyond the grasp of ordinary intellects. Glencoe possessed a kind of philosophic chivalry, in imitation of the old peripatetic sages, and was continually dreaming of romantic enter-prizes in morals, and splendid systems for the improvement of society. He had a fanciful mode of illustrating abstract subjects, peculiarly to my taste; clothing them with the language of poetry and throwing round them almost the magic hues of fiction. "How charming," thought I, "is divine philosophy;" not harsh and crabbed, as dull fools suppose,

> "But a perpetual feast of nectar'd sweets
> Where no crude surfeit reigns."

I felt a wonderful self-complacency at being on such excellent terms with a man whom I considered on a parallel with the sages of antiquity, and looked down with a sentiment of pity on the feebler intellects of my sisters, who could comprehend nothing of metaphysics. It is true, when I attempted to study them by myself, I was apt to get in a fog; but when Glencoe came to my aid, every thing was soon as clear to me as day. My ear drank in the beauty of his words; my imagination was dazzled with the splendor of his illustrations. It caught up the sparkling sands of poetry, that glittered through his speculation, and mistook them for the golden ore of wisdom. Struck with the facility with which I seemed to imbibe and relish the most abstract doctrines, I conceived a still higher opinion of my mental power, and was convinced that I was also a philosopher.

I was now verging toward man's estate, and, though my education had been extremely irregular—following the caprices of my humor, which I mistook for the impulses of my genius—yet I was regarded with wonder and delight, by my mother and sisters, who considered me almost as wise and infallible as I considered myself. This high opinion of me was strengthened by a declamatory habit, which made me an oracle and orator at the domestic board. The time was now at hand, however, that was to put my philosophy to the test.

We had passed through a long winter, and the spring ground at length opened upon us, with unusual sweetness. The soft serenity of the weather; the beauty of the surrounding country; the joyous notes of the birds; the balmy breath of flower and blossom, all combined to fill my bosom with indistinct sensations, and nameless wishes. Amid the soft seductions of the season, I lapsed into a state of utter indolence both of body and mind.

Philosophy had lost its charms for me. Metaphysics—faugh! I tried to study; took down volume after volume, ran my eye vacantly over a few pages, and threw them by with distaste. I loitered about the house, with my hands in my pockets and an air of complete vacancy. Something was necessary to make me happy; but what was that something? I sauntered to the apartments of my sisters, hoping their conversation might amuse me. They had walked out, and the room was vacant. On the table lay a volume which they had been reading. It was a novel. I had never read a novel, having conceived a contempt for works of the kind, from hearing them universally condemned. It is true, I had remarked they were as universally read; but I considered them beneath the attention of a philosopher, and never would venture to read them, lest I should lessen my mental superiority in the eyes of my sisters. Nay, I had taken up a work of the kind, now and then, when I knew my sisters were observing me, looked into it for a moment, and then laid it down, with a slight super-cilious smile. On the present occasion, out of mere listlessness, I took up the volume, and turned over a few of the first pages. I thought I heard some one coming, and laid it down, I was mistaken; no one was near, and what I had read, tempted my curiosity to read a little farther. I leaned against a window-frame, and in a few minutes was completely lost in the story. How long I stood there reading, I know not; but I believe for nearly two hours. Suddenly I heard my sisters on the stairs, when I thrust the book into my bosom, and the two other volumes, which lay near, into my pockets, and hurried out of the house to my beloved woods. Here I remained all day beneath the trees, bewildered, bewitched; devouring the contents of these delicious volumes; and only returned to the house when it was too dark to peruse their pages.

This novel finished, I replaced it in my sister's apartment, and looked for others. Their stock was ample, for they had brought home all that were current in the city; but my appetite demanded an immense supply. All this course of reading was carried on clandestinely, for I was a little ashamed of it, and fearful that my wisdom might be called in question; but this very privacy gave it additional zest. It was "bread eaten in secret;" it had the charm of a private amour.

But think what must have been the effect of such a course of reading, on a youth of my temperament, and turn of mind; indulged, too, amidst romantic scenery, and in the romantic season of the year. It seemed as if I had entered upon a new scene of existence. A train of combustible feelings were lighted up in me, and my soul was all tenderness and passion. Never was youth more completely love-sick, though as yet it was a mere general sentiment and wanted a definite object. Unfortunately our neighborhood was particularly deficient in female society, and I languished in vain for some divinity, to whom I might offer up this most uneasy burthen of affections. I was at one time seriously enamoured of a lady whom I saw occasionally in my rides, reading at the window of a country-seat; and actually serenaded her with my flute; when, to my confusion, I discovered that she was old enough to be my mother. It was a sad damper to my romance; especially as my father heard of it, and made it the subject of one of those household jokes which he was apt to serve up at every meal-time.

I soon recovered from this check, however, but it was only to relapse into a state of amorous excitement, I passed whole days in the fields, and along the brooks; for there is something in the tender passion, that makes us alive to the beauties of nature. A soft sunshine morning infused a sort of rapture into my breast. I flung open my arms, like the Grecian youth in Ovid, as if I would take in and embrace the balmy atmosphere.* The song of the birds melted me to tenderness. I would lie by the side of some rivulet, for hours, and form garlands of the flowers on its banks, and muse on ideal beauties, and sigh from the crowd of undefined emotions that swelled my bosom.

* OVID's Metamorphoses: Book VII.

In this state of amorous delirium, I was strolling one morning along
a beautiful wild brook, which I had discovered in a glen. There was
one place where a small waterfall, leaping from among rocks into a
natural basin, made a scene such as a poet might have chosen as the
haunt of some shy Naiad. It was here I usually retired to banquet on
my novels. In visiting the place this morning, I traced distinctly, on
the margin of the basin, which was of fine clear sand, the prints of a
female foot, of the most slender and delicate proportions. This was
sufficient for an imagination like mine. Robinson Crusoe himself, on
the beach of his lonely island, would not have been more suddenly
assailed with thick-coming fancies. I endeavoured to track the steps,
but they only passed for a few paces along the fine sand, and then
were lost among the herbage. I remained gazing in reverie upon this
passing trace of loveliness. It evidently was not made by any of my
sisters, for they knew nothing of this haunt; besides, the foot was
smaller than theirs; it was remarkable for its beautiful delicacy.

My eye accidentally caught two or three half-withered wild flowers
lying on the ground. The unknown nymph had doubtless dropped them
from her bosom! Here was a new document of taste and sentiment. I
treasured them up as invaluable reliques. The place, too, where I
found them, was remarkably picturesque, and the most beautiful part
of the brook. It was overhung with a fine elm entwined with grape-
vines. She who could select such a spot who could delight in wild
brooks, and wild flowers and silent solitudes, must have fancy and
feeling and tenderness; and with all these qualities she must be beautiful!

But who could be this Unknown, that had thus passed by as in a
morning dream, leaving merely flowers and fairy footsteps, to tell of
her loveliness! There was a mystery in it, that bewildered me. It
was so vague and disembodied, like those "airy tongues that syllable
mens' names" in solitude. Every attempt to solve the mystery was vain.
I could hear of no being in the neighborhood to whom this trace could
be ascribed. I haunted the spot, and became more and more enamoured.
Never, surely, was passion more pure and spiritual, and never lover
in more dubious situation. My case could only be compared with
that of the amorous Prince, in the fairy tale of Cinderella; but he
had a glass slipper on which to lavish his tenderness. I, alas! was
in lover with a footstep!

The imagination is alternately a cheat and a dupe; nay more, it is
the most subtle of cheats, for its cheats itself, and becomes the dupe
of its own delusions. It conjures up "airy nothings," gives to them a
"local habitation and a name," and then bows to their control as implicitly as if they were realities. Such was now my case. The good
Numa could not more thoroughly have persuaded himself that the

nymph Egeria hovered about her sacred fountain, and communed with him in spirit, than I had deceived myself into a kind of visionary intercourse with the airy phantom fabricated in my brain. I constructed a rustic seat at the foot of the tree where I had discovered the footsteps. I made a kind of bower there, where I used to pass my mornings, reading poetry and romances. I carved hearts and darts on the tree, and hung it with garlands. My heart was full to overflowing, and wanted some faithful bosom into which it might relieve itself. What is a lover without a confidante? I thought at once of my sister Sophy, my early play-mate, the sister of my affections. She was so reasonable, too and of such correct feelings; always listening to my words as oracular sayings, and admiring my scraps of poetry as the very inspirations of the muse. From such a devoted, such a rational being, what secrets could I have!

I accordingly took her, one morning, to my favorite retreat. She looked around, with delighted surprise upon the rustic seat, the bower, the tree carved with emblems of the tender passion. She turned her eyes upon me, to enquire the meaning.

"Oh Sophy," exclaimed I, clasping both her hands in mine, and looking earnestly in her face: "I am in love!"

She started with surprize.

"Sit down," said I "and I will tell you all."

She seated herself upon the rustic bench, and I went into a full history of the footstep, with all the associations of idea that had been conjured up by my imagination.

Sophy was enchanted; it was like a fairy tale: She had read of such mysterious visitations, in books, and the loves thus conceived were always for beings of superior order, and were always happy. She caught the illusion, in all its force; her cheek glowed; her eye brightened.

"I dare say she's pretty;" said Sophy.

"Pretty!" echoed I, "She is beautiful!" I went through all the reasoning by which I had logically proved the fact to my own satisfaction. I dwelt upon the evidences of her taste, her sensibility to the beauties of nature; her soft meditative habit, that delighted in solitude; "oh," said I, clasping my hands, "to have such a companion to wander through these scenes; to sit with her by this murmuring stream, to wreathe garlands round her brows; to hear the music of her voice mingling with the whisperings of these groves; to—"

"Delightful! delightful!" cried Sophy; "What a sweet creature she must be! She is just the friend I want. How I shall dote upon her. Oh my dear brother! You must not keep her all to yourself. You must let *me* have some share of her!"

I caught her to my bosom: "You shall—you shall!" cried I, "My dear Sophy; we will all live for each other!"

The conversation with Sophy heightened the illusions of my mind; and the manner in which she had treated my day-dream, identified it with facts and persons, and gave it still more the stamp of reality. I walked about as one in a trance heedless of the world around, and lapped in an elysium of the fancy.

In this mood I met, one morning, wih Glencoe. He accosted me with his usual smile; was proceeding wih some general observations, but paused and fixed on me an enquiring eye.

"What is the matter with you?" said he; "you seem agitated; has any thing in particular happened?"

"Nothing," said I hesitating; "at least nothing worth communicating to you."

"Nay, my dear young friend," said he, "whatever is of sufficient importance to agitate you, is worthy of being communicated to me."

"Well; but my thoughts are running on what you would think a frivolous subject."

"No subject is frivolous, that has the power to awaken strong feelings."

"What think you," said I, hesitating, "what think you of love?"

Glencoe almost started at the question, "Do you call that a frivolous subject?" replied he. "Believe me, there is none fraught with such deep, such vital interest. If you talk, indeed, of the capricious inclination awakened by the mere charm of perishable beauty, I grant it to be idle in the extreme; but that love which springs from the concordant sympathies of virtuous hearts; that love which is awakened by the perception of moral excellence, and fed by meditation on intellectual as well as personal beauty; that is a passion which refines and ennobles the human heart. Oh, where is there a sight more nearly approaching to the intercourse of angels, than that of two young and innocent beings, free from the sins and follies of the world, mingling pure thoughts, and looks, and feelings, and becoming as it were soul of one soul, and heart of one heart! How exquisite the silent converse that they hold; the soft devotion of the eye, that needs no words to make it eloquent! Yes, my friend, if there be any thing in this weary world worthy of heaven, it is the pure bliss of such a mutual affection!"

The words of my worthy tutor overcame all farther reserve. "Mr. Glencoe," cried I, blushing still deeper, "I am in love!"

"And is that what you were ashamed to tell me? Oh never seek to conceal from your friend so important a secret. If your passion be unworthy, it is for the steady hand of friendship to pluck it forth; if honorable, none but an enemy would seek to stifle it. On nothing does the character and happiness so much depend, as on the first affection of the heart. Were you caught by some fleeting and superficial charm—a bright eye, a blooming cheek, a soft voice, or a voluptuous form—I would warn you to beware; I would tell you that beauty is but a passing gleam of the morning, a perishable flower; that accident may becloud and blight it, and that at best it must soon pass away. But were you in love with such a one as I could describe; young in years, but still younger in feelings; lovely in person, but as a type of the mind's beauty; soft in voice, in token of gentleness of spirit; blooming in countenance, like the rosy tints of morning kindling with the promise of a genial day; an eye beaming with the benignity of a happy heart; a cheerful temper, alive to all kind impulses, and frankly diffusing its own felicity; a self-poised mind, that needs not lean on others for support; an elegant taste, that can embellish solitude, and furnish out its own enjoyments—"

"My dear Sir," cried I, for I could contain myself no longer, "you have described the very person!"

"Why then, my dear young friend," said he, affectionately pressing my hand, "In God's name, love on!"

For the remainder of the day, I was in some such state of dreamy beatitude as a Turk is said to enjoy, when under the influence of opium. It must be already manifest, how prone I was to bewilder myself with picturings of the fancy, so as to confound them with existing realities. In the present instance, Sophy and Glencoe had contributed to promote the transient delusion. Sophy, dear girl, had as usual, joined with me in my castle-buildings, and indulged in the same train of imaginings; while Glencoe duped by my enthusiasm, firmly believed that I spoke of a being I had seen and known. By their sympathy with my feelings, they in a manner became associated with the unknown in my mind, and thus linked her with the circle of my intimacy.

In the evening, our family party was assembled in the hall, to enjoy the refreshing breeze. Sophy was playing some favorite Scotch airs on the piano, while Glencoe, seated apart with his forehead resting on his hand, was buried in one of those pensive reveries, that made him so interesting to me.

"What a fortunate being I am!" thought I; "blessed with such a sister and such a friend! I have only to find out this amiable Unknown, to wed her, and be happy! What a paradise will be my home, graced with a partner of such exquisite refinement! It will be a perfect fairy bower, buried among sweets and roses. Sophy shall live with us, and be the companion of all our enjoyments. Glencoe, too, shall no more be the solitary being that he now appears. He shall have a home with us. He shall have his study, where, when he pleases, he may shut himself up from the world, and bury himself in his own reflections. His retreat shall be held sacred; no one shall intrude there; no one but myself, who will visit him now and then, in his seclusion, where we will devise grand schemes together for the improvement of mankind. How delightfully our days will pass, in a round of rational pleasures and elegant employments! Sometimes we will have music; sometimes we will read; sometimes we will wander through the flower-garden, when I will smile with complacency on every flower my wife has planted while, in the long winter evenings, the ladies will sit at their work, and listen, with hushed attention, to Glencoe and myself, as we discuss the abstruse doctrines of metaphysics."

From this delectable reverie, I was startled by my father's slapping me on the shoulder: "What possesses the lad?" cried he; "here have I been speaking to you half a dozen times, without receiving an answer."

"Pardon me, Sir," replied I; "I was so completely lost in thought, that I did not hear you."

"Lost in thought! And pray what were you thinking of? Some of your philosophy, I suppose."

"Upon my word," said my sister Charlotte, with an arch laugh, "I suspect Harry's in love again."

"And if I were in love, Charlotte," said I, somewhat nettled, and recollecting Glencoe's enthusiastic eulogy of the passion, "if I were in love, is that a matter of jest and laughter? Is the tenderest and most fervid affection that can animate the human breast, to be made a matter of cold-hearted ridicule?"

My sister coloured. "Certainly not, brother!—Nor did I mean to make it so, or to say any thing that should wound your feelings. Had I really suspected you had formed some genuine attachment, it would have been sacred in my eyes; but—but," said she, smiling, as if at some whimsical recollection, "I thought that you—you might be indulging in another little freak of the imagination."

"I'll wager any money," cried my father, "he has fallen in love again with some old lady at a window!"

"Oh no!" cried my dear sister Sophy, with the most gracious warmth; "she is young and beautiful."

"From what I understand," said Glencoe, rousing himself, "she must be lovely in mind as in person."

I found my friends were getting me into a fine scrape. I began to perspire at every pore, and felt my ears tingle.

"Well, but," cried my father, "who is she? What is she? Let us hear something about her."

This was no time to explain so delicate a matter. I caught up my hat, and vanished out of the house.

The moment I was in the open air, and alone, my heart upbraided me. Was this respectful treatment to my father—to *such* a father too—who had always regarded me as the pride of his age,—the staff of his hopes? It is true, he was apt, sometimes, to laugh at my enthusiastic flights; and did not treat my philosophy with due respect; but when had he ever thwarted a wish of my heart? Was I then to act with reserve toward him, in a matter which might affect the whole current of my future life? "I have done wrong," thought I; "but it is not too late to remedy it. I will hasten back, and open my whole heart to my father!"

I returned accordingly, and was just on the point of entering the house, with my heart full of filial piety, and a contrite speech upon my lips, when I heard a burst of obstreperous laughter from my father, and a loud titter from my two elder sisters.

"A foot step!" shouted he, as soon as he could recover himself; "in love with a footstep! Why this beats the old lady at the window!" And then there was another appalling burst of laughter. Had it been a clap of thunder, it could hardly have astounded me more completely. Sophy, in the simplicity of her heart, had told all, and had set my father's risible propensities in full action.

Never was poor mortal so thoroughly crest-fallen as myself. The whole delusion was at an end. I drew off silently from the house, shrinking smaller and smaller at every fresh peal of laughter; and wandering about until the family had retired, stole quietly to my bed. Scarce any sleep, however, visited my eyes that night! I lay overwhelmed with mortification, and meditating how I might meet the family in the morning. The idea of ridicule was always intolerable to me; but to endure it on a subject by which my feelings had been so much excited, seemed worse than death. I almost determined, at one time, to get up, saddle my horse, and ride off. I knew not whither.

At length, I came to a resolution. Before going down to breakfast, I sent for Sophy, and employed her as ambassador to treat formally in the matter. I insisted that the subject should be buried in oblivion; otherwise, I would not show my face at table. It was readily agreed to; for not one of the family would have given me pain for the world. They faithfully kept their promise. Not a word was said of the matter; but there were wry faces and suppressed titters, that went to my soul;

and whenever my father looked me in the face, it was with such a tragic-comical leer; such an attempt to pull down a serious brow upon a whimsical mouth, that I had a thousand times rather he had laughed outright.

———

For a day or two after the mortifying occurrence, I kept as much as possible out of the way of the family, and wandered about the fields and woods by myself. I was sadly out of tune, my feelings were all jarred and unstrung. The birds sang from every grove, but I took no pleasure in their melody and the flowers of the field bloomed unheeded around me. To be crossed in love, is bad enough; but then one can fly to poetry for relief; and turn one's woes to account in soul-subduing stanzas. But to have one's whole passion; object and all, annihilated, dispelled, proved to be such stuff as dreams are made of; or, worse than all, to be turned into a proverb and a jest—what consolation is there in such a case?

I avoided the fatal brook where I had seen the footstep. My favorite resort was now the banks of the Hudson, where I sat upon the rocks, and mused upon the current that dimpled by, or the waves that laved the shore; or watched the bright mutations of the clouds and the shifting lights and shadows of the distant mountain. By degrees a returning serenity stole over my feelings; and a sigh now and then, gentle and easy, and unattended by pain, showed that my heart was recovering its susceptibility.

As I was sitting in this musing mood, my eye became gradually fixed upon an object that was borne along by the tide. It proved to be a little pinnace, beautifully modelled, and gaily painted, and decorated. It was an unusual sight in this neighborhood, which was rather lonely: indeed, it was rare to see any pleasure-barks in this part of the river. As it drew nearer, I perceived that there was no one on board; it had apparently drifted from its anchorage. There was not a breath of air: the little bark came floating along on the glassy stream, wheeling about with the eddies. At length it ran aground, almost at the foot of the rock on which I was seated. I descended to the margin of the river, and drawing the bark to shore, admired its light and elegant proportions, and the taste with which it was fitted up. The benches were covered with cushions, and its long streamer was of silk. On one of the cushions lay a lady's glove, of delicate size and shape, with beautifully tapered fingers. I instantly seized it and thrust it in my bosom: it seemed a match for the fairy footstep that had so fascinated me.

In a moment, all the romance of my bosom was again in a glow. Here was one of the very incidents of fairy tale. A bark sent by some invisible power, some good genius or benevolent fairy; to waft to me some delectable adventure. I recollected something of an enchanted bark, drawn by white swans, that conveyed a knight down the current of the Rhine, on some enterprize connected with love and beauty. The glove, too, showed that there was a lady fair concerned in the present adventure. It might be a gauntlet of definance, to dare me to the enterprize.

In the spirit of romance, and the whim of the moment, I sprang on board, hoisted the light sail, and pushed from shore. As if breathed by some presiding power, a light breeze at that moment sprang up, swelled out the sail, and dallied with the silken streamer. For a time I glided along under steep umbrageous banks, or across deep sequestered bays; and then stood out over a wide expansion of the river, toward a high rocky promontory. It was a lovely evening: the sun was setting in a congregation of clouds that threw the whole heavens in a glow, and were reflected in the river. I delighted myself with all kinds of fantastic fancies, as to what enchanted island, or mystic bower, or necromantic palace, I was to be conveyed by the fairy bark.

In the revel of my fancy, I have not noticed that the gorgeous congregation of clouds which had so much delighted me, was in fact a gathering thunder-gust. I perceived the truth too late. The clouds came hurrying on, darkening as they advanced. The whole face of nature was suddenly changed, and assumed that baleful and livid tint, predictive of a storm. I tried to gain the shore, but before I could reach it, a blast of wind struck the water, and lashed it at once into foam. The next moment it over took the boat. Alas! I was nothing of a sailor; and my protecting fairy forsook me in the moment of peril. I endeavored to lower the sail; but in so doing, I had to quit the helm; the bark was overturned in an instant, and I was thrown into the water. I endeavored to cling to the wreck, but missed my hold, being a poor swimmer, I soon found myself sinking, but grasped a light oar that was floating by me. It was not sufficient for any support; I again sank beneath the surface: there was a rushing and bubbling sound in my ears, and all sense forsook me.

How long I remained insensible, I know not. I had a confused notion of being moved and tossed about, and of hearing strange beings and strange voices around me; but all was like a hideous dream. When I at length recovered full consciousness and perception, I found myself

in bed, in a spacious chamber, furnished with more taste than I had
been accustomed to. The bright rays of a morning son were intercepted
by curtains of a delicate rose colour, that gave a soft, voluptuous tinge
to every object. Not far from my bed, on a classic tripod, was a basket
of beautiful exotic flowers, breathing the sweetest fragrance.

"Where am I? How came I here?" I tasked my mind to catch at
some previous event, from which I might trace up the thread of
existence to the present moment. By degrees, I called to mind the
fairy pinnace, my daring embarcation, my adventurous voyage, my
disastrous ship wreck. Beyond that, all was chaos. How came I here?
What unknown region had I landed upon? The people that inhabited
it must be gentle and amiable, and of elegant tastes, for they loved
downy beds, fragrant flowers, and rose-coloured curtains.

While I lay thus musing, the tones of a harp reached my ear.
Presently they were accompanied by a female voice. It came from the
room below; but in the profound stillness of my chamber, not a
modulation was lost. My sisters were all considered good musicians, and
sang very tolerably, but I had never heard a voice like this. There was
no attempt at difficult execution, or striking effect; but there were
exquisite inflexions, and tender turns, which art could not reach.
Nothing but feeling and sentiment could produce them. It was soul
breathed forth in sound. I was always alive to the influence of music:
indeed, I was susceptible of voluptuous influences of every kind—
sounds, colors, shapes and, fragrant odors. I was the very slave of
sensation.

I lay mute and breathless, and drank in every note of this syren
strain. It thrilled through my whole frame, and filled my soul with
melody and love. I pictured to myself, with curious logic, the form
of the unseen musician. Such melodious sounds and exquisite inflexions
could only be produced by organs of the most delicate flexibility. Such
organs do not belong to coarse, vulgar forms; they are the harmonious
results of fair proportions, and admirable symmetry. A being so organized,
must be lovely.

Again my busy imagination was at work. I called to mind the
Arabian story of a prince, borne away during sleep by a good genius,
to the distant abode of a princess, of ravishing beauty. I do not pretend to say that I believed in having experienced a similar transporta-
tion; but it was my inveterate habit to cheat myself with fancies of the
kind, and to give the tinge of illusion to surrounding realities.

The witching sound had ceased, but its vibrations still played round
my heart, and filled it with a tumult of soft emotions. At this moment,
a self-upbraiding pang shot through my bosom. "Ah, recreant!" a voice
seemed to exclaim, "is this the stability of thine affections? What! hast

thou so soon forgotten the nymph of the fountain? Has one song, idly piped in thine ear, been sufficient to charm away the cherished tenderness of a whole summer?"

The wise may smile—but I am in a confiding mood, and must confess my weakness. I felt a degree of compunction at this sudden infidelity, yet I could not resist the power of present fascination. My peace of mind was destroyed by conflicting claims. The nymph of the fountain came over my memory, with all the associations of fairy footsteps, shady groves, soft echoes, and wild streamlets; but this new passion was produced by a strain of soul-subduing melody, still lingering in my ear, aided by a downy bed, fragrant flowers, and rose-colored curtains. "Unhappy youth!" sighed I to myself, "distracted by such rival passions, and the empire of thy heart thus violently contested by the sound of a voice, and the print of a footstep!"

———

I had not remained long in this mood, when I heard the door of the room gently opened. I turned my head to see what inhabitant of this enchanted palace should appear; whether page in green, hideous dwarf, or haggard fairy. It was my own man Scipio. He advanced with cautious step, and was delighted, as he said, to find me so much myself again. My first questions were as to where I was, and how I came there? Scipio told me a long story of his having been fishing in a canoe, at the time of my hare-brained cruise; of his noticing the gathering squall, and my impending danger; of his hastening to join me, but arriving just in time to snatch me from a watery grave; of the great difficulty in restoring me to animation; and of my being subse-quently conveyed, in a state of insensibility, to this mansion.

"But where am I?" was the reiterated demand.

"In the house of Mr. Somerville."

"Somerville—Somerville!" I recollected to have heard that a gentleman of that name had recently taken up his residence at some distance from my father's abode, on the opposite side of the Hudson. He was commonly known by the name of "French Somerville," from having passed part of his early life in France, and from his exhibiting traces of French taste in his mode of living, and the arrangements of his house. In fact, it was in his pleasure-boat, which had got adrift, that I made my fanciful and disastrous cruise. All this was simple, straight-forward matter of fact, and threatened to demolish all the cobweb romance I had been spinning, when fortunately I again heard the tinkling of a harp. I raised myself in bed, and listened.

"Scipio," said I, with some little hesitation, "I heard some one singing just now. Who was it?"

"Oh, that was Miss Julia."

"Julia! Julia! Delightful! what a name! And, Scipio—is she—is she pretty?"

Scipio grinned from ear to ear. "Except Miss Sophy, she was the most beautiful young lady he had ever seen."

I should observe, that my sister Sophia was considered by all the servants a paragon of perfection.

Scipio now offered to remove the basket of flowers; he was afraid their odor might be too powerful; but Miss Julia had given them that morning to be placed in my room.

These flowers, then, had been gathered by the fairy fingers of my unseen beauty; that sweet breath which had filled my ear with melody, had passed over them. I made Scipio hand them to me, culled several of the most delicate, and laid them on my bosom.

Mr. Somerville paid me a visit not long afterward. He was an interesting study for me, for he was the father of my unseen beauty, and probably resembled her. I scanned him closely. He was a tall and elegant man, with an open, affable manner, and an erect and graceful carriage. His eyes were bluish-gray, and, though not dark, yet at times were sparkling and expressive. His hair was dressed and powdered, and being lightly combed up from his forehead, added to the loftiness of his aspect. He was fluent in discourse, but his conversation had the quiet tone of polished society, without any of those bold flights of thought, and picturings of fancy, which I so much admired.

My imagination was a little puzzled, at first, to make out of this assemblage of personal and mental qualities, a picture that should harmonize with my previous idea of the fair unseen. By dint, however, of selecting what it liked, and rejecting what it did not like, and giving a touch here and a touch there, it soon finished out a satisfactory portrait.

"Julia must be tall," thought I, "and of exquisite grace and dignity. She is not quite so courtly as her father, for she has been brought up in the retirement of the country. Neither is she of such vivacious deportment; for the tones of her voice are soft and plaintive, and she loves pathetic music. She is rather pensive—yet not too pensive; just what is called interesting. Her eyes are like her father's, except that they are of a purer blue, and more tender and languishing. She has light hair—not exactly flaxen, for I do not like flaxen hair, but between that and auburn. In a word, she is a tall, elegant, imposing, languishing, blue-eyed, romantic looking beauty." And having thus finished her picture, I felt ten times more in love with than ever.

———

I felt so much recovered, that I would at once have left my room, but Mr. Somerville objected to it. He had sent early word to my family of my safety; and my father arrived in the course of the morning. He was shocked at learning the risk I had run, but rejoiced to find me so much restored, and was warm in his thanks to Mr. Somerville for his kindness. The other only required, in return, that I might remain two or three days as his guest, to give time for my recovery, and for our forming a closer acquaintance; a request which my father readily granted. Scipio accordingly accompanied my father home, and returned with a supply of clothes, and with affectionate letters from my mother and sisters.

The next morning, aided by Scipio, I made my toilet with rather more care than usual, and descended the stairs, with some trepidation, eager to see the original of the portrait which had been so completely pictured in my imagination.

On entering the parlor, I found it deserted. Like the rest of the house, it was furnished in a foreign style. The curtains were of French silk; there were Grecian couches, marble tables, pier-glasses, and chandeliers. What chiefly attracted my eye, were documents of female taste that I saw around me; a piano, with an ample stock of Italian music; a book of poetry lying on the sofa; a vase of fresh flowers on a table, and a port-folio open with a skilful and half-finished sketch of them. In the window was a Canary bird, in a gilt cage, and near by, the harp that had been in Julia's arms. Happy harp! But where was the being that reigned in this little empire of delicacies?—that breathed poetry and song, and dwelt among birds and flowers, and rose-colored curtains?

Suddenly I heard the hall door fly open, the quick pattering of light steps, a wild, capricious strain of music, and the shrill barking of a dog. A light frolic nymph of fifteen came tripping into the room, playing on a flageolet, with a little spaniel ramping after her. Her gipsy hat had fallen back upon her shoulders; a profusion of glossy brown hair was blown in rich ringlets about her face, which beamed through them with the brightness of smiles and dimples.

At sight of me, she stopped short, in the most beautiful confusion, stammered out a word or two about looking for her father, glided out of the door, and I heard her bounding up the stair-case, like a frightened fawn, with the little dog barking after her.

When Miss Somerville returned to the parlor, she was quite a different being. She entered, stealing along by her mother's side with noiseless step, and sweet timidity: her hair was prettily adjusted, and a soft blush mantled on her damask cheek. Mr. Somerville accompanied the ladies, and introduced me regularly to them. There were many kind inquiries, and much sympathy expressed, on the subject of my nautical accident, and some remarks upon the wild scenery of the neighborhood, with which the ladies seemed perfectly acquainted.

"You must know," said Mr. Somerville, "that we are great navigators, and delight in exploring every nook and corner of the river. My daughter, too, is a great hunter of the picturesque, and transfers every rock and glen to her port-folio. By the way, my dear, show Mr. Mountjoy that pretty scene you have lately sketched." Julia complied, blushing, and drew from her port-folio a colored sketch. I almost started at the sight. It was my favorite brook. A sudden thought darted across my mind. I glanced down my eye, and beheld the divinest little foot in the world. Oh, blissful conviction! The struggle of my affections was at an end. The voice and the footstep were no longer at variance. Julia Somerville was the nymph of the fountain!

What conversation passed during breakfast, I do not recollect, and hardly was conscious of at the time, for my thoughts were in complete confusion. I wished to gaze on Miss Somerville, but did not dare. Once, indeed, I ventured a glance. She was at that moment darting a similar one from under a covert of ringlets. Our eyes seemed shocked by the rencontre, and fell; hers through the natural modesty of her sex, mine through a bashfulness produced by the previous workings of my imagination. That glance, however, went like a sun-beam to my heart.

A convenient mirror favored my diffidence, and gave me the reflection of Miss Somerville's form. It is true it only presented the back of her head, but she had the merit of an ancient statue; contemplate her from any point of view, she was beautiful. And yet she was totally different from every thing I had before conceived of beauty. She was not the serene, meditative maid that I had pictured the nymph of the fountain; nor the tall, soft, languishing, blue-eyed, dignified being, that I had fancied the minstrel of the harp. There was nothing of dignity about her: she was girlish in her appearance, and scarcely of the middle size; but then there was the tenderness of budding youth; the sweetness of the half-blown rose, when not a tint or perfume has been withered or exhaled; there were smiles and dimples, and all the soft witcheries of ever-varying expression. I wondered that I could ever have admired any other style of beauty.

After breakfast, Mr. Somerville departed to attend to the concerns of his estate, and gave me in charge of the ladies. Mrs. Somerville also was called away by household cares, and I was left alone with

Julia! Here then was the situation which of all others I had most coveted. I was in the presence of the lovely being that had so long been the desire of my heart. We were alone; propitious opportunity for a lover! Did I seize upon it? Did I break out in one of my accustomed rhaphsodies? No such thing! Never was being more awkwardly embarrassed.

"What can be the cause of this?" thought I. "Surely, I cannot stand in awe of this young girl. I am of course her superior in intellect, and am never embarrassed in company with my tutor, notwithstanding all his wisdom."

It was passing strange. I felt that if she were an old woman, I should be quite at my ease; if she were even an ugly woman, I should make out very well: it was her beauty that overpowered me. How little do lovely women know what awful beings they are, in the eyes of inexperienced youth! Young men brought up in the fashionable circles of our cities will smile at all this. Accustomed to mingle incessantly in female society, and to have the romance of the heart deadened by a thousand frivolous flirtations, women are nothing but women in their eyes; but to a susceptible youth like myself, brought up in the country, they are perfect divinities.

Miss Somerville was at first a little embarrassed herself, but somehow or other, women have a natural adroitness in recovering their self-possession; they are more alert in their minds, and graceful in their manners. Besides, I was but an ordinary personage in Miss Somerville's eyes; she was not under the influence of such a singular course of imaginings as had surrounded her, in my eyes, with the illusions of romance. Perhaps, too, she saw the confusion in the opposite camp, and gained courage from the discovery. At any rate, she was the first to take the field.

Her conversation, however, was only on common-place topics, and in an easy, well-bred style. I endeavored to respond in the same manner; but I was strangely incompetent to the task. My ideas were frozen up; even words seemed to fail me. I was excessively vexed at myself, for I wished to be uncommonly elegant. I tried two or three times to turn a pretty thought, or to utter a fine sentiment; but it would come forth so trite, so forced, so mawkish, that I was ashamed of it. My very voice sounded discordantly, though I sought to modulate it into the softest tones. "The truth is," I thought to myself, "I cannot bring my mind down to the small talk necessary for young girls; it is too masculine and robust for the mincing pleasure of parlor gossip. I am a philosopher—and that accounts for it."

The entrance of Mrs. Somerville at length gave me relief. I at once breathed freely, and felt a vast deal of confidence come over me.

"This is strange," thought I, "that the appearance of another woman should revive my courage; that I should be a better match for two women than one. However, since it is so, I will take advantage of the circumstance, and let this young lady see that I am not so great a simpleton as she probably thinks me."

I accordingly took up the book of poetry which lay upon the sofa. It was Milton's Paradise Lost. Nothing could have been more fortunate; it afforded a fine scope for my favorite vein of grandiloquence. I went largely into a discussion of its merits, or rather an enthusiastic eulogy of them. My observations were addressed to Mrs. Somerville, for I found I could talk to her with more ease than to her daughter. She appeared perfectly alive to the beauties of the poet, and disposed to meet me in the discussion; but it was not my object to hear her talk; it was to talk myself. I anticipated all she had to say, overpowered her with the copiousness of my ideas, and supported and illustrated them by long citations from the author.

While thus holding forth, I cast a side glance to see how Miss Somerville was affected. She had some embroidery stretched on a frame before her, but had paused in her labor, and was looking down as if lost in mute attention. I felt a glow of self-satisfaction, but I recollected, at the same time, with a kind of pique, the advantage she had enjoyed over me in our tête-à-tête. I determined to push my triumph, and accordingly kept on with redoubled ardor, until I had fairly exhausted my subject, or rather my thoughts.

I had scarce come to a full stop, when Miss Somerville raised her eyes from the work on which they had been fixed, and turning to her mother, observed: "I have been considering, mamma, whether to work these flowers plain, or in colors."

Had an ice-bolt been shot to my heart, it could not have chilled me more effectually. "What a fool," thought I, "have I been making myself—squandering away fine thoughts, and fine language, upon a light mind, and an ignorant ear! This girl knows nothing of poetry. She has no soul, I fear, for its beauties. Can any one have real sensibility of heart, and not be alive to poetry? However, she is young; this part of her education has been neglected: there is time enough to remedy it. I will be her preceptor. I will kindle in her mind the sacred flame, and lead her through the fairy land of song. But after all, it is rather unfortunate, that I should have fallen in love with a woman who knows nothing of poetry."

———

I passed a day not altogether satisfactory. I was a little disappointed that Miss Somerville did not show more poetical feeling. "I am afraid, after all," said I to myself, "she is light and girlish, and more fitted to pluck wild flowers, play on the flageolet, and romp with little dogs, than to converse with a man of my turn."

I believe, however, to tell the truth, I was more out of humor with myself. I thought I had made the worst first appearance that ever hero made, either in novel or fairy tale. I was out of all patience, when I called to mind my awkward attempts at ease and elegance, in the tête-à-tête. And then my intolerable long lecture about poetry, to catch the applause of a heedless auditor! But there I was not to blame. I had certainly been eloquent: it was her fault that the eloquence was wasted. To meditate upon the embroidery of a flower when I was expatiating on the beauties of Milton! She might at least have admired the poetry, if she did not relish the manner in which it was delivered; though that was not despicable, for I had recited passages in my best style, which my mother and sisters had always considered equal to a play. "Oh, it is evident," thought I, "Miss Somerville has very little soul!"

Such were my fancies and cogitations, during the day, the greater part of which was spent in my chamber, for I was still languid. My evening was passed in the drawing-room, where I overlooked Miss Somerville's port-folio of sketches. They were executed with great taste, and showed a nice observation of the peculiarities of nature. They were all her own, and free from those cunning tints and touches of the drawing-master, by which young ladies' drawings, like their heads, are dressed up for company. There was no garish and vulgar trick of colors, either; all was executed with singular truth and simplicity.

"And yet," thought I, "this little being, who has so pure an eye to take in, as in a limpid brook, all the graceful forms and magic tints of nature, has no soul for poetry!"

Mr. Somerville, toward the latter part of the evening, observing my eye to wander occasionally to the harp, interpreted and met my wishes with his accustomed civility.

"Julia, my dear," said he, "Mr. Mountjoy would like to hear a little music from your harp; let us hear, too, the sound of your voice."

Julia immediately complied, without any of that hesitation and difficulty, by which young ladies are apt to make the company pay dear for bad music. She sang a sprightly strain, in a brilliant style, that came trilling playfully over the ear; and the bright eye and dimpling smile showed that her little heart danced with the song. Her pet Canary bird, who hung close by, was wakened by the music, and burst forth into an emulating strain. Julia smiled with a pretty air of defiance, and played louder.

After some time, the music changed, and ran into a plaintive strain,

in a minor key. Then it was, that all the former witchery of her voice
came over me; then it was, that she seemed to sing from the heart
and to the heart. Her fingers moved about the chords as if they scarcely
touched them. Her whole manner and appearance changed; her eyes
beamed with the softest expression; her countenance, her frame, all
seemed subdued into tenderness. She rose from the harp, leaving
it still vibrating with sweet sounds, and moved toward her father, to
bid him good night.

His eyes had been fixed on her intently, during her performance.
As she came before him, he parted her shining ringlets with both
his hands, and looked down with the fondness of a father on her innocent face. The music seemed still lingering in its lineaments, and
the action of her father brought a moist gleam in her eye. He kissed
her fair forhead, after the French mode of parental caressing: "Good
night, and God bless you," said he, "my good little girl!"

Julia tripped away, with a tear in her eye, a dimple in her cheek,
and a light heart in her bosom. I thought it the prettiest picture of
paternal and filial affection I had ever seen.

When I retired to bed, a new train of thoughts crowded into my
brain. "After all," said I to myself, "it is clear this girl has a soul though
she was not moved by my eloquence. She has all the outward signs
and evidences of poetic feeling. She paints well, and has an eye for
nature. She is a fine musician, and enters into the very soul of song.
What a pity that she knows nothing of poetry! But we will see what
is to be done. I am irretrievably in love with her what then am I to do?
Come down to the level of her mind, or endeavor to raise her to some
kind of intellectual equality with myself! That is the most generous
course. She will look up to me as a benefactor. I shall become associated
in her mind with the lofty thoughts and harmonious graces of poetry.
She is apparently docile: besides, the difference of our ages will
give me an ascendancy over her. She cannot be above sixteen years
of age, and I am full turned of twenty." So, having built this most
delectable of air-castles, I fell asleep.

————

The next morning, I was quite a different being. I no longer felt
fearful of stealing a glance at Julia; on the contrary, I contemplated
her steadily, with the benignant eye of a benefactor. Shortly after
breakfast, I found myself alone with her, as I had on the preceding
morning; but I felt nothing of the awkwardness of our previous
tête-à-tête. I was elevated by the consciousness of my intellectual
superiority, and should almost have felt a sentiment of pity for the

ignorance of the lovely little being, if I had not felt also the assurance
that I should be able to dispel it. "But it is time," thought I, "to
open school."

Julia was occupied in arranging some music on her piano. I looked
over two or three songs; they were Moore's Irish melodies.

"These are pretty things," said I, flirting the leaves over lightly,
and giving a slight shrug, by way of qualifying the opinion.

"Oh I love them of all things!" said Julia, "they're so touching!"

"Then you like them for the poetry," said I, with an encouraging
smile.

"Oh yes; she thought them charmingly written."

Now was my time. "Poetry," said I, assuming a didactic attitude
and air, "poetry is one of the most pleasing studies that can occupy
a youthful mind. It renders us susceptible of the gentle impulses of
humanity, and cherishes a delicate perception of all that is virtuous
and elevated in morals, and graceful and beautiful in physics. It_____"

I was going on in a style that would have graced a professor of
rhetoric, when I saw a light smile playing about Miss Somerville's
mouth, and that she began to turn over the leaves of a music book. I
recollected her inattention to my discourse of the preceding morning.
"There is no fixing her light mind," thought I, "by abstract theory;
we will proceed practically." As it happened, the identical volume
of Milton's Paradise Lost was lying at hand.

"Let me recommend to you, my young friend," said I, in one of
those tones of persuasive admonition, which I had so often loved in
Glencoe, "let me recommend to you this admirable poem: you will
find in it sources of intellectual enjoyment far superior to those songs
which have delighted you." Julia looked at the book, and then at
me, with a whimsically dubious air. "Milton's Paradise Lost?" said
she; "oh I know the greater part of that by heart."

I had not expected to find my pupil so far advanced; however, the
Paradise Lost is a kind of school book, and its finest passages are
given to young ladies as tasks.

"I find," said I to myself, "I must not treat her as so complete a
novice; her inattention, yesterday, could not have proceeded from
absolute ignorance, but merely from a want of poetic feeling. I'll
try her again."

I now determined to dazzle her with my own erudition, and
launched into a harangue that would have done honor to an institute.
Pope, Spenser, Chaucer, and the old dramatic writers, were all dipped
into, with the excursive flight of a swallow. I did not confine myself
to English poets, but gave a glance at the French and Italian schools:
I passed over Ariosto in full wing, but paused on Tasso's Jerusalem

Delivered. I dwelt on the character of Clorinda: "There's a character," said I, "that you will find well worthy a woman's study. It shows to what exalted heights of heroism the sex can rise; how gloriously they may share even in the stern concerns of men."

"For my part," said Julia, gently taking advantage of a pause, "for my part, I prefer the character of Sophronia."

I was thunderstruck. She then had read Tasso! This girl that I had been treating as an ignoramus in poetry! She proceeded, with a slight glow of the cheek, summoned up perhaps by a casual glow of feeling:

"I do not admire those masculine heroines," said she, "who aim at the bold qualities of the opposite sex. Now Sophronia only exhibits the real qualities of a woman, wrought up to their highest excitement. She is modest, gentle, and retiring, as it becomes a woman to be; but she has all the strength of affection proper to a woman. She cannot fight for her people, as Clorinda does, but she can offer herself up, and die, to serve them. You may admire Clorinda, but you surely would be more apt to love Sophronia; at least," added she, suddenly appearing to recollect herself, and blushing at having launched into such a discussion, "at least, that is what papa observed, when we read the poem together."

"Indeed," said I dryly, for I felt disconcerted and nettled at being unexpectedly lectured by my pupil; "indeed, I do not exactly recollect the passage."

"Oh," said Julia, "I can repeat it to you;" and she immediately gave it in Italian.

Heavens and earth!—here was a situation! I knew no more of Italian than I did of the language of Psalmanazar. What a dilemma for a would-be-wise man to be placed in! I saw Julia waited for my opinion.

"In fact," said I, hesitating, "I—I do not exactly understand Italian."

"Oh," said Julia, with the utmost naïveté, "I have no doubt it is very beautiful in the translation."

I was glad to break up school, and get back to my chamber, full of the mortification which a wise man in love experiences on finding his mistress wiser than himself. "Translation! translation!" muttered I to myself, as I jerked the door shut behind me: "I am surprised my father has never had me instructed in the modern languages. They are all-important. What is the use of Latin and Greek? No one speaks them; but here, the moment I make my appearance in the world, a little girl slaps Italian in my face. However, thank Heaven, a language is easily learned. The moment I return home, I'll set about studying Italian; and to prevent future surprise, I will study Spanish and German at the same time; and if any young lady attempts to quote Italian upon me again, I'll bury her under a heap of High Dutch poetry!"

I felt now like some mighty chieftain, who has carried the war into a weak country, with full confidence of success, and been repulsed and obliged to draw off his forces from before some inconsiderable fortress.

"However," thought I, "I have as yet brought only my light artillery into action; we shall see what is to be done with my heavy ordnance. Julia is evidently well versed in poetry; but it is natural she should be so; it is allied to painting and music, and is congenial to the light graces of the female character. We will try her on graver themes."

I felt all my pride awakened; it even for a time swelled higher than my love. I was determined completely to establish my mental superiority, and subdue the intellect of this little being: it would then be time to sway the sceptre of gentle empire, and win the affections of her heart.

Accordingly, at dinner I again took the field, *en potence*. I now addressed myself to Mr. Sommerville, for I was about to enter upon topics in which a young girl like her could not be well versed. I led, or rather forced, the conversation into a vein of historical erudition, discussing several of the most prominent facts of ancient history, and accompanying them with sound, indisputable apothegms.

Mr. Somerville listened to me with the air of a man receiving information. I was encouraged, and went on gloriously from theme to theme of school declamation. I sat with Marius on the ruins of Carthage; I defended the bridge with Horatius Cocles; thrust my hand into the flame with Martius Scævola, and plunged with Curtius into the yawning gulph; I fought side by side with Leonidas, at the straits of Thermopylæ; and was going full drive into the battle of Platæa, when my memory, which is the worst in the world, failed me, just as I wanted the name of the Lacedemonian commander.

"Julia, my dear," said Mr. Somerville, "perhaps you may recollect the name of which Mr. Mountjoy is in quest?"

Julia colored slightly: "I believe," said she, in a low voice, "I believe it was Pausanias."

This unexpected sally, instead of reinforcing me, threw my whole scheme of battle into confusion, and the Athenians remained unmolested in the field.

I am half inclined, since, to think Mr. Somerville meant this as a sly hit at my school-boy pedantry; but he was too well bred not to seek to relieve me from my mortification. "Oh!" said he, "Julia is our family book of reference for names, dates, and distances, and has an excellent memory for history and geography."

I now became desperate; as a last resource, I turned to metaphysics.

"If she is a philosopher in petticoats," thought I, "it is all over with me."

Here, however, I had the field to myself. I gave chapter and verse of my tutor's lectures, heightened by all his poetical illustrations: I even went farther than he had ever ventured, and plunged into such depths of metaphysics, that I was in danger of sticking in the mire at the bottom. Fortunately, I had auditors who apparently could not detect my flounderings. Neither Mr. Somerville nor his daughter offered the least interruption.

When the ladies had retired, Mr. Somerville sat sometime with me; and as I was no longer anxious to astonish, I permitted myself to listen, and found that he was really agreeable. He was quite communicative, and from his conversation I was enabled to form a juster idea of his daughter's character, and the mode in which she had been brought up. Mr Somerville had mingled much with the world, and with what is termed fashionable society. He had experienced its cold elegancies, and gay insincerities; its dissipation of the spirits, and squanderings of the heart. Like many men of the world, though he had wandered too far from nature ever to return to it, yet he had the good taste and good feeling to look back fondly to its simple delights, and to determine that his child, if possible should never leave them. He had superintended her education with scrupulous care, storing her mind with the graces of polite literature, and with such knowledge as would enable it to furnish its own amusement and occupation, and giving her all the accomplishments that sweeten and enliven the circle of domestic life. He had been particularly sedulous to exclude all fashionable affectations; all false sentiment, false sensibility, and false romance. "Whatever advantages she may possess," said he, "she is quite unconscious of them. She is a capricious little being, in every thing but her affections; she is however, free from art. Simple, ingenuous, innocent, amiable and, I thank God! happy."

Such was the Eulogy of a fond father, delivered with a tenderness that touched me. I could not help making a casual enquiry, whether, among the graces of polite literature, he had included a slight tincture of metaphysics. He smiled, and told me he had not.

On the whole, when, as usual, that night, I summed up the day's observations on my pillow, I was not altogether dissatisfied. "Miss Somerville," said I, "loves poetry, and I like her the better for it. She has the advantage of me in Italian: agreed; what is it to know a variety of languages, but merely to have a variety of sounds to express the same idea? Original thought is the ore of the mind; language is but the accidental stamp and coinage, by which it is put into circulation. If I can furnish an original idea, what care I how many languages she can translate it into? She may be able, also, to quote names, and dates, and latitudes, better than I; but that is a mere effort of the memory. I admit she is more accurate in history and geography than I; but then she knows nothing of metaphysics."

———

I had now sufficiently recovered, to return home; yet I could not think of leaving Mr. Somerville's, without having a little farther conversation with him on the subject of his daughter's education.

"This Mr. Somerville," thought I, "is a very accomplished, elegant man; he has seen a good deal of the world, and, upon the whole, has profited by what he has seen. He is not without information, and, as far as he thinks, appears to think correctly; but after all, he is rather superficial, and does not think profoundly. He seems to take no delight in those metaphysical abstractions, that are the proper aliment of masculine minds." I called to mind various occasions in which I had indulged largely in metaphysical discussions, but could recollect no instance where I had been able to draw him out. He had listened, it is true, with attention, and smiled, as if in acquiescence; but had always appeared to avoid reply. Besides, I had made several sad blunders in the glow of eloquent declamation; but he had never interrupted me, to notice and correct them, as he would have done, had he been versed in the theme.

"Now it is really a great pity," resumed I, "that he should have the entire management of Miss Somerville's education. What a vast advantage it would be, if she would be put for a little time under the superintendance of Glencoe. He would throw some deeper shades of thought into her mind, which at present, is all sunshine: not but that Mr. Somerville has done very well, as far as he has gone; but then he has merely prepared the soil for the strong plants of useful knowledge. She is well versed in the leading facts of history, and the general course of Belles lettres," said I; "a little moral Philosophy would do wonders."

I accordingly took occasion to ask Mr. Somerville for a few moments' conversation in his study, the morning I was to depart. When we were alone, I opened the matter fully to him. I commenced with the warmest eulogium of Glencoe's powers of mind, and vast acquirements, and ascribed to him all my proficiency in the higher branches of knowledge; I begged, therefore, to recommend him as a friend calculated to direct the studies of Miss Somerville; to lead her mind, by degrees, to the contemplation of abstract principles, and to produce habits of philosophical analysis; "which," added I, gently smiling, "are not often cultivated by young ladies." I ventured to hint, in addition,

that he would find Mr. Glencoe a most valuable and interesting acquaintance for himself; one who would stimulate and evolve the
powers of his mind; and who might open to him tracts of inquiry and
speculation, to which perhaps he had hitherto been a stranger.

Mr. Somerville listened with grave attention. When I had finished,
he thanked me in the politest manner for the interest I took in the
welfare of his daughter and himself. He observed that, as regarded
himself, he was afraid he was too old to benefit by the instructions
of Mr. Glencoe, and that as to his daughter, he was afraid her mind
was but little fitted for the study of metaphysics. "I do not wish,"
continued he, "to strain her intellects with subjects they cannot grasp,
but to make her familiarly acquainted with those that are within the
limits of her capacity. I do not pretend to prescribe the boundaries
of female genius and am far from indulging the vulgar opinion, that
women are unfitted by nature for the highest intellectual pursuits. I
speak only with reference to my daughter's taste and talents. She will
never make a learned woman; nor in truth do I desire it; for such is
the jealousy of our sex, as to mental as well as physical ascendancy,
that a learned woman is not always the happiest. I do not wish my
daughter to excite envy, nor to battle with the prejudices of the world;
but to glide peaceably through life on the good will and kind opinion
of her friends. She has ample employment for her little head, in the
course I have marked out for her; and is busy at present with some
branches of natural history, calculated to awaken her perceptions to
the beauties and wonders of nature, and to the inexhaustable volume
of wisdom constantly spread open before her eyes. I consider that
woman most likely to make an agreeable companion, who can draw
topics of pleasing remark from every natural object; and most likely
to be cheerful and contented, who is continually sensible of the order,
the harmony, and the invariable beneficence, that reign throughout
the beautiful world we inhabit."

"But," added he, smiling, "I am betraying myself into a lecture
instead of merely giving a reply to your kind offer. Permit me to take
the liberty in return, of enquiring a little about your own pursuits.
You speak of having finished your education; but of course you have
a line of private study and mental occupation marked out; for you
must know the importance, both in point of interest and happiness,
of keeping the mind employed. May I ask what system you observe
in your intellectual exercises?"

"Oh, as to system," I observed, "I could never bring myself into
any thing of the kind. I thought it best to let my genius take its own
course, as it always acted the most vigorously when stimulated by
inclination."

Mr. Somerville shook his head. "This same genius," said he, "is a wild quality, that runs away with our most promising young men. It has become so much the fashion, too, to give it the reins, that it is now thought an animal of too noble and generous a nature to be brought to the harness. But it is all a mistake. Nature never designed these high endowments to run riot through society, and throw the whole system into confusion. No, my dear Sir, genius, unless it acts upon system, is very apt to be a useless quality to society, sometimes an injurious, and certainly a very uncomfortable one, to its possessor. I have had many opportunities of seeing the progress through life of young men who were accounted geniuses, and have found it too often end in early exhaustion and bitter disappointment; and have as often noticed that these effects might be traced to a total want of system. There were no habits of business, of steady purpose and regular application superinduced upon the mind: every thing was left to chance and impulse, and native luxuriance, and every thing of course ran to waste, and wild entanglement. Excuse me if I am tedious on this point, for I feel solicitous to impress it upon you, being an error extremely prevalent in our country, and one into which too many of our youth have fallen. I am happy however, to observe the zeal which still appears to actuate you for the acquisition of knowledge, and augur every good from the elevated bent of your ambition. May I ask what has been your course of study for the last six months?"

Never was question more unluckily timed. For the last six months, I had been absolutely buried in novels and romances.

Mr. Somerville perceived that the question was embarrassing, and with his invariable good breeding, immediately resumed the conversation, without waiting for a reply. He took care, however, to turn it in such a way as to draw from me an account of the whole manner in which I had been educated, and the various currents of reading into which my mind had run. He then went on to discuss briefly, but impressively, the different branches of knowledge most important to a young man in my situation; and to my surprize I found him a complete master of those studies on which I had supposed him ignorant, and on which I had been descanting so confidently.

He complimented me, however, very graciously upon the progress I had made, but advised me for the present to turn my attention to the physical rather than the moral sciences. "These studies," said he, "store a man's mind with valuable facts, and at the same time repress self confidence, by letting him know how boundless are the realms of knowledge, and how little we can possibly know. Where as metaphysical studies, though an ingenious order of intellectual employment, are apt to bewilder some minds with vague speculations. They never know how far they have advanced, or what may be the correctness of their favorite theory. They render many of our young men verbose and declamatory, and prone to mistake the aberrations of their fancy for the inspirations of divine philosophy."

I could not but interrupt him, to assent to the truth of these remarks, and to say that it had been my lot, in the course of my limited experience, to encounter young men of the kind, who had overwhelmed me by their verbosity.

Mr. Somerville smiled. "I trust," said he, kindly, "that you will guard against these errors. Avoid the eagerness with which a young man is apt to hurry into conversation, and to utter the crude and ill-digested notions which he has picked up in his recent studies. Be assured that extensive and accurate knowledge is the slow acquisition of a studious life time; that a young man, however pregnant his wit, and prompt his talent, can have mastered but the rudiments of learning, and, in a manner, attained the implements of study. Whatever may have been your past assiduity, you must be sensible that as yet you have but reached the threshold of true knowledge; but at the same time, you have the advantage that you are still very young, and have ample time to learn."

Here our conference ended. I walked out of the study, a very different being from what I was on entering it. I had gone in with the air of a professor about to deliver a lecture; I came out like a student, who had failed in his examination, and been degraded in his class.

"Very young," and "on the threshold of knowledge!" This was extremely flattering, to one who had considered himself an accomplished scholar, and profound philosopher!

"It is singular," thought I; "there seems to have been a spell upon my faculties, ever since I have been in this house. I certainly have not been able to do myself justice. Whenever I have undertaken to advise, I have had the tables turned upon me. It must be that I am strange and diffident among people I am not accustomed to. I wish they could hear me talk at home!"

"After all," added I, on farther reflection, "after all, there is a great deal of force in what Mr. Somerville has said. Some how or other, these men of the world do now and then hit upon remarks that would do credit to a philosopher. Some of his general observations came so home, that I almost thought they were meant for myself. His advice about adopting a system of study, is very judicious. I will immediately put it into practice. My mind shall operate henceforward with the regularity of clock-work."

How far I succeeded in adopting this plan; how I fared in the farther pursuit of knowledge, and how I succeeded in my suit to Julia Somerville may afford matter for a farther communication to the public, if this simple record of my early life is fortunate enough to excite any curiosity.

THE BERMUDAS

A SHAKESPEARIAN RESEARCH

"Who did not think, till within these foure yeares, but that these islands had begun rather a habitation for Divells, than fit for men to dwell in? Who did not hate the name, when hee was on land, and shun the place when he was in the seas? But behold the misprision and conceits of the world! For true and large experience hath now told us, it is one of the sweetest paradises that be upon earth."

"A PLAINE DESCRIPT. OF THE BARMUDAS," 1613.

In the course of a voyage home from England, our ship had been struggling, for two or three weeks, with perverse headwinds and a stormy sea. It was in the month of May, yet the weather had at times a wintry sharpness, and it was apprehended that we were in the neighborhood of floating islands of ice, which at that season of the year drift out of the Gulf of Saint Lawrence, and sometimes occasion the wreck of noble ships.

Wearied out by the continued oppositions of the elements our Captain bore away to the south, in hopes of catching the expiring breath of the trade winds, and making what is called the Southern passage. A few days wrought, as it were, a magical "sea change" in every thing around us. We seemed to emerge into a different world. The late dark and angry sea lashed up into roaring and swashing surges, became calm and sunny; the rude winds died away; and gradually a light breeze sprang up directly aft, filling out every sail, and wafting us smoothly along on an even keel. The air softened into a bland and delightful temperature. Dolphins began to play about us; the nautilus came floating by, like a fairy ship, with its mimic sail and rainbow tints; and flying fish, from time to time, made their short excursive flights, and occasionally fell upon the deck. The cloaks and over-coats in which we had hitherto wrapped ourselves, and moped about the vessel, were thrown aside: for a summer warmth had succeeded to the late wintry chills. Sails were stretched as awnings over the quarter deck, to protect us from the mid day sun. Under these we lounged away the day, in luxurious indolence, musing with half-shut eyes, upon the quiet ocean. The night was scarcely less beautiful than the day. The rising moon sent a quivering column of silver along the undulating surface of the deep, and, gradually climbing the heaven lit up our towering top sails and swelling main-sails, and spread a pale, mysterious light around. As our ship made her whispering way through this dreamy world of waters,

every boisterous sound on board was charmed to silence; and the low
whistle or drowsy song, of a sailor from the forecastle, or the tinkling
of a guitar, and the soft warbling of a female voice from the quarter-
deck, seemed to derive a witching melody from the scene and hour. I
was reminded of Oberon's exquisite description of music and moonlight on the ocean.

> ————."Thou rememberest
> Since once I sat upon a promontory, and heard a mermaid on
>   a dolphin's back,
> Uttering such dulcet and harmonious breath,
> That the rude sea grew civil at her song; and certain stars shot
>   madly from their spheres
> To hear the sea-maid's music."

Indeed, I was in the very mood to conjure up all the imaginary beings with which poetry has peopled old ocean, and almost ready to
fancy I heard the distant song of the mermaid, or the mellow shell of
the triton, and to picture to myself Neptune and Amphitrite with all
their pageant sweeping along the dim horizon.

A day or two of such fanciful voyaging, brought us in sight of the
Bermudas, which first looked like mere summer clouds, peering above
the quiet ocean. All day we glided along in sight of them, with just wind
enough to fill our sails; and never did land appear more lovely. They were
clad in emerald verdure beneath the serenest of skies: not an angry
wave broke upon their quiet shores, and small fishing craft riding the
crystal waves, seemed as if hung in air. It was such a scene, that Fletcher
pictured to himself, when he extolled the halcyon lot of the fisher man:

> Ah! would thou knew'st how much it better were
>   To bide among the simple fisher-swains:
> No shrieking owl, no night-crow lodgeth here,
>   Nor is our simple pleasure mixed with pains.
> Our sports begin with the beginning year;
>   In calms to pull the leaping fish to land,
>   In roughs, to sing and dance along the yellow sand.

In contemplating these beautiful islands, and the peaceful sea around
them, I could hardly realize that these were the "still vext Bermoothes" of
Shakespeare, once the dread of mariners, and infamous in the narratives
of the early discoverers, for the dangers and disasters which beset them.
Such, however, was the case; and the islands derived additional interest in my eyes, from fancying that I could trace, in their early his-

tory, and in the superstitious notions connected with them, some of the elements of Shakespeare's wild and beautiful drama of the Tempest. I shall take the liberty of citing a few historical facts, in support of this idea, which may claim some additional attention from the American reader, as being connected with the first settlement of Virginia.

At the time when Shakespeare was in the fullness of his talent, and seizing upon every thing that could furnish aliment to his imagination, the colonization of Virginia was a favorite object of enterprise among people of condition in England, and several of the courtiers of the court of Queen Elizabeth were personally engaged in it. In the year 1609, a noble armament of nine ships and five hundred men sailed for the relief of the Colony. It was commanded by Sir George Somers, as Admiral, a gallant and generous gentleman, above sixty years of age, and possessed of an ample fortune, yet still bent upon hardy enterprise, and ambitious of signalizing himself in the service of his country.

On board of his flag-ship, the Sea-Venture, sailed also Sir Thomas Gates, Lieutenant-general of the Colony. The voyage was long and boisterous. On the twenty-fifth of July, the admiral's ship was separated from the rest, in a hurricane. For several days, she was driven about at the mercy of the elements, and so strained and racked, that her seams yawned open, and her hold was half filled with water. The storm subsided, but left her a mere foundering wreck. The crew stood in the hold to their waists in water, vainly endeavoring to bail her with kettles, buckets, and other vessels. The leaks rapidly gained on them, while their strength was as rapidly declining. They lost all hope of keeping the ship afloat, until they should reach the American coast; and wearied with fruitless toil, determined, in their despair, to give up all farther attempt, shut down the hatches, and abandon themselves to providence. Some, who had spiritous liquors, or "Comfortable waters:" as the old record quaintly terms them, brought them forth, and shared them with their comrades, and they all drank a sad farewell to one another, as men who were soon to part company in this world.

In this moment of extremity, the worthy Admiral, who kept sleepless watch from the high stern of the vessel, gave the thrilling cry of "land!" All rushed on deck, in a frenzy of joy, and nothing now was to be seen or heard on board but the transports of men who felt as if rescued from the grave. It is true the land in sight would not, in ordinary circumstances, have inspired much self gratulation. It could be nothing else but the groups of islands called after their discoverer, one Juan Bermudas, a Spaniard, but stygmatized among the mariners of those days as the islands of Devils! "For the islands of the Barmudas," says the old narrative of this voyage, "as every man knoweth that hath heard or read of them, were never inhabited by any christian or heathen people, but were ever esteemed and reputed a most prodigious and enchanted place, affording nothing but gusts, stormes, and foul weather, which made every navigator and mariner to avoide them as Scylla and Charybdis, or as they would shun the divell himself."*

"Sir George Somers and his tempest-tossed comrades, however, hailed them with rapture, as if they had been a terrestrial paradise. Every sail was spread, and every exertion made to urge the foundering ship to land. Before long, she struck upon a rock. Fortunately, the late stormy winds had subsided, and there was no surf. A swelling wave lifted her from off the rock, and bore her to another; and thus she was borne on from rock to rock, until she remained wedged between two, as firmly as if set upon the stocks. The boats were immediately lowered, and, though the shore was above a mile distant, the whole crew were landed in safety.

Every one had now his task assigned him. Some made all haste to unload the ship, before she should go to pieces; some constructed wigwams of palmetto leaves, and others ranged the island in quest of wood and water. To their surprize and joy, they found it far different from the desolate and frightful place they had been taught, by seamen's stories, to expect. It was well wooded and fertile; there were birds of various kinds, and herds of swine roaming about, the progeny of a number that had swum ashore, in former years, from a Spanish wreck. The island abounded with turtle, and great quantities of their eggs were to be found among the rocks. The bays and inlets were full of fish; so tame, that if any one stepped into the water, they would throng around him. Sir George Somers in a little while, caught enough with hook and line to furnish a meal to his whole ship's company. Some of them were so large, that two were as much as a man could carry. Crawfish, also, were taken in abundance. The air was soft and salubrious, and the sky beautifully serene. Waller, in his "Summer Islands" has given us a faithful picture of the climate:

> For the kind spring, (which but salutes us here,)
> Inhabits these, and courts them all the year:
> Ripe fruits and blossoms on the same trees live;
> At once they promise, and at once they give:
> So sweet the air, so moderate the clime,
> None sickly lives, or dies before his time.
> Heaven sure has kept this spot of earth uncurst,
> To show how all things were created first."

* A Plaine Description of the Barmudas.

We may imagine the feelings of the ship-wrecked mariners, on finding themselves cast by stormy seas upon so happy a coast; where abundance was to be had without labor; where, what in other climes constituted the costly luxuries of the rich, were within every man's reach; and
where life promised to be a mere holiday. Many of the common sailors
especially, declared they no better lot than to pass the rest of their lives
on this favored island.

The commanders, however, were not so ready to console themselves
with mere physical comforts, for the severance from the enjoyments of
cultivated life, and all the objects of honorable ambition. Despairing of
the arrival of any chance ship on these shunned and dreaded islands,
they fitted out the long-boat, making a deck of the ships hatches, and,
having manned her with eight picked men, dispatched her, under the
command of an able and hardy mariner, named Raven, to proceed to
Virginia, and procure shipping to be sent to their relief.

While waiting in anxious idleness for the arrival of the looked-for aid,
dissensions arose between Sir George Somers and Sir Thomas Gates,
originating, very probably, in jealousy of the lead which the nautical experience and professional station of the Admiral gave him in the present
emergency. Each Commander of course had his adherents: these dissensions ripened into a complete schism; and this handful of shipwrecked
men, thus thrown together on an uninhabited island, separated into two
parties and lived asunder in bitter feud, as men rendered fickle by prosperity, instead of being brought into brotherhood by a common calamity.

Weeks and months elapsed, without bringing the looked-for aid from
Virginia, though that colony was within but a few days' sail. Fears were
now entertained that the long-boat had been either swallowed up in
the sea, or wrecked on some savage coast, one or other of which most
probably was the case, as nothing was ever heard of Raven and his
comrades.

Each party now set to work to build a vessel for itself out of the cedar
with which the island abounded. The wreck of the Sea Venture furnished rigging, and various other articles; but they had no iron for bolts
and other fastenings; and for want of pitch and tar, they payed the
seams of their vessels with lime and turtles' oil, which soon dried, and
became as hard as stone.

In the tenth of May, 1610, they set sail, having been about nine months
on the island. They reached Virginia without farther accident, but found
the colony in great distress for provisions. The account that they gave of
the abundance that reigned in the Bermudas, and especially of the herds
of swine that roamed the island, determined Lord Delaware, the Governor of Virginia, to send thither for supplies. Sir George Somers, with
his wonted promptness and generosity, offered to undertake what was

still considered a dangerous voyage. Accordingly, on the nineteenth of June, he set sail, in his own cedar vessel of thirty tons, accompanied by another small vessel, commanded by Captain Argall.

The gallant Somers was doomed again to be tempest-tossed. His companion vessel was soon driven back to port, but he kept the sea; and, as usual, remained at his post on deck in all weathers. His voyage was long and boisterous, and the fatigues and exposures which he under went were too much for a frame impaired by age and by previous hardships. He arrived at Bermudas completely exhausted and broken down.

His nephew, Captain Matthew Somers, attended him in his illness with affectionate assiduity. Finding his end approaching, the veteran called his men together, and exhorted them to be true to the interests of Virginia; to procure provisions, with all possible despatch, and hasten back to the relief of the colony. With this dying charge, he gave up the ghost, leaving his nephew and crew overwhelmed with grief and consternation. Their first thought was to pay honor to his remains. Opening the body, they took out the heart and entrails, and buried them, erecting a cross over the grave. They then embalmed the body, and set sail with it for England; thus, while paying empty honors to their deceased commander, neglecting his earnest wish and dying injunction, that they should return with relief to Virginia.

The little bark arrived safely at Whitechurch, in Dorsetshire, with its melancholy freight. The body of the worthy Somers was interred with the military honors due to a brave soldier, and many vollies fired over his grave. The Bermudas have since received the name of the Somer Islands, as a tribute to his memory.

The accounts given by Captain Matthew Somers and his crew of the delightful climate, and the great beauty, fertility, and abundance of these islands, excited the zeal of enthusiasts, and the cupidity of speculators, and a plan was set on foot to colonize them. The Virginia company sold their right to the islands to one hundred and twenty of their own members, who erected themselves into distinct corporation, under the name of the "Somer Island Society;" and Mr. Richard Moore was sent out in 1612 as governor, with sixty men, to found a Colony; and this leads me to the second branch of this research.

THE THREE KINGS OF BERMUDA
AND THEIR TREASURE OF AMBERGRIS

At the time that Sir George Somers was preparing to launch his cedar-built bark, and sail for Virginia, there were three culprits among his men, who had been guilty of capital offenses. One of them was shot; the others, named Christopher Carter and Edward Waters, escaped. Waters, indeed made a very narrow escape, for he had actually been tied to a tree to be executed, but cut the rope with a knife, which he had concealed about his person, and fled to the woods, where he was joined by Carter. These two worthies kept themselves concealed in the secret parts of the island, until the departure of the two vessels. When Sir George Somers revisited the island, in quest of supplies for the Virginia Colony, these culprits hovered about the landing-place, and suceeded in persuading another seaman, named Edward Chard, to join them, giving him the most seductive picture of the ease and abundance in which they revelled.

Whe the bark that bore Sir George's body to England had faded from the watery horizon these three vagabonds walked forth in their majesty and might, the lords and sole inhabitants of these islands. For a time their little commonwealth went on prosperously and happily. They built a house, sowed corn, and the seeds of various fruits: and, having plenty of hogs, wild fowl, and fish of all kinds, with turtle in abundance, carried on their tripartite sovereignty with great harmony and much feasting. All kingdoms, however, are doomed to revolution, convulsion, or decay; so it fared with the empire of these three kings of Bermuda, albeit they were monarchs without subjects. In an evil hour, in their search after turtle, among the fissures of the rocks, they came upon a great treasure of ambergris, which had been cast on shore by the ocean. Besides a number of pieces of smaller dimensions, there was one great mass, the largest that had ever been known, weighing eighty pounds, and which, of itself, according to the market value of ambergris in those days, was worth about nine or ten thousand pounds!

From that moment, the happiness and harmony of the three kings of Bermuda were gone forever. While poor devils, with nothing to share but the common blessings of the island, which administered to prevent enjoyment, but had nothing of convertible value, they were loving and united; but here was actual wealth, which would make them rich men, whenever they could transport it to market.

Adieu the delights of the island! They now became flat and insipid. Each pictured to himself the consequence he might now aspire to in civilized life, could he once get there with this mass of ambergris. No longer a poor Jack Tar, frolicking in the low taverns of Wapping, he might roll through London in his coach, and, perchance arrive, like Whittington at the dignity of Lord Mayor.

With riches came envy and covetousness. Each was now for assuming the supreme power, and getting the monopoly of the ambergris. A civil war at length broke out; Chard and Waters defied each other to mortal combat, and the kingdom of the Bermudas was on the point of being deluged with royal blood. Fortunately, Carter took no part in the bloody feud. Ambition might have made him view it with secret exultation, for if either or both of his brother potentates were slain in the conflict, he would be a gainer in purse and ambergris. But he dreaded to be left alone in this uninhabited island, and to find himself the monarch of a solitude: So he secretly purloined and hid the weapons of the belligerent rivals, who, having no means of carrying on the war, gradually cooled down into a sullen amistice.

The arrival of Governor More, with an overpowering force of sixty men, put an end to the empire. He took possession of the kingdom, in the name of the Somer Island Company, and forthwith proceeded to make a settlement. The three kings tacitly relinquished their sway, but stood up stoutly for their treasure. It was determined, however that, they had been fitted out at the expense, and employed in the service of the Virginia Company; that they had found the ambergris while in the service of that company, and on that company's land; that the ambergris therefore, belonged to that company, or rather to the Somer Island Company, in consequence of their recent purchase of the islands, and all their appurtenances. Having thus legally established their right, and being moreover able to back it by might, the company laid the lion's paw upon the spoil; and nothing more remains on historic record of the Three Kings of Bermuda, and their treasure of ambergris.

The reader will now determine whether I am more extravagant than most of the commentators on Shakespeare, in my surmise that the story of Sir George Somer's shipwreck, and the subsequent occurences that took place on the uninhabited island, may have furnished the bard with some of the elements of his drama of the Tempest.

The tidings of the shipwreck, and of the incidents connected with it, reached England not long before the production of this drama, and made a great sensation there. A narrative of the whole matter, from which most of the foregoing particulars are extracted, was published at the time in London, in a pamphlet form, and could not fail to be eagerly perused by Shakespeare, and to make a vivid impression on his fancy. His expression in the Tempest of "the still vext Bermoothes," accords exactly with the storm-beaten character of those islands, The enchantments, too, with which he has clothed the island of Prospero, may they not be traced to the wild and superstitiuus notions entertained about the Bermudas? I have already cited two passages from a pamphlet published at the time, showing that they were esteemed "a most *prodigious* and *enchanted* place," and the "habitation of divells;" and another

pamphlet, published shortly afterward, observes: "and whereas it is re-
ported that this land of the Barmudas, with the islands about, (which
are many, at least an hundred,) are enchanted and kept with evill and
wicked spirits, it is a most idle false report."*

The description, too, given in the same pamphlets, of the real beauty
and fertility of the Bermudas, and of their serene and happy climate,
so opposite to the dangerous and inhospitable character with which they
had been stygmatized, accords with the eulogium of Sebastian on the
island of Prospero:

"Though this island seem to be desert, uninhabitable, and almost in-
acessible, it most needs be of subtle, tender, and delicate temperance.
The air breathes upon us here most sweetly. Here is every thing advantageous to life. How lush and lusty the grass looks! how green!"

I think too, in the exulting consciousness of ease, security, and abundance, felt by the late tempest-tossed mariners, while revelling in the
plentiousness of the island, and their inclination to remain there, released
from the labours, the cares, and the artificial restraints, of civilized life.
I can see something of the golden commonwealth of honest Gonzalo:

> "Had I a plantation of this isle, my lord,
> And were the king of it, what would I do?
> I' the commonwealth I would by contraries
> Execute all things: for no kind of traffick
> Would I admit: no name of magistrate;
> Letters should not be known; riches, poverty,
> And use of service, none; contract, succession,
> Bourn, bound of land, tilth, vineyard, none.
> No use of metal, corn, or wine, or oil:
> No occupation; all men idle, all.
>
>   .   .   .   .   .   .
>
> All things in common, nature should produce,
> Without sweat or endeavour: Treason, felony,
> Sword, pike, knife, gun, or need of any engine,
> Would I not have; but nature should bring forth,
> Of its own kind all foizon, all abundance,
> To feed my innocent people."

But above all, in three fugitive vagabonds who remained in possession
of the island of Bermuda, on the departure of their comrades, and in
their squabbles about supremacy, on the finding of their treasure, I see
typified Sebastian, Trinculo, and their worthy companion Caliban:

* 'Newes from the Barmudas:' 1612.

"Trinculo, the king and all our company being drowned, we will inherit here!"

"Monster, I will kill this man; his daughter and I will be king and queen, (save our graces!) and Trinculo and thyself shall be viceroys."

I do not mean to hold up the incidents and characters in the narrative and in the play as parallel, or as being strikingly similar; neither would I insinuate that the narrative suggested the play; I would only suppose that Shakespeare, being occupied about that time on the drama of the Tempest; the main story of which, I believe, is of Italian origin, had many of the fanciful ideas of it suggested to his mind, by the shipwreck of Sir George Somers on the "still vex't Bermoothes," and by the popular superstitions connected with these islands, and suddenly put in circulation, by that event.

THE WIDOW'S ORDEAL

OR

A JUDICIAL TRIAL BY COMBAT

The world is daily growing older and wiser. Its institutions vary with its years, and mark its growing wisdom; and none more so than its modes of investigating truth, and ascertaining guilt or innocence. In its nonage, when man was yet a fallible being, and doubted the accuracy of his own intellect, appeals were made to heaven in dark and doubtful cases of atrocious accusation.

The accused was required to plunge his hand in boiling oil, or to walk across redhot ploughshares, or to maintain his innocence in armed fight and listed field, in person or by champion. If he passed these ordeals unscathed, he stood acquitted, and the result was regarded as a verdict from on high.

It is somewhat remarkable that, in the gallant age of chivalry, the gentler sex should have been most frequently the subjects of these rude trials and perilous ordeals; and that, too, when assailed in their most delicate and vulnerable part—their honor.

In the present very old and enlightened age of the world, when the human intellect is perfectly competent to the management of its own concerns, and needs no special interposition of heaven in its affairs, the trial by jury has superseded these superhuman ordeals; and the unanimity of twelve discordant minds is necessary to constitute a verdict. Such a unanimity would, at first sight, appear also to require a miracle from heaven; but it is produced by a simple device of human ingenuity. The twelve jurors are locked up in their box, there to fast until abstinence shall have so clarified their intellects that the whole jarring panel can discern the truth, and concur in a unanimous decision. One point is certain, that truth is one, and is immutable—until the jurors all agree, they cannot all be right.

It is not our intention, however, to discuss this great judicial point, or to question the avowed superiority of the mode of investigating truth, adopted in this antiquated and very sagacious era. It is our object merely to exhibit to the curious reader, one of the most memorable cases of judicial combat we find in the annals of Spain. It occurred at the bright commencement of the reign, and in the youthful, and, as yet, glorious days, of Roderick the Goth; who subsequently tarnished his fame at home by his misdeeds, and, finally, lost his kingdom and his life on the banks of the Guadalete, in that disastrous battle, which gave up Spain a conquest to the Moors. The following is the story:—

There was, once upon a time, a certain duke of Lorraine, who was acknowledged throughout his domains to be one of the wisest princes that ever lived. In fact, there was no one measure adopted by him that did not astonish his privy counsellors and gentlemen in attendance; and he said such witty things, and made such sensible speeches, that the jaws of his high chamberlain were nigh dislocated from laughing with delight at one, and gaping with wonder at the other.

This very witty and exceedingly wise potentate lived for half a century in single blessedness, at length his courtiers began to think it a great pity so wise and wealthy a prince should not have a child after his own likeness, to inherit his talents and domains; so they urged him most respectfully to marry, for the good of his estate, and the welfare of his subjects.

He turned their advice over in his mind some four or five years and then sent forth emissaries to summon to his court all the beautiful maidens in the land, who were ambitious of sharing a ducal crown. The court was soon crowded with beauties of all styles and complexions, from among whom he chose one in the earliest budding of her charms, and acknowledged by all the gentlemen to be unparalleled for grace and loveliness. The courtiers extolled the duke to the skies for making such a choice, and considered it another proof of his great wisdom. "The duke," said they, "is waxing a little too old, the damsel, on the other hand, is a little too young; if one is lacking in years, the other has a superabundance; thus a want on one side, is balanced by an excess on the other, and the result is a well-assorted marriage."

The duke, as is often the case with wise men who marry rather late, and take damsels rather youthful to their bosoms, became dotingly fond of his wife, and very properly indulged her in all things. He was, consequently, cried up by his subjects in general, and by the ladies in particular, as a pattern for husbands; and, in the end, from the wonderful docility with which he submitted to be reined and checked, acquired the amiable and enviable appellation of duke Philibert, the wife-ridden.

There was only one thing that disturbed the conjugal felicity of this paragon of husbands—though a considerable time lapsed after his marriage, there was still no prospect of an heir. The good duke left no means untried to propitiate heaven. He made vows and pilgrimages, he fasted and he prayed, but all to no purpose. The courtiers were all astonished at the circumstance. They could not account for it. While the meanest peasant in the country had sturdy brats by dozens, without putting up a prayer, the duke wore himself to skin and bone with penances and fastings, yet seemed farther off from his object than ever.

At length, the worthy prince fell dangerously ill, and felt his end approaching. He looked sorrowfully and dubiously upon his young and tender spouse, who hung over him with tears and sobbings. "Alas!" said he, "tears are soon dried from youthful eyes, and sorrow lies lightly on a youthful heart. In a little while thou wilt forget in the arms of another husband him who has loved thee so long."

"Never! never!" cried the duchess. "Never will I cleave to another! Alas, that my lord should think me capable of such inconstancy!"

The worthy and wife-ridden duke was soothed by her assurances; for he could not brook the thought of giving her up even after he should be dead. Still he wished to have some pledge of her enduring constancy:

"Far be it from me, my dearest wife," said he, "to control thee through a long life. A year and a day of strict fidelity will appease my troubled spirit. Promise to remain faithful to my memory for a year and a day, and I will die in peace."

The duchess made a solemn vow to that effect, but the uxorious feelings of the duke were not yet satisfied. "Safe bind, safe find," thought he; so he made a will, bequeathing to her all his domains, on condition of her remaining true to him for a year and a day after his decease; but, should it appear that, within that time, she had in anywise lapsed from her fidelity, the inheritance should go to his nephew, the lord of a neighboring territory.

Having made his will, the good duke died and was buried. Scarcely was he in his tomb, when his nephew came to take possession, thinking, as his uncle had died without issue, that the domains would be devised to him of course. He was in a furious passion, when the will was produced, and the young widow declared inheritor of the dukedom. As he was a violent, high-handed man, and one of the sturdiest knights in the land, fears were entertained that he might attempt to seize on the territories by force. He had, however, two bachelor uncles for bosom counsellors—swaggering rakehelly old cavaliers, who, having led loose and riotous lives, prided themselves upon knowing the world, and being deeply experienced in human nature. "Prithee, man, be of good cheer," said they, "the duchess is a young and buxom widow. She has just buried our brother, who, God rest his soul! was somewhat too much given to praying and fasting, and kept his pretty wife always tied to his girdle. She is now like a bird from a cage. Think you she will keep her vow? Pooh, pooh—impossible!—Take our words for it—we know mankind, and, above all, womankind. She cannot hold out for such a length of time; it is not in womanhood—it is not in widowhood—we know it, and that's enough. Keep sharp look-out upon the widow, therefore, and within the twelvemonth you will catch her tripping—and then the dukedom is your own."

The nephew was pleased with this counsel, and immediately placed spies round the duchess, and bribed several of her servants to keep a watch upon her, so that she could not take a single step, even from one apartment of her palace to another, without being observed. Never was young and beautiful widow exposed to so terrible an ordeal.

The duchess was aware of the watch thus kept upon her. Though confident of her own rectitude, she knew that it is not enough for a woman to be virtuous—she must be above the reach of slander. For the whole term of her probation, therefore, she proclaimed a strict nonintercourse with the other sex. She had females for cabinet ministers and chamberlains, through whom she transacted all her public and private concerns; and it is said that never were the affairs of the dukedom so adroitly administered.

All males were rigorously excluded from the palace; she never went out of its precincts, and whenever she moved about its courts and gardens, she surrounded herself with a bodyguard of young maids of honor, commanded by dames renowned for discretion. She slept in a bed without curtains, placed in the centre of a room illuminated by innumerable wax tapers. Four ancient spinsters, virtuous as Virginia, perfect dragons of watchfulness, who only slept during the daytime, kept vigils throughout the night, seated in the four corners of the room on stools without backs or arms, and with seats cut in checquers of the hardest wood, to keep them from dozing.

Thus wisely and warily did the young duchess conduct herself for twelve long months, and slander almost bit her tongue off in despair, at finding no room even for a surmise. Never was ordeal more burdensome, or more enduringly sustained.

The year passed away. The last, odd day arrived, and a long, long day it was. It was the twenty-first of June, the longest day in the year. It seemed as if it would never come to an end. A thousand times did the duchess and her ladies watch the sun from the windows of the palace, as he slowly climbed the vault of heaven, and seemed still more slowly to roll down. They could not help expressing their wonder, now and then, why the duke should have tagged this supernumerary day to the end of the year, as if three hundred and sixty-five days were not sufficient to try and task the fidelity of any woman. It is the last grain that turns the scale—the last drop that overflows the goblet—and the last moment of delay that exhausts the patience. By the time the sun sank below the horizon, the duchess was in a fidget that passed all bounds, and, though several hours were yet to pass before the day regularly expired, she could not have remained those hours in durance to gain a royal crown, much less a ducal coronet. So she gave her orders, and her paltrey, magnificently caparisoned, was brought into the court-yard of the castle, with palfreys for all her ladies in attendance. In this way she sallied forth, just as the sun had gone down. It was a mission of piety—

a pilgrim cavalcade to a convent at the foot of a neighboring mountain
—to return thanks to the blessed Virgin, for having sustained her through
this fearful ordeal.

The orisons performed, the duchess and her ladies returned, ambling
gently along the border of a forest. It was about that mellow hour of
twilight when night and day are mingled, and all objects are indistinct.
Suddenly, some monstrous animal sprang from out a thicket, with fearful
howlings. The female body-guard was thrown into confusion, and fled
different ways. It was some time before they recovered from their panic,
and gathered once more together; but the duchess was not to be found.
The greatest anxiety was felt for her safety. The hazy mist of twilight
had prevented their distinguishing perfectly the animal which had aff-
righted them. Some thought it a wolf, others a bear, others a wild man
of the woods. For upwards of an hour did they beleaguer the forest,
without daring to venture in, and were on the point of giving up the
duchess as torn to pieces and devoured, when, to their great joy, they
beheld her advancing in the gloom, supported by a stately cavalier.

He was a stranger knight, whom nobody knew. It was impossible to
distinguish his countenance in the dark; but all the ladies agreed that
he was of noble presence and captivating address. He had rescued the
duchess from the very fangs of the monster, which, he assured the ladies,
was neither a wolf, nor a bear, nor yet a wild man of the woods, but a
veritable fiery dragon, a species of monster peculiarly hostile to beautiful
females in the days of chivalry, and which all the efforts of knight errantry had not been able to extirpate.

The ladies crossed themselves when they heard of the danger from
which they had escaped, and could not enough admire the gallantry of
the cavalier. The duchess would fain have prevailed on her deliverer to
accompany her to her court; but he had no time to spare, being a knight
errant, who had many adventures on hand, and many distressed damsels
and afflicted widows to rescue and relieve in various parts of the country. Taking a respectful leave, therefore, he pursued his wayfaring, and
the duchess and her train returned to the palace. Throughout the whole
way, the ladies were unwearied in chanting the praises of the stranger
knight; nay, many of them would willingly have incurred the danger of
the dragon to have enjoyed the happy deliverance of the duchess. As to
the latter, she rode pensively along, but said nothing.

No sooner was the adventure of the wood made public, than a whirl-
wind was raised about the ears of the beautiful duchess. The blustering
nephew of the deceased duke went about, armed to the teeth, with a
swaggering uncle at each shoulder, ready to back him, and swore the
duchess had forfeited her domain. It was in vain that she called all the
saints, and angels, and her ladies in attendance into the bargain, to wit-

ness that she had passed a year and a day of immaculate fidelity. One fatal hour remained to be accounted for; and into the space of one little hour sins enough may be conjured up by evil tongues, to blast the fame of a whole life of virtue.

The two graceless uncles, who had seen the world, were ever ready to bolster the matter through, and, as they were brawny, broad-shouldered warriors, and veterans in brawl as well as debauch, they had great sway with the multitude. If any one pretended to assert the innocence of the duchess, they interrupted him with a loud ha! ha! of derision. "A pretty story, truly," would they cry, "about a wolf and a dragon, and a young widow rescued in the dark by a sturdy varlet, who dares not show his face in the daylight. You may tell that to those who do not know human nature; for our parts, we know the sex, and that's enough."

If, however, the other repeated his assertion, they would suddenly knit their brows, swell, look big, and put their hands upon their swords. As few people like to fight in a cause that does not touch their own interests, the nephew and the uncles were suffered to have their way, and swagger uncontradicted.

The matter was at length referred to a tribunal composed of all the dignitaries of the dukedom, and many and repeated consultations were held. The character of the duchess, throughout the year, was as bright and spotless as the moon in a cloudless night; one fatal hour of darkness alone intervened to eclipse its brightness. Finding human sagacity incapable of dispelling the mystery, it was determined to leave the question to heaven; or, in other words, to decide it by the ordeal of the sword —a sage tribunal in the age of chivalry. The nephew and two bully uncles were to maintain their accusation in listed combat, and six months were allowed to the duchess to provide herself with three champions, to meet them in the field. Should she fail in this, or should her champions be vanquished, her honor would be considered as attainted, her fidelity as forfeit, and her dukedom would go to the nephew, as a matter of right.

With this determination the duchess was fain to comply. Proclamations were accordingly made, and heralds sent to various parts; but day after day, week after week, and month after month elapsed, without any champion appearing to assert her loyalty throughout that darksome hour. The fair widow was reduced to despair, when tidings reached her of grand tournaments to be held at Toledo, in celebration of the nuptials of Don Roderick, the last of the Gothic kings, with the Morisco princess Exilona. As a last resort, the duchess repaired to the Spanish court, to implore the gallantry of its assembled chivalry.

The ancient city of Toledo was a scene of gorgeous revelry on the event of the royal nuptials. The youthful king, brave, ardent, and mag-

nificent, and his lovely bride, beaming with all the radiant beauty of
the east, were hailed with shouts and acclamations whenever they appeared. Their nobles vied with each other in the luxury of their attire,
their prancing steeds, and splendid retinues; and the haughty dames of
the court appeared in a blaze of jewels.

In the midst of all this pageantry, the beautiful, but afflicted duchess
of Lorraine made her approach to the throne. She was dressed in black,
and closely veiled; four duennas of the most staid and severe aspect, and
six beautiful demoiselles, formed her female attendants. She was guarded
by several very ancient, withered, and grayheaded cavaliers; and her
train was borne by one of the most deformed and diminutive dwarfs in
existence.

Advancing to the foot of the throne, she knelt down, and, throwing up
her veil, revealed a countenance so beautiful that half the courtiers
present were ready to renounce wives and mistresses, and devote themselves to her service; but when she made known that she came in quest
of champions to defend her fame, every cavalier pressed forward to offer
his arm and sword, without inquiring into the merits of the case; for it
seemed clear that so beauteous a lady could have done nothing but what
was right; and that, at any rate, she ought to be championed in following
the bent of her humors, whether right or wrong.

Encouraged by such gallant zeal, the duchess suffered herself to be
raised from the ground, and related the whole story of her distress. When
she concluded, the king remained for some time silent, charmed by the
music of her voice. At length: "As I hope for salvation, most beautiful
duchess," said he, "were I not a sovereign king, and bound in duty to
my kingdom, I myself would put lance in rest to vindicate your cause;
as it is, I here give full permission to my knights, and promise lists and
a fair field, and that the contest shall take place before the walls of
Toledo, in presence of my assembled court."

As soon as the pleasure of the king was known, there was a strife among
the cavaliers present, for the honor of the contest. It was decided by lot,
and the successful candidates were objects of great envy, for every
one was ambitious of finding favor in the eyes of the beautiful widow.

Missives were sent, summoning the nephew and his two uncles to
Toledo, to maintain their accusations, and a day was appointed for the
combat. When the day arrived, all Toledo was in commotion at an early
hour. The lists had been prepared in the usual place, just without the
walls, at the foot of the rugged rocks on which the city is built, and on
that beautiful meadow along the Tagus, known by the name of the king's
garden. The populace had already assembled, each one eager to secure
a favorable place; the balconies were filled with the ladies of the court,
clad in their richest attire, and bands of youthful knights, splendidly

armed, and decorated with their ladies' devices, were managing their superbly caparisoned steeds about the field. The king at length came forth in state, accompanied by the queen Exilona. They took their seats in a raised balcony, under a canopy of rich damask; and, at sight of them, the people rent the air with acclamations.

The nephew and his uncles now rode into the field, armed *cap-a-pie*, and followed by a train of cavaliers of their own roystering cast, great swearers and carousers, arrant swashbucklers, with clanking armor and jingling spurs. When the people of Toledo beheld the vaunting and discourteous appearance of these knights, they were more anxious than ever for the success of the gentle duchess; but, at the same time, the sturdy and stalwart frames of these warriors, showed that whoever won the victory from them, must do it at the cost of many a bitter blow.

As the nephew and his riotous crew rode in at one side of the field, the fair widow appeared at the other, with her suite of grave gray-headed courtiers, her ancient duennas and dainty demoiselles, and the little dwarf toiling along under the weight of her train. Every one made way for her as she passed, and blessed her beautiful face, and prayed for success to her cause. She took her seat in a lower balcony, not far from the sovereigns; and her pale face, set off by her mourning weeds, was as the moon, shining forth from among the clouds of night.

The trumpets sounded for the combat. The warriors were just entering the lists, when a stranger knight, armed in panoply, and followed by two pages and an esquire, came galloping into the field, and, riding up to the royal balcony, claimed the combat as a matter of right.

"In me," cried he, "behold the cavalier who had the happiness to rescue the beautiful duchess from the peril of the forest, and the misfortune to bring on her this grievous calumny. It was but recently, in the course of my errantry, that tidings of her wrongs have reached my ears, and I have urged hither at all speed, to stand forth in her vindication."

No sooner did the duchess hear the accents of the knight than she recognized his voice, and joined her prayers with his that he might enter the lists. The difficulty was, to determine which of the three champions already appointed should yield his place, each insisting on the honor of the combat. The stranger knight would have settled the point, by taking the whole contest upon himself; but this the other knights would not permit. It was at length determined, as before, by lot, and the cavalier who lost the chance retired murmuring and disconsolate.

The trumpets again sounded—the lists were opened. The arrogant nephew and his two drawcansir uncles appeared so completely cased in steel, that they and their steeds were like moving masses of iron.

When they understood the stranger knight to be the same that had rescued the duchess from her peril, they greeted him with the most boisterous derision:

"O ho! sir Knight of the Dragon," said they; "you who pretend to champion fair widows in the dark, come on, and vindicate your deeds of darkness in the open day."

The only reply of the cavalier was, to put lance in rest, and brace himself for the encounter. Needless is it to relate the particulars of a battle, which was like so many hundred combats that have been said and sung in prose and verse. Who is there but must have foreseen the event of a contest, where heaven had to decide on the guilt or innocence of the most beautiful and immaculate of widows?

The sagacious reader, deeply read in this kind of judicial combats, can imagine the encounter of the graceless nephew and the stranger knight. He sees their concussion, man to man, and horse to horse, in mid career, and sir Graceless hurled to the ground, and slain. He will not wonder that the assailants of the brawny uncles were less successful in their rude encounter; but he will picture to himself the stout stranger spurring to their rescue, in the very critical moment; he will see him transfixing one with his lance, and cleaving the other to the chine with a back stroke of his sword, thus leaving the trio of accusers dead upon the field, and establishing the immaculate fidelity of the duchess, and her title to the dukedom, beyond the shadow of a doubt.

The air rang with acclamations; nothing was heard but praises of the beauty and virtue of the duchess, and of the prowess of the stranger knight; but the public joy was still more increased when the champion raised his visor, and revealed the countenance of one of the bravest cavaliers of Spain, renowned for his gallantry in the service of the sex, and who had been round the world, in quest of similar adventures.

That worthy knight, however, was severely wounded, and remained for a long time ill of his wounds. The lovely duchess, grateful for having twice owed her protection to his arm, attended him daily during his illness; and finally rewarded his gallantry with her hand.

The king would fain have had the knight establish his title to such high advancement by farther deeds of arms; but his courtiers declared that he already merited the lady, by thus vindicating her fame and fortune in a deadly combat à l'outrance; and the lady herself hinted that she was perfectly satisfied of his prowess in arms, from the proofs she had received in his achievement in the forest.

Their nuptials were celebrated with great magnificence. The present husband of the duchess did not pray and fast like his predecessor, Philibert the wife-ridden; yet he found greater favor in the eyes of heaven, for their union was blessed with a numerous progeny—the daughters chaste and beauteous as their mother; the sons stout and valiant as their sire, and renowned, like him, for relieving disconsolate damsels and desolated widows.

THE KNIGHT OF MALTA

In the course of a tour in Sicily, in the days of my junvenility, I passed
some little time at the ancient city of Catania, at the foot of Mount
Aetna. Here I became acquainted with the Chevalier L——, an old
Knight of Malta. It was not many years after the time that Napoleon
had dislodged the Knights from their island, and he still wore the
insignia of his order. He was not, however, one of those reliques of
that once chivalrous body, who have been described as "a few worn-out
old men, creeping about certain parts of Europe with the maltese cross
on their breasts;" on the contrary, though advanced in life his form was
still light and vigorous; he had a pale, thin, intellectual visage, with a
high forehead, and a bright visionary eye. He seemed to take a fancy
to me, as I certainly did to him, and we soon became intimate. I visited
him occasionally, at his apartments, in the wing of an old palace, looking
toward Mt. Ætna. He was an antiquary, a virtuoso, and a connoisseur.
His rooms were decorated with mutilated statues, dug up from Grecian
and Roman ruins; old vases, lachrymals, and sepulchral lamps. He had
astronomical and chemical instruments, and black-letter books, in various
languages. I found that he had dipped a little in chimerical studies, and
had a hankering after astrology and alchymy. He affected to believe
in dreams and visions, and delighted in the fanciful Rosicrucian doctrines.
I cannot persuade myself, however, that he really believed in all these;
I rather think he loved to let his imagination carry him away into the
boundless fairly land which they unfolded.

In company with the chevalier, I took several excursions on horseback
about the environs of Catania, and the picturesque skirts of Mount
Ætna. One of those led us through a village which had sprung up on
the very tract of an ancient eruption, the houses being built of lava.
At one time we passed, for some distance, along a narrow lane, between
two high dead convent walls. It was a cut-throat looking place in a
country where assassinations are frequent; and just about midway
through it, we observed blood upon the pavement and the walls, as if
a murder had actually been committed there.

The chevalier spurred on his horse until he had extricated himself
completely from this suspicious neighborhood. He then observed, that
it reminded him of a similar blind alley in Malta, infamous on account
of the many assassinations that had taken place there; concerning one
of which he related a long and tragical story, that lasted until we
reached Catania. It involved various circumstances of a wild and super-

82

natural character, but which he assured me were handed down in tradition, and generally credited by the old inhabitants of Malta.

As I like to pick up strange stories, and as I was particularly struck with several parts of this, I made a minute of it on my return to my lodgings. The memorandum was lost, with several of my travelling papers, and the story had faded from my mind, when recently, on perusing a French memoir, I came suddenly upon it, dressed up, it is true, in a very different manner, but agreeing in the leading facts, and given upon the word of that famous adventurer the Count Cagliostro.

I have amused myself, during a snowy day in the country, by rendering it roughly into English, for the entertainment of a youthful circle round the Christmas fire. It was well received by my auditors, who however, are rather easily pleased. One proof of its merits is, that it sent some of the youngest of them quaking to their beds, and gave them very fearful dreams. Hoping that it may have the same effect upon the ghost-hunting reader, I subjoin it. I would observe, that wherever I have modified the French version of the story, it has been in conformity to some recollection of the narrative of my friend, the Knight of Malta.

THE GRAND PRIOR OF MINORCA
A VERITABLE GHOST STORY

Keep my wits heaven! They say spirits appear
To melancholy minds, and the graves open!
FLETCHER.

About the middle of the last century, while the Knights of Saint John of Jerusalem still maintained something of their ancient state and sway in the Island of Malta, a tragical event took place there, which is the ground work of the following narrative.

It may be as well to premise, that at the time we are treating of, the order of Saint John of Jerusalem, grown excessively wealthy, had degenerated from its originally devout and warlike character. Instead of being a hardy body of "monk-knights" sworn soldiers of the cross, fighting the Paynim in the Holy land, or scouring the Mediterranean, and scourging the Barbary coasts with their galleys, or feeding the poor, and attending upon the sick at their hospitals, they led a life of luxury and libertinism, and were to be found in the most voluptuous courts of Europe. The order, in fact, had become a mode of providing for the needy branches of the Catholic aristocracy of Europe. "A commandery," we are told, was a splendid provision for a younger brother; and men of rank, however dissolute, provided they belonged to the highest aristocracy, became Knights of Malta, just as they did bishops, or colonels of regiments, or Court chamberlains. After a brief residence at Malta, the Knights passed the rest of their time in their own countries, or only made a visit now and then to the island. While there, having but little military duty to perform, they beguiled their idleness by paying attentions to the fair.

There was one circle of society, however, into which they could not obtain currency. This was composed of a few families of the old Maltese nobility, natives of the island. These families, not being permitted to enroll any of their members in the order, affected to hold no intercourse with its chevaliers; admitting none into their exclusive coteries but the Grand Master whom they acknowledged as their soverign, and the members of the chapter which formed his council.

To indemnify themselves for this exclusion, the chevaliers carried their gallantries into the next class of society, composed of those who held civil, administrative, and judicial situations. The ladies of this class were called *honorate,* or honorables, to distinguish them from the inferior orders; and among them were many of superior grace, beauty, and fascination.

Even in this more hospitable class, the chevaliers were not all equally favored. Those of Germany had the decided preference, owing to their fair and fresh complexions, and the kindliness of their manners; next to these came the Spanish cavaliers, on account of their profound and courteous devotion, and most discreet secrecy. Singular as it may seem, the chevaliers of France fared the worst. The Maltese ladies dreaded their volatility, and their proneness to boast of their amours, and shunned all entanglement with them. They were forced, therefore, to content themselves with conquests among females of the lower orders. They revenged themselves, after the gay French manner, by making the "honorate" the objects of all kinds of jests and mystifications; by prying into their tender affairs with the more favored chevaliers, and making them the theme of song and epigram.

About this time, a French vessel arrived at Malta, bringing out a distinguished personage of the order of St. John of Jerusalem, the Commander de Foulquerre; who came to solicit the post of commander in chief of the gallies. He was descended from an old and warrior line of French nobility, his ancestors having long been Seneschals of Poitou, and claiming descent from the first counts of Angouleme.

The arrival of the commander caused a little uneasiness among the peaceably inclined, for he bore the character, in the island, of being fiery, arrogant, and quarrelsome. He had already been three times at Malta, and on each visit, had signalized himself by some rash and deadly affray. As he was now thirty-four years of age, however, it was hoped that time might have taken off the fiery edge of his spirit, and that he might prove more quiet and sedate than formerly. The commander set up an establishment befitting his rank and pretensions; for he arrogated to himself an importance greater even than that of the Grand Master. His house immediately became the rallying place of all the young French chevaliers. They informed him of all the slights they had experienced or imagined, and indulged their petulant and satirical vein at the expense of the honorate and their admirers. The chevaliers of other nations soon found the topics and tone of conversation at the commander's irksome and offensive, and gradually ceased to visit there. The commander remained at the head of a national *clique,* who looked up to him as their model. If he was not as boisterous and quarrelsome as formerly, he had become haughty and overbearing. He was fond of talking over his past affairs of punctilio and bloody duel. When walking the streets, he has generally attended by a ruffling train of young French chevaliers, who caught his own air of assumption and bravado. These he would conduct to the scenes of his deadly encounters, point out the very spot where each fatal lunge had been given, and dwell vaingloriously on every particular.

Under his tuition, the young French chevaliers began to add bluster and arrogance, to their former petulance and levity; they fired up on the most trivial occasions, particularly with those who had been most successful with the fair; and would put on the most intolerable drawcansir airs. The other chevaliers conducted themselves with all popular forbearance and reserve; but they saw it would be impossible to keep on long in this manner, without coming to an open rupture.

Among the Spanish cavaliers, was one named Don Luis de Lima Vasconcellos. He was distantly related to the Grand Master, and had been enrolled at an early age among his pages, but had been rapidly promoted by him, until, at the age of twenty-six, he had been given the richest Spanish commandery in the order. He had, moreover, been fortunate with the fair, with one of whom, the most beautiful honorata of Malta; he had long maintained the most tender correspondence.

The character, rank, and connexions of Don Luis put him on a par with the imperious Commander de Foulquerre, and pointed him out as a leader and champion to his countrymen. The Spanish cavaliers repaired to him, therefore, in a body; represented all the grievances they had sustained, and the evils they apprehended, and urged him to use his influence with the commander and his adherents, to put a stop to the growing abuses.

Don Luis was gratified by this mark of confidence and esteem, on the part of his countrymen, and promised to have an interview with the Commander de Foulquerre on the subject. He resolved to conduct himself with the utmost caution and delicacy on the occasion; to represent to the commander the evil consequences which might result from the inconsiderate conduct of the young French chevaliers; and to entreat him to exert the great influence he so deservedly possessed over them, to restrain their excesses. Don Luis was aware however, of the peril that attended any interview of the kind with this imperious and fractious man, and apprehended, however it might commence, that it would terminate in a duel. Still it was an affair of honor, in which Castilian dignity was concerned; beside he had a lurking disgust at the over-bearing manner of De Foulguerre, and perhaps had been somewhat offended by certain intrusive attentions which he had presumed to pay to the beautiful honorata.

It was now Holy Week; a time too sacred for worldly feuds and passions, especially in a community under the dominion of a religious order; it was agreed, therefore, that the dangerous interview in question should not take place, until after the Easter holy days. It is probable, from subsequent circumstances, that the Commander de Foulquerre had some information of this arrangement among the Spanish cavaliers, and was determined to be beforehand, and to mortify the pride of their champion, who was thus preparing to read him a lecture. He chose Good Friday for his purpose. On this sacred day, it is customary, in Catholic countries, to make a tour of all the churches, offering up prayers in each. In every Catholic church, as is well known, there is a vessel of holy water near the door. In this, every one on entering, dips his fingers, and makes therewith the sign of the cross on his forehead and breast. An office of gallantry among the young Spaniards, is to stand near the door, dip their hands in the holy vessel, and extend them courteously and respectfully to any lady of their acquaintance who may enter, who thus receives the sacred water at second hand on the tips of her fingers, and proceeds to cross herself with all due decorum. The Spaniards, who are the most jealous of lovers, are impatient when this piece of devo-tional gallantry is proffered to the object of their affections by any other hand: on Good Friday, therefore, when a lady makes a tour of the churches, it is the usage among them, for the inamorato to follow her from church to church, so as to present her the holy water at the door of each; thus testifying his own devotion, and at the same time preventing the officious services of a rival.

On the day in question, Don Luis followed the beautiful honorata, to whom, as has already been observed, he had long been devoted. At the very first church she visited, the Commander de Foulquerre was stationed at the portal, with several of the young French chevaliers about him. Before Don Luis could offer her the holy water, he was anticipated by the Commander, who thrust himself between them, and, while he performed the gallant office to the lady, turned his back upon her admirer, and trod upon his feet. The insult was enjoyed by the young French men who were present. It was too deep and grave to be forgiven by Spanish pride, and at once put an end to all Don Luis' plans of caution and forebearance. He repressed his passion for the moment, however, and waited until all the parties left the church; then accosting the Commander with an air of coolness and unconcern, he enquired after his health, and asked to what church he proposed making his second visit "To the Magisterial church of Saint John." Don Luis offered to conduct him thither, by the shortest route. His offer was accepted, apparently without suspicion, and they proceeded together. After walking some distance, they entered a long, narrow lane, without door or window opening upon it, called the "Strada Stretta," or narrow street. It was a street in which duels were tacitly permitted or connived at in Malta, and were suffered to pass as accidental encounters. Every where else, they were prohibited. This restriction had been instituted to diminish the number of duels, formerly so frequent in Malta. As a further precaution to render these encounters less fatal it was an offense punishable with death for any one to enter this street armed with either poniard or pistol. It was a lonely, dismal street, just wide enough for two men to stand upon their guard and cross their swords; few persons ever traversed it, unless with some sinister design; and on any pre-concerted duello the seconds posted themselves at each end to stop all passengers, and prevent interruption.

In the present instance, the parties had scarce entered the street, when Don Luis drew his sword and called upon the Commander to defend himself.

De Foulquerre was evidently taken by surprise; he drew back, and attempted to expostulate; but Don Luis persisted in defying him to the combat.

After a second or two, he likewise drew his sword, but immediately lowered the point.

"Good Friday!" ejaculated he, shaking his head. "One word with you; it is full six years since I have been in a confessional; I am shocked at the state of my conscience; but wither three days; that is to say, on Monday next—"

Don Luis would listen to nothing. Though naturally of a peaceable disposition, he had been stung to fury, and people of that character, when once incensed, are deaf to reason. He compelled the Commander to put himself on his guard. The latter, though a man accustomed to brawl and battle, was singularly dismayed. Terror was visible in all his features. He placed himself with his back to the wall, and the weapons were crossed. The contest was brief and fatal. At the very first thrust, the sword of Don Luis passed through the body of his antagonist. The Commander staggered to the wall, and leaned against it.

"On Good Friday–" ejaculated he again, with a failing voice, and despairing accents "Heaven pardon you!" added he; "Take my sword to Têtefoulque, and have a hundred masses performed in the chapel of the castle for the repose of my soul!" With these words he expired.

The fury of Don Luis was at an end. He stood aghast, gazing at the bleeding body of the commander. He called to mind the prayer of the deceased for three days respite, to make his peace with heaven; he had refused it; had sent him to the grave with all his sins upon his head!—His conscience smote him to the core: he gathered up the sword of the Commander, which he had been enjoined to take to Têtefoulques, and hurried from the fatal Strada Stretta.

The duel of course made a great noise in Malta, but had no injurious effect on the worldly fortunes of Don Luis. He made a full declaration of the whole matter before the proper authorities; the chapter of the order considered it one of those casual encounters of the Strada Stretta, which were mourned over but tolerated; the public, by whom the late Commander had been generally detested, declared that he deserved his fate. It was but three days after the event, that Don Luis was advanced to one of the highest dignities of the order, being invested by the Grand Master with the priorship of the Kingdom of Majorca.

From that time forward, however, the whole character and conduct of Don Luis underwent a change. He became a prey to a dark melancholy, which nothing could assuage. The most austere piety, the severest penances, had no effect in allaying the horror which preyed upon his mind. He was absent for a long time from Malta; having gone, it was said, on remote pilgrimages; when he returned, he was more haggard than ever. There seemed something mysterious and inexplicable in this disorder of his mind. The following is the revelation made by himself, of the horrible visions or chimeras by which he was haunted.

"When I had made my declaration before the chapter," said he, "my provocations were publicly known, I had made my peace with man, but it was not so with God, nor with my confessor, nor with my own conscience. My act was doubly criminal, from the day on which it was committed; and from my refusal to a delay of three days, for the victim of my resentment to receive the sacraments. His despairing ejaculation, 'Good Friday! Good Friday!' continually rang in my ears. 'Why did I not grant the respite!' cried I to myself; 'was it not enough to kill the body, but must I seek to kill the soul.'"

"On the night of the following Friday, I started suddenly from my sleep. An unaccountable horror was upon me. I looked wildly around. It seemed as if I were not in my apartment nor in my bed, but in the fatal Strada Stretta, lying on the pavement. I again saw the Commander leaning against the wall; I again heard his dying words: 'Take my sword to Têtefoulques, and have a hundred masses performed in the chapel of the castle, for the repose of my soul!' "

On the following night, I caused one of my servants to sleep in the same room with me. I saw and heard nothing either on that night or any of the nights following, until the next Friday; when I had again the same vision, with this difference, that my valet seemed to be lying some distance from me on the pavement of the Strada Stretta. The vision continued to be repeated on every Friday night, the commander always appearing in the same manner, and uttering the same words: "Take my sword to Têtefoulques, and have a hundred masses performed in the chapel of the castle for the repose of my soul!"

On questioning my servant on the subject, he stated that on these occasions he dreamt that he was lying in a very narrow street, but he neither saw nor heard any thing of the commander.

I knew nothing of this Têtefoulques, whither the defunct was so urgent I should carry his sword. I made enquiries therefore, concerning it among the French chevaliers. They informed me that it was an old castle, situated about four leagues from Poitiers, in the midst of a forest. It had been built in old times, several centuries since, by Foulques Taillefer, (or Fulke Hackiron) a redoubtable hard-fighting Count of Angouleme, who gave it to an illegitimate son, afterwards created Grand Seneschal of Poitou, which son became the progenitor of the Foulquerres of Têtefoulques, hereditary seneschals of Poitou. They farther informed me, that strange stories were told of this old castle, in the surrounding country, and that it contained many curious reliques. Among these were the arms of Foulques Taillefer, together with those of all the warriors he had slain; and that it was an immemorial usage with the Foulquerres to have the weapons deposited there which they had wielded either in war or single combat." This, then, was the reason of the dying injunction of the Commander respecting his sword. I carried this weapon with me, wherever I went, but still I neglected to comply with his request.

"The visions still continued to harrass me with undiminished horror. I repaired to Rome, where I confessed myself to the Grand Cardinal penitentiary, and informed him of the terrors with which I was haunted. He promised me absolution, after I should have performed certain acts of penance, the principal of which was, to execute the dying request of the Commander, by carrying his sword to Têtefoulques, and having the hundred masses performed in the chapel of the castle for the repose of his soul.

I set out for France as speedily as possible, and made no delay in my journey. On arriving at Poitiers, I found that the tidings of the death of the Commander had reached there, but had caused no more affliction than among the people of Malta. Leaving my equipage in the town, I put on the garb of a pilgrim and, taking a guide, set out on foot for Têtefoulques. Indeed the roads in this part of the country were impracticable for carriages.

I found the castle of Têtefoulques a grand but gloomy and dilapidated pile. All the gates were closed, and their reigned over the whole place an air of almost savage loneliness and desertion. I had understood that its only inhabitants were the concierge, or warder, and a kind of hermit who had charge of the chapel. After ringing for some time at the gate, I at length succeeded in bringing forth the warder, who bowed with reverence to my pilgrim's garb. I begged him to conduct me to the chapel, that being the end of my pilgrimage. We found the hermit there, chanting the funeral service; a dismal sound to one who came to perform a penance for the death of a member of the family. When he had ceased to chant, I informed him that I came to accomplish an obligation of conscience, and that I wished him to perform a hundred masses for the repose of the soul of the commander. He replied that, not being in orders, he was not authorized to perform mass, but that he would willingly undertake to see that my debt of conscience was discharged.

"I laid my offering on the altar, and would have placed the sword of the commander there, likewise. 'Hold!' said the hermit, with a melancholy shake of the head, 'this is no place for so deadly a weapon, that has so often been bathed in christian blood. Take it to the armory, you will find there trophies enough of like character. It is a place into which I never enter.'"

"The warder here took up the theme abandoned by the peaceful man of God. He assured me that I would see in the armory the swords of all the warrior race of Foulquerres, together with those of the enemies over whom they had triumphed. This, he observed, had been a usage kept up since the time of Mellusine, and of her husband Geoffrey à la Grand Dent, or Geoffrey with the Great-tooth.

I followed the gossiping warder to the armory. It was a great dusty hall, hung round with Gothic-looking portraits, of a stark line of warriors, each with his weapons, and the weapons of those he had slain in battle, hung beside his picture. The most conspicuous portrait was that of Foulques Taillefer (Fulke Hackiron) Count of Angouleme, and founder of the castle. He was represented at full length, armed cap-à-pie, and grasping a huge buckler, on which were emblazoned three lions passant. The figure was so striking, that it seemed ready to start from the canvass; and I observed beneath this picture, a trophy composed of many weapons, proofs of the numerous triumphs of this hard-fighting old cavalier. Beside the weapons connected with the portraits, there were swords of all shapes, sizes, and centuries, hung round the hall; with piles of armour, placed as it were in effigy.

"On each side of an immense chimney, were suspended the portraits of the first Seneschal of Poitou (the illegitimate son of Foulques Taillefer) and his wife Isabella de Lusignan; the progenitors of the grim race of Foulquerres that frowned around. They had the look of being perfect likenesses and as I gazed on them, I fancied I could trace in their antiquated features some family resemblance to their unfortunate descendant, whom I had slain! This was a dismal neighborhood, yet the armory was the only part of the castle that had a habitable air; so I asked the warder whether he could not make a fire, and give me something for supper there, and prepare me a bed in one corner.

" 'A fire and a supper you shall have, and that cheerfully, most worthy pilgrim,' said he; 'but as to a bed, I advise you to come and sleep in my chamber.'

" 'Why so?' enquired I; 'why shall I not sleep in this hall?'

" 'I have my reasons; I will make a bed for you close to mine.'

I made no objections, for I recollected that it was Friday, and I dreaded the return of my vision. He brought in billets of wood; kindled a fire in the great overhanging chimney, and then went forth to prepare my supper. I drew a heavy chair before the fire, and seating myself in it, gazed musingly round upon the portraits of the Foulquerres, and the antiquated armour and weapons, the mementos of many a bloody deed. As the day declined, the smoky draperies of the hall gradually became confounded with the dark ground of the paintings, and the lurid gleams from the chimney only enabled me to see visages staring at me from the gathering darkness. All this was dismal in the extreme, and somewhat appalling; perhaps it was the state of my conscience that rendered me peculariarly sensitive, and prone to fearful imaginings.

At length the warder brought in my supper. It consisted of a dish of trout, and some craw-fish, taken in the fossé of the castle. He procured also a bottle of wine, which he informed me was wine of Poitou. I requested him to invite the hermit to join me in my repast; but the holy man sent back word that he allowed himself nothing but roots and herbs, cooked with water. I took my meal, therefore, alone, but prolonged it as much as possible, and sought to cheer my drooping spirits by the wine of Poitou, which I found very tolerable.

When supper was over, I prepared for my evening devotions. I have always been very punctual in reciting my breviary; it is the prescribed and bounden duty of all cavaliers of the religious orders; and I can answer for it, is faithfully performed by those of Spain. I accordingly drew forth from my pocket a small missal and a rosary; and told the warder he need only designate to me the way to his chamber, where I could come and rejoin him when I had finished my prayers.

He accordingly pointed out a winding stair-case opening from the hall. "You will descend this stair-case," said he, "until you come to the fourth landing place, where you enter a vaulted passage terminated by an arcade, with a statue of the blessed Jeanne of France: you cannot help finding my room, the door of which I will leave open; it is the sixth door from the landing place. I advise you not to remain in this hall after midnight. Before that hour you will hear the hermit ring the bell in going the rounds of the corridors. Do not linger here after that signal."

The warder retired, and I commenced my devotions. I continued at them earnestly; pausing from time to time to put wood upon the fire. I did not dare to look much around me; for I felt myself becoming a prey to fearful fancies. The pictures appeared to become animated. If I regarded one attentively for any length of time, it seemed to move the eyes and lips. Above all, the portraits of the Grand Seneschal and his lady, which hung on each side of the great chimney, the progenitors of the Foulquerres of Têtefoulque, regarded me, I thought, with angry and baleful eyes; I even fancied they exchanged significant glances with each other. Just then a terrible blast of wind shook all the casements, and, rushing through the hall, made a fearful rattling and clashing among the armour. To my startled fancy, it seemed something super-natural.

At length I heard the bell of the hermit, and hastened to quit the hall. Taking a solitary light, which stood on the supper table, I descended the winding stair-case; but before I had reached the vaulted passage, leading to the statue of the blessed Jeanne of France, a blast of wind extinguished my taper. I hastily re-mounted the stairs to light it again at the chimney; but judge of my feelings, when, on arriving at the entrance to the armory, I beheld the Seneschal and his lady, who had descended from their frames and seated themselves on each side of the fire place!

"Madam, my love," said the Seneschal, with great formality, and in antiquated phrase, "What think you of the presumption of this Castilian, who comes to harbour himself and make wassail in this our castle, after having slain our descendant the Commander, and that without granting him time for confession?"

"Truly, my lord," answered the female spectre, with no less stateliness of manner, and with great asperity of tone: "Truly, my lord, I opine that this Castilian did a grievous wrong in this encounter; and he should never be suffered to depart hence without your throwing him the gauntlet."

I paused to hear no more, but rushed again down stairs, to seek the chamber of the warder. It was impossible to find it in the darkness, and in the perturbation of my mind. After an hour and a half of fruitless search, and mortal horrors and anxieties, I endeavored to persuade myself that the day was about to break, and listened impatiently for the crowing of the cock; for I thought if I could hear his cheerful note, I should be rëassured; catching, in the disordered state of my nerves, at the popular notion that ghosts never appear after the first crowing of the cock.

At length I rallied myself, and endeavored to shake off the vague terrors which haunted me. I tried to persuade myself that the two figures which I had seemed to see and hear, had existed only in my troubled imagination. I still had the end of a candle in my hand, and determined to make another effort to re-light it, and find my way to bed; for I was ready to sink with fatigue. I accordingly sprang up the stair-case. Three steps at a time, stopped at the door of the armory, and peeped cautiously in. The two gothic figures were no longer in the chimney corners, but I neglected to notice whether they had reascended to their frames. I entered and made desperately for the fire-place, but scarce had I advanced three strides, when Messire Foulques Taillefer stood before me, in the center of the hall, armed cap-à-pie, and standing in guard, with the point of his sword silently presented to me. I would have retreated to the stair-case, but the door of it was occupied by the phantom figure of an esquire, who rudely flung a gauntlet in my face. Driven to fury, I snatched down a sword from the wall; by chance it was that of the commander which I had placed there. I rushed upon my fantastic adversary, and seemed to pierce him through and through; but at the same time I felt as if something pierced my heart, burning like a red-hot iron. My blood inundated the hall, and I fell senseless.

"When I recovered consciousness, it was broad day, and I found myself in a small chamber, attended by the warder and the hermit. The former told me that on the previous night, he had awakened long after the midnight hour, and perceiving that I had not come to his chamber, he had furnished himself with a vase of holy water, and set out to seek me. He found me stretched senseless on the pavement of the armory, and bore me to his room. I spoke of my wound; and of the quantity of blood that I had lost. He shook his head, and knew nothing about it; and to my surprise, on examination, I found myself perfectly sound and unharmed. The wound and blood, therefore, had been all delusion. Neither the warder nor the hermit put any questions to me, but advised me to leave the castle as soon as possible. I lost no time in complying with their counsel, and felt my heart relieved from an oppressive weight, as I left the gloomy and fate-bound battlements of Têtefoulques behind me.

I arrived at Bayonne, on my way to Spain, on the following Friday. At midnight I was startled from my sleep, as I had formerly been; but it was no longer by the vision of the dying Commander. It was old Foulques Taillefer who stood before me, armed, cap-à-pie, and presenting the point of his sword. I made the sign of the cross, and the spectre vanished, but I received the same red-hot thrust in the heart which I had felt in the armory, and I seemed to be bathed in blood. I would have called out, or have risen from my bed and gone in quest of succor, but I could neither speak nor stir. This agony endured until the crowing of the cock, when I fell asleep again; but the next day I was ill, and in a most pitiable state. I have continued to be harrassed by the same vision every Friday night: no acts of penitence and devotion, have been able to relieve me from it; and it is only a lingering hope in divine mercy, that sustains me, and enables me to support so lamentable a visitation.'

————

The Grand Prior of Majorca wasted gradually away under this constant remorse of conscience, and this horrible incubus. He died some time after, having revealed the preceding particulars of his case, evidently the victim of a diseased imagination.

The above relation has been rendered in many parts literally, from the French memoir, in which it, is given as a true story: if so, it is one of those instances in which truth is more romantic than fiction.

"A TIME OF UNEXAMPLED PROSPERITY"

In the course of a voyage from England, I once fell in with a convoy of merchant ships, bound for the West Indies. The weather was uncommonly bland; and the ships vied with each other in spreading sail to catch a light, favoring breeze, until their hulls were almost hidden beneath a cloud of canvass. The breeze went down with the sun, and his last yellow rays shone upon a thousand sails, idly flapping against the masts.

I exulted in the beauty of the scene, and augured a prosperous voyage; but the veteran master of the ship shook his head, and pronounced this halcyon calm a "weather-breeder." And so it proved. A storm burst forth in the night; the sea roared and raged; and when the day broke, I beheld the late gallant convoy scattered in every direction; some dismasted, others scudding under bare poles, and many firing signals of distress.

I have since been occasionally reminded of this scene, by those calm, sunny seasons in the commercial world, which are known by the name of "times of unexampled prosperity." They are the sure weather-breeders of traffic. Every now and then the world is visited by one of these delusive seasons, when 'the credit system,' as it is called, expands to full luxuriance: every body trusts every body; a bad debt is a thing unheard of; the broad way to certain and sudden wealth lies plain and open; and men are tempted to dash forward boldly, from the facility of borrowing.

Promissory notes, interchanged between scheming individuals, are liberally discounted at the banks, which become so many mints to coin words into cash; and as the supply of words is inexhaustible, it may readily be supposed what a vast amount of promissory capital is soon in circulation. Every one now talk in thousands; nothing is heard but gigantic operations in trade; great purchases and sales of real property, and immense sums made at every transfer. All, to be sure, as yet exists in promise; but the believer in promises calculates the aggregate as solid capital, and falls back in amazement at the amount of public wealth, the "unexampled state of public prosperity!"

Now is the time for speculative and dreaming or designing men. They relate their dreams and projects to the ignorant and credulous, dazzle them with golden visions, and set them maddening after shadows. The example of one stimulates another; speculation rises on speculation; bubble rises on bubble; every one helps with his breath to swell the windy superstructure, and admires and wonders at the magnitude of the inflation he has contributed to produce.

Speculation is the romance of trade, and casts contempt upon all its sober realities. It renders the stock-jobber a magician, and the exchange a region of enchantment. It elevates the merchant into a kind of knight errant, or rather a commercial Quixotte. The slow but sure gains of snug per centage become despicable in his eyes: no "operation" is thought worthy of attention, that does not double or treble the invest-ment. No business is worth following, that does not promise an immediate fortune. As he sits musing over his ledger, with pen behind his ear, he is like La Mancha's hero in his study, dreaming over his books of chivalry. His dusty counting-house fades before his eyes, or changes into a Spanish mine: he gropes after diamonds, or dives after pearls. The subterranean garden of Aladdin is nothing to the realms of wealth that break upon his imagination.

Could this delusion always last, the life of a merchant would indeed be a golden dream; but it is as short as it is brilliant. Let but a doubt enter, and the "season of unexampled prosperity" is at end. The coinage of words is suddenly curtailed; the promissory capital begins to vanish into smoke; a panic succeeds, and the whole superstructure, built upon credit, and reared by speculation, crumbles to the ground, leaving scarce a wreck behind:

"It is such stuff as dreams are made of."

When a man of business, therefore, hears on every side rumors of fortunes suddenly acquired; when he finds banks liberal, and brokers busy; when he sees adventurers flush of paper capital, and full of scheme and enterprise; when he perceives a greater disposition to buy than to sell; when trade overflows its accustomed channels, and deluges the country; when he hears of new regions of commercial adventure; of distant marts and distant mines, swallowing merchandise and disgorging gold; when he finds joint stock companies of all kinds forming; rail-roads, canals, and locomotive engines, springing up on every side; when idlers suddenly become men of business, and dash into the game of commerce as they would into the hazards of the faro table; when he beholds the streets glittering with new equipages, palaces conjured up by the magic of speculation; tradesmen flushed with sudden success, and vying with each other in ostentatious expense; in a word, when he hears the whole community joining in the theme of "unexampled pros-perity," let him look upon the whole as a "weather-breeder," and prepare for the impending storm.

The foregoing remarks are intended merely as a prelude to a narrative I am about to lay before the public, of one of the most memorable instances of the infatuation of gain, to be found in the whole history of

commerce. I allude to the famous Mississippi bubble. It is a matter that
has passed into a proverb, and become a phrase in every one's mouth,
yet of which not one merchant in ten has probably a distinct idea. I
have therefore thought that an authentic account of it would be interesting and salutary, at the present moment, when we are suffering under
the effects of a severe access of the credit system, and just recovering
from one of its ruinous delusions.

THE GREAT MISSISSIPPI BUBBLE.

Before entering into the story of this famous chimera, it is proper to
give a few particulars concerning the individual who engendered it.
JOHN LAW was born in Edinburgh, in 1671. His father, William Law,
was a rich goldsmith, and left his son an estate of considerable value,
called Lauriston, situated about four miles from Edinburgh. Goldsmiths,
in those days, acted occasionally as bankers, and his father's operations,
under this character, may have originally turned the thoughts of the
youth to the science of calculation, in which he became an adept; so that
at an early age he excelled in playing at all games of combination.

In 1694, he appeared in London, where a handsome person, and an
easy and insinuating address, gained him currency in the first circles,
and the nick-name of "Beau Law." The same personal advantages gave
him success in the world of gallantry, until he became involved in a
quarrel with Beau Wilson, his rival in fashion, whom he killed in a duel,
and then fled to France, to avoid prosecution.

He returned to Edinburgh in 1700, and remained there several years;
during which time he first broached his great credit system, offering to
supply the deficiency of coin by the establishment of a bank, which, according to his views, might emit a paper currency equivalent to the
whole landed estate of the kingdom.

His scheme excited great astonishment in Edinburgh; but, though the
government was not sufficiently advanced in financial knowledge to
detect the fallacies upon which it was founded, Scottish caution and suspicion served in place of wisdom, and the project was rejected. Law met
with no better success with the English parliament; and the fatal affair
of the death of Wilson still hanging over him, for which he had never
been able to procure a pardon, he again went to France.

The financial affairs of France were at this time in a deplorable condition. The wars, the pomp, and profusion, of Louis XIV., and his religious persecutions of whole classes of the most industrious of his subjects, had exhausted his treasury, and overwhelmed the nation with
debt. The old monarch clung to his selfish magnificence, and could not be
induced to diminish his enormous expenditure; and his minister of

finance was driven to his wits' end to devise all kinds of disastrous expedients to keep up the royal state, and to extricate the nation from its
embarrassments.

In this state of things, Law ventured to bring forward his financial
project. It was founded on the plan of the Bank of England, which had
already been in successful operation several years. He met with immediate patronage, and a congenial spirit, in the Duke of Orleans, who had
married a natural daughter of the king. The duke had been astonished
at the facility with which England had supported the burthen of a
public debt, created by the wars of Anne and William, and which exceeded in amount that under which France was groaning. The whole
matter was soon explained by Law to his satisfaction. The latter maintained that England had stopped at the mere threshold of an art capable
of creating unlimited sources of national wealth. The duke was dazzled
with his splendid views and specious reasonings, and thought he clearly
comprehended his system. Demarets, the Comptroller General of
Finance, was not so easily deceived. He pronounced the plan of Law
more pernicious than any of the disastrous expedients that the government had yet been driven to. The old King also, Louis XIV., detested all
innovations, especially those which came from a rival nation: the project
of a bank, therefore, was utterly rejected.

Law remained for a while in Paris, leading a gay and affluent existence, owing to his handsome person, easy manners, flexible temper, and
a faro-bank which he had set up. His agreeable career was interrupted
by a message from D'Argenson, Lieutenant General of Police, ordering
him to quit Paris, alleging that he was *rather too skilful at the game
which he had introduced!*

For several succeeding years, he shifted his residence from state to
state of Italy and Germany; offering his scheme of finance to every court
that he visited, but without success. The Duke of Savoy, Victor Ama-
deas, afterward King of Sardinia. was much struck with his project; but
after considering it for a time, replied, *"I am not sufficiently powerful,
to ruin myself."*

The shifting, adventurous life of Law, and the equivocal means by
which he appeared to live, playing high, and always with great success,
threw a cloud of suspicion over him, wherever he went, and caused him
to be expelled by the magistracy from the semi-commercial, semi-
aristocratical cities of Venice and Genoa.

The events of 1715, brought Law back again to Paris. Louis XIV.
was dead. Louis XV. was a mere child, and during his minority, the
Duke of Orleans held the reins of government as Regent. Law had at
length found his man.

The Duke of Orleans has been differently represented by different contemporaries. He appears to have had excellent natural qualities, per-verted by a bad education. He was of the middle size, easy and grace-ful, with an agreeable countenance, and open, affable demeanor. His mind was quick and sagacious, rather than profound; and his quickness of intellect, and excellence of memory, supplied the lack of studious application. His wit was prompt and pungent; he expressed himself with vivacity and precision; his imagination was vivid, his temperament san-guine and joyous; his courage daring. His mother, the Duchess of Or-leans, expressed his character in a jeu d'esprit. "The fairies," said she, "were invited to be present at his birth, and each one conferring a talent on my son, his possesses them all. Unfortunately, we had forgotten to invite an old fairy, who, arriving after all the others, exclaimed, "He shall have all the talents, excepting that to make a good use of them."

Under proper tuition, the Duke might have risen to real greatness; but in his early years, he was put under the tutelage of the Abbé Dubois, one of the subtlest and basest spirits that ever intrigued its way into eminent place and power. The Abbé was of low origin, and despicable exterior, totally destitute of morals, and perfidious in the extreme; but with a supple, insinuating address, and an accommodating spirit, tol-erant of all kinds of profligacy in others. Conscious of his own inherent baseness, he sought to secure an influence over his pupil, by corrupting his principles, and fostering his vices: he debased him, to keep him-self from being despised. Unfortunately, he succeeded. To the early precepts of this infamous pander, have been attributed those excesses that disgraced the manhood of the Regent, and gave a licentious char-acter to his whole course of government. His love of pleasure, quickened and indulged by those who should have restrained it, led him into all kinds of sensual indulgence. He had been taught to think lightly of the most serious duties and sacred ties; to turn virtue into a jest, and con-sider religion mere hypocrisy. He was a gay misanthrope, that had a sovereign but sportive contempt for mankind; believed that his most de-voted servant would be his enemy, if interest prompted; and maintained that an honest man was he who had the art to conceal that he was the contrary.

He surrounded himself with a set of dissolute men like himself; who, let loose from the restraint under which they had been held, during the latter hypocritical days of Louis XIV., now gave way to every kind of debauchery. With these men the Regent used to shut himself up, after the hours of business, and excluding all graver persons and graver con-cerns, celebrate the most drunken and disgusting orgies; where obscenity and blasphemy formed the seasoning of conversation. For the profligate companions of these revels, he invented the appellation of his roués, the literal meaning of which is, men broken on the wheel; intended, no doubt, to express their broken-down characters and dislocated fortunes; although a contemporary asserts that it designated the punishment that most of them merited. Madame de Labran, who was present at one of the Regent's suppers, was disgusted by the conduct and conversation of the host and his guests, and observed at table, that God, after he had created man, took the refuse clay that was left, and made of it the souls of lacqueys and princes.

Such was the man that now ruled the destinies of France. Law found him full of perplexities, from the disastrous state of the finances. He had already tampered with the coinage, calling in the coin of the nation, re-stamping it, and issuing it at a nominal increase of one-fifth; thus de-frauding the nation out of twenty per cent. of its capital. He was not likely, therefore, to be scrupulous about any means likely to relieve him from financial difficulties: he had even been led to listen to the cruel alternative of a national bankruptcy.

Under these circumstances, Law confidently brought forward his scheme of a bank, that was to pay off the national debt, increase the revenue, and at the same time diminish the taxes. The following is stated as the theory by which he recommended his system to the Regent. The credit enjoyed by a banker or a merchant, he observed, increases his capital ten fold; that is to say, he who has a capital of one hundred thou-sand livres, may, if he possess sufficient credit, extend his operations to a million, and reap profits to that amount. In like manner, a state that can collect into a bank all the current coin of the kingdom, would be as powerful as if its capital were increased ten fold. The specie must be drawn into the bank, not by way of loan, or by taxations, but in the way of deposit. This might be effected in different modes, either by in-spiring confidence, or by exerting authority. One mode, he observed, had already been in use. Each time that a state makes a re-coinage, it be-comes momentarily the depositary of all the money called in, belonging to the subjects of that state. His bank was to effect the same purpose; that is to say, to receive in deposit all the coin of the kingdom, but to give in exchange its bills, which, being of an invariable value, bearing an interest, and being payable on demand, would not only supply the place of coin, but prove a better and more profitable currency.

The Regent caught with avidity at the scheme. It suited his bold, reck-less spirit, and his grasping extravagance. Not that he was altogether the dupe of Law's specious projects: still he was apt, like many other men, unskilled in the arcana of finance, to mistake the multiplication of money, for the multiplication of wealth; not understanding that it was a mere agent or instrument in the interchange of traffic, to represent the value of the various productions of industry; and that an increased cir-culation of coin or bank bills, in the shape of currency, only adds a proportionably increased and fictitious value to such productions. Law enlisted the vanity of the Regent in his cause. He persuaded him that he saw more clearly than others into sublime theories of finance, which were quite above the ordinary apprehension. He used to declare that, excepting the Regent and the Duke of Savoy, no one had thoroughly comprehended his system.

It is certain that it met with strong opposition from the Regent's ministers, the Duke de Noailles and the Chancellor d'Anguesseau; and it was no less strenuously opposed by the parliament of Paris. Law, however, had a potent though secret coadjutor in the Abbé Dubois, now rising, during the regency, into great political power, and who retained a baneful influence over the mind of the Regent. This wily priest, as avaricious as he was ambitious, drew large sums from Law as subsidies, and aided him greatly in many of his most pernicious operations. He aided him, in the present instance, to fortify the mind of the Regent against all the remonstrances of his ministers and the parliament.

Accordingly, on the 2nd of May, 1716, letters patent were granted to Law, to establish a bank of deposite, discount, and circulation, under the firm of "Law and Company," to continue for twenty years. The capital was fixed at six millions of livres, divided into shares of five hundred livres each, which were to be sold for twenty-five per cent. of the regent's debased coin, and seventy-five per cent. of the public securities; which were then at a great reduction from their nominal value, and which then amounted to nineteen hundred millions. The ostensible object of the bank, as set forth in the patent, was to encourage the commerce and manufactures of France. The louis-d'ors and crowns of the bank were always to retain the same standard of value, and its bills to be payable in them on demand.

At the outset, while the bank was limited in its operations, and while its paper really represented the specie in its vaults, it seemed to realize all that had been promised from it. It rapidly acquired public confidence, and an extended circulation, and produced an activity in commerce, unknown under the baneful government of Louis XIV. As the bills of the bank bore an interest, and as it was stipulated they would be of invariable value, and as hints had been artfully circulated that the coin would experience successive diminution, every body hastened to the bank to exchange gold and silver for paper. So great became the throng of depositors, and so intense their eagerness, that there was quite a press and struggle at the back door, and a ludicrous panic was awakened, as if there was danger of their not being admitted. An anecdote of the time relates, that one of the clerks, with an ominous smile, called out to the struggling multitude, "Have a little patience, my friends; we mean to take all your money;" an assertion disastrously verified in the sequel.

Thus, by the simple establishment of a bank, Law and the Regent obtained pledges of confidence for the consummation of farther and more complicated schemes, as yet hidden from the public. In a little while, the bank shares rose enormously, and the amount of its notes in circulation exceeded one hundred and ten millions of livres. A subtle stroke of policy had rendered it popular with the aristocracy. Louis XIV. had several years previously imposed an income tax of a tenth, giving his royal word that it should cease in 1717. This tax had been exceedingly irksome to the privileged orders; and, in the present disastrous times, they had dreaded an augmentation of it. In consequences of the successful operation of Law's scheme, however, the tax was abolished, and now nothing was to be heard among the nobility and clergy, but praises of the Regent and the bank.

Hitherto, all had gone well, and all might have continued to go well, had not the paper system been farther expanded. But Law had yet the grandest part of his scheme to develop. He had to open his ideal world of speculation, his El Dorado of unbounded wealth. The English had brought the vast imaginary commerce of the South Seas in aid of their banking operations. Law sought to bring, as an immense auxiliary of his bank, the whole trade of the Mississippi. Under this name was included not merely the river so called, but the vast region known as Louisiana, extending from north latitude 29° up to Canada in north latitude 40°. This country had been granted by Louis XIV. to the Sieur Crozat, but he had been induced to resign his patent. In conformity to the plea of Mr. Law, letters patent were granted in August 1717, for the creation of a commercial company, which was to have the colonizing of this country, and the monopoly of its trade and resources, and of the beaver or fur trade with Canada. It was called the Western, but became better known as the Mississippi Company. The capital was fixed at one hundred millions of livres, divided into shares, bearing an interest of four per cent., which were subscribed for in the public securities. As the bank was to cooperate with the company, the regent ordered that its bills should be received the same as coin, in all payments of the public revenue. Law was appointed chief director of this company, which was an exact copy of the Earl of Oxford's South Sea Company, set on foot in 1711, and which distracted all England with the frenzy of speculation. In like manner with the delusive picturings given in that memorable scheme of the sources of rich trade to be opened in the South Sea countries, Law held forth magnificent prospects of the fortunes to be made in colonizing Louisiana, which was represented as a veritable land of promise, capable of yielding every variety of the most precious produce. Reports, too, were artfully circulated, with great mystery, as if to the "chosen few," of mines of gold and silver recently discovered in

Louisiana, and which would insure instant wealth to the early pur-
chasers. These confidential whispers of course soon became public; and
were confirmed by travellers fresh from the Mississippi, and doubtless
bribed, who had seen the mines in question, and declared them superior
in richness to those of Mexico and Peru. Nay more, ocular proof was
furnished to public credulity, in ingots of gold, conveyed to the mint,
as if just brought from the mines of Louisiana.

Extraordinary measures were adopted to force a colonization. An edict
was issued to collect and transport settlers to the Mississippi. The police
lent its aid. The streets and prisons of Paris, and of the provincial cities,
were swept of mendicants and vagabonds of all kinds, who were conveyed to Havre de Grace. About six thousand were crowded into ships,
where no precautions had been taken for their health or accommodation. Instruments of all kinds proper for the working of mines were os-
tentatiously paraded in public, and put on board the vessels; and the
whole set sail for this fabled El Dorado, which was to prove the grave
of the greater part of its wretched colonists.

D'Anguesseau, the chancellor, a man of probity and integrity, still
lifted his voice against the paper system of Law, and his project of colonization, and was eloquent and prophetic in picturing the evils they
were calculated to produce; the private distress and public degradation;
the corruption of morals and manners; the triumph of knaves and
schemers; the ruin of fortunes, and downfall of families. He was incited
more and more to this opposition by the Duke de Noailles, the Minister of
Finance, who was jealous of the growing ascendancy of Law over the
mind of the Regent, but was less honest than the chancellor in his opposition. The Regent was excessively annoyed by the difficulties they
conjured up in the way of his darling schemes of finance, and the countenance they gave to the opposition of parliament; which body, disgusted more and more with the abuses of the regency, and the system
of Law, had gone so far as to carry its remonstrances to the very foot
of the throne.

He determined to relieve himself from these two ministers, who, either
through honesty or policy, interfered with all his plans. Accordingly, on
the 28th of January, 1718, he dismissed the chancellor from office, and
exiled him to his estate in the country; and shortly afterward, removed the
Duke de Noailles from the administration of the finance.

The opposition of parliament to the Regent and his measures, was carried on with increasing violence. That body aspired to an equal authority
with the Regent, in the administration of affairs, and pretended, by its
decree, to suspend an edict of the regency, ordering a now coinage, and
altering the value of the currency. But its chief hostility was levelled
against Law, a foreigner and a heretic, and one who was considered by

a majority of the members in the light of a malefactor. In fact, so far was this hostility carried, that secret measures were taken to investigate his malversations, and to collect evidence against him; and it was resolved in parliament that, should the testimony collected justify their suspicions, they would have him seized and brought before them; would give him a brief trial, and if convicted, would hang him in the courtyard of the palace, and throw open the gates after the execution, that the public might behold his corpse!

Law received intimation of the danger hanging over him, and was in terrible trepidation. He took refuge in the Palais Royal, the residence of the Regent, and implored his protection. The Regent himself was embarrassed by the sturdy opposition of parliament, which contemplated nothing less than a decree reversing most of his public measures, especially those of finance. His indecision kept Law for a time in an agony of terror and suspense. Finally, by assembling a board of justice, and bringing to his aid the absolute authority of the king, he triumphed over parliament, and relieved Law from his dread of being hanged.

The system now went on with flowing sail. The Western, or Mississippi Company, being identified with the bank, rapidly increased in power and privileges. One monopoly after another was granted to it; the trade of the Indian seas; the slave trade with Senegal and Guinea; the farming of tobacco; the national coinage, etc. Each new privilege was made a pretext for issuing more bills, and caused an immense advance in the price of stock. At length, on the 4th of December, 1718, the Regent gave the establishment the imposing title of THE ROYAL BANK, and proclaimed that he had effected the purchase of all the shares, the proceeds of which he had added to its capital. This measure seemed to shock the public feeling more than any other connected with the system, and roused the indignation of parliament. The French nation had been so accustomed to attach an idea of every thing noble, lofty, and magnificent, to the royal name and person, especially during the stately and sumptuous reign of Louis XIV., that they could not at first tolerate the idea of royalty being in any degree mingled with matters of traffic and finance, and the king being in a manner a banker. It was one of the downward steps, however, by which royalty lost its illusive splendor in France, and became gradually cheapened in the public mind.

Arbitrary measures now began to be taken to force the bills of the bank into artificial currency. On the 27th of December, appeared an order in council, forbidding, under severe penalties, the payment of any sum above six hundred livres in gold or silver. This decree rendered bank bills necessary in all transactions of purchase and sale, and called for a new emission. The prohibition was occasionally evaded or opposed; confiscations were the consequence; informers were rewarded, and spies and traitors began to spring up in all the domestic walks of life.

The worst effect of this illusive system was the mania for gain, or rather for gambling in stocks, that now seized upon the whole nation. Under the exciting effects of lying reports, and the forcing effects of government decrees, the shares of the Company went on rising in value, until they reached thirteen hundred per cent. Nothing was now spoken of, but the price of shares, and the immense fortunes suddenly made by lucky speculators. Those whom Law had deluded, used every means to delude others. The most extravagant dreams were indulged, concerning the wealth to flow in upon the Company, from its colonies, its trade, and its various monopolies. It is true, nothing as yet had been realized, nor could in some time be realized, from these distant sources, even if productive: but the imaginations of speculators are ever in the advance, and their conjectures are immediately converted into facts. Lying reports now flew from mouth to mouth, of sure avenues to fortune suddenly thrown open. The more extravagant the fable, the more readily was it believed. To doubt, was to awaken anger, or incur ridicule. In a time of public infatuation, it requires no small exercise of courage to doubt a popular fallacy.

Paris now became the centre of attraction for the adventurous and the avaricious, who flocked to it, not merely from the provinces, but from neighboring countries. A stock exchange was established in a house in the Rue Quincampoix, and became immediately the gathering place of stock-jobbers. The exchange opened at seven o'clock, with the beat of drum and sound of bell, and closed at night with the same signals. Guards were stationed at each end of the street, to maintain order, and exclude carriages and horses. The whole street swarmed throughout the day like a bee-hive. Bargains of all kinds were seized upon with avidity. Shares of stock passed from hand to hand, mounting in value, one knew not why. Fortunes were made in a moment, as if by magic; and every lucky bargain prompted those around to a more desperate throw of the die. The fever went on, increasing in intensity as the day declined; and when the drum beat, and the bell rang, at night, to close the exchange, there were exclamations of impatience and despair, as if the wheel of fortune had suddenly been stopped, when about to make its luckiest evolution.

To engulf all classes in this ruinous vortex, Law now split the shares of fifty millions of stock each into one hundred shares; thus, as in the splitting of lottery tickets, accommodating the venture to the humblest purse. Society was thus stirred up to its very dregs, and adventurers of the lowest order hurried to the stock market. All honest, industrious pursuits, and modest gains, were now dispised. Wealth was to be obtained instantly, without labor, and without stint. The upper classes were as base in their venality as the lower. The highest and most powerful nobles, abandoning all generous pursuits and lofty aims, engaged in the vile scuffle for gain. They were even baser than the lower classes; for some of them, who were members of the council of the regency, abused their station and their influence, and promoted measures by which shares arose while in their hands, and they made immense profits.

The Duke de Bourbon, the prince of Conti, the Dukes de la Force and D'Antin were among the foremost of these illustrious stock-jobbers. They were nick-named the Mississippi Lords, and they smiled at the sneering title. In fact, the usual distinctions of society had lost their consequence, under the reign of this new passion. Rank, talent, military fame, no longer inspired deference. All respect for others, all self-respect, were forgotten in the mercenary struggle of the stock-market. Even prelates and ecclesiastical corporations, forgetting their true objects of devotion, mingled among the votaries of Mammon. They were not behind those who wielded the civil power in fabricating ordinances suited to their avaricious purposes. Theological decisions forthwith appeared, in which the anathema launched by the church against usury, was conveniently construed as not extending to the traffic in bank shares!

The Abbé Dubois entered into the mysteries of stock-jobbing with all the zeal of an apostle, and enriched himself by the spoils of the credulous; and he continually drew large sums from Law, as considerations for his political influence. Faithless to his country, in the course of his gambling speculations he transferred to England a great amount of specie, which had been paid into the royal treasury; thus contributing to the subsequent dearth of the precious metals.

The female sex participated in this sordid frenzy. Princesses of the blood, and ladies of the highest nobility, were among the most rapacious of stock-jobbers. The Regent seemed to have the riches of Crœsus at his command, and lavished money by hundreds of thousands upon his female relatives and favorites, as well as upon his *roués*, the dissolute companions of his debauches. "My son," writes the Regent's mother, in her correspondence, "gave me shares to the amount of two millions, which I distributed among my household. The king also took several millions for his own household. All the royal family have had them; all the children and grand-children of France, and the princes of the blood."

Luxury and extravagance kept pace with this sudden inflation of fancied wealth. The hereditary palaces of nobles were pulled down, and rebuilt on a scale of augmented splendor. Entertainments were given, of incredible cost and magnificence. Never before had been such display in houses, furniture, equipages, and amusements. This was particularly the case among persons of the lower ranks, who had suddenly become possessed of millions. Ludicrous anecdotes are related of some of these upstarts. One, who had just launched a splendid carriage, when about to use it for the first time, instead of getting in at the door, mounted, through habitude, to his accustomed place behind. Some ladies of quality, seeing a well-dressed woman covered with diamonds, but whom no-body knew, alight from a very handsome carriage, inquired who she was, of the footman. He replied, with a sneer: "It is a lady who has recently tumbled from a garret into this carriage." Mr. Law's domestics were said to become in like manner suddenly enriched by the crumbs that fell from his table. His coachman, having made a fortune, retired from his service. Mr. Law requested him to procure a coachman in his place. He appeared the next day with two, whom he pronounced equally good, and told Mr. Law: "Take which of them you choose, and I will take the other!"

Nor were these *novi homini* treated with the distance and disdain they would formerly have experienced from the haughty aristocracy of France. The pride of the old noblesse had been stifled by the stronger instinct of avarice. They rather sought the intimacy and confidence of these lucky upstarts; and it has been observed that a nobleman would gladly take his seat at the table of the fortunate lacquey of yesterday, in hopes of learning from him the secret of growing rich!

Law now went about with a countenance radiant with success, and apparently dispensing wealth on every side. "He is admirably skilled in all that relates to finance," writes the Duchess of Orleans, the Regent's mother, "and has put the affairs of the state in such good order, that all the king's debts have been paid. He is so much run after, that he has no repose night or day. A duchess even kissed his hand publicly. If a duchess can do this, what will other ladies do!"

Wherever he went, his path, we are told, was beset by a sordid throng, who waited to see him pass, and sought to obtain the favor of a word, a nod, or smile, as if a mere glance from him would bestow for-tune. When at home, his house was absolutely besieged by furious can-didates for fortune. "They forced the doors," says the Duke de St. Simon; "they scaled his windows from the garden; they made their way into his cabinet down the chimney!"

The same venal court was paid by all classes to his family. The highest ladies of the court vied with each other in meannesses, to purchase the lucrative friendship of Mrs. Law and her daughter. They waited upon them with as much assiduity and adulation as if they had been princesses of the blood. The Regent one day expressed a desire that some duchess should accompany his daughter to Genoa. "My Lord," said some one present, "if you would have a choice from among the duchesses, you need but send to Mrs. Law's; you will find them all assembled there."

The wealth of Law rapidly increased with the expansion of the bubble. In the course of a few months, he purchased fourteen titled estates, paying for them in paper; and the public hailed these sudden and vast acquisitions of landed property, as so many proofs of the soundness of his system. In one instance, he met with a shrewd bargainer, who had not the general faith in his paper money. The President de Novion insisted on being paid for an estate in hard coin. Law accordingly brought the amount, four hundred thousand livres, in specie, saying, with a sarcastic smile, that he preferred paying in money, as its weight rendered it a mere incumbrance. As it happened, the President could give no clear title to the land, and the money had to be refunded. He paid it back *in paper*, which Law dared not refuse, lest he should depreciate it in the market!

The course of illusory credit went on triumphantly for eighteen months. Law had nearly fulfilled one of his promises, for the greater part of the public debt had been paid off; but how paid? In bank shares, which had been trumped up several hundred per cent. above their value, and which were to vanish like smoke in the hands of the holders.

One of the most striking attributes of Law, was the imperturbable assurance and self-possession with which he replied to every objection, and found a solution for every problem. He had the dexterity of a juggler in evading difficulties; and what was peculiar, made figures themselves, which are the very elements of exact demonstration, the means to dazzle and bewilder.

Toward the latter end of 1719, the Mississippi scheme had reached its highest point of glory. Half a million of strangers had crowded into Paris, in quest of fortune. The hotels and lodging-houses were overflowing; lodgings were procured with excessive difficulty; granaries were turned into bed-rooms; provisions had risen enormously in price; splendid houses were multiplying on every side; the streets were crowded with carriages; above a thousand new equipages had been launched.

On the eleventh of December, Law obtained another prohibitory decree, for the purpose of sweeping all the remaining specie in circulation into the bank. By this it was forbidden to make any payments in silver, above ten livres, or in gold, above three hundred.

The repeated decrees of this nature, the object of which was to depreciate the value of gold, and increase the illusive credit of paper, began to awaken doubts of a system which required such bolstering. Capitalists gradually awoke from their bewilderment. Sound and able financiers consulted together, and agreed to make common cause against this continual expansion of a paper system. The shares of the bank and of the Company began to decline in value. Wary men took the alarm, and began to *realize*, a word now first brought into use, to express the conversion of *ideal* property into something *real*.

The Prince of Conti, one of the most prominent and grasping of the Mississippi lords, was the first to give a blow to the credit of the bank. There was a mixture of ingratitude in his conduct, that characterized the venal baseness of the times. He had received, from time to time, enormous sums from Law, as the price of his influence and patronage. His avarice had increased with every acquisition, until Law was compelled to refuse one of his exactions. In revenge, the prince immediately sent such an amount of paper to the bank to be cashed, that it required four wagons to bring away the silver, and he had the meanness to loll out of the window of his hotel, and jest and exult, as it was trundled into his port cochère.

This was the signal for other drains of like nature. The English and Dutch merchants, who had purchased a great amount of bank paper at low prices, cashed them at the bank, and carried the money out of the country. Other strangers did the like, thus draining the kingdom of its specie, and leaving paper in its place.

The Regent, perceiving these symptoms of decay in the system, sought to restore it to public confidence, by conferring marks of confidence upon its author. He accordingly resolved to make Law Comptroller General of the Finances of France. There was a material obstacle in the way. Law was a protestant, and the Regent, unscrupulous as he was himself, did not dare publicly to outrage the severe edicts which Louis XIV, in his bigot days, had fulminated against all heretics. Law soon let him know that there would be no difficulty on that head. He was ready at any moment to abjure his religion in the way of business. For decency's sake, however, it was judged proper he should previously be convinced and converted. A ghostly instructor was soon found, ready to accomplish his conversion in the shortest possible time. This was the Abbé Tencin, a profligate creature of the profligate Dubois, and like him working his way to ecclesiastical promotion and temporal wealth, by the basest means.

Under the instructions of the Abbé Tencin, Law soon mastered the mysteries and dogmas of the Catholic doctrine; and, after a brief course of ghostly training, declared himself thoroughly convinced and converted. To avoid the sneers and jests of the Parisian public, the ceremony of abjuration took place at Melun. Law made a pious present of one hundred thousand livres to the Church of St. Roque, and the Abbé Tencin was rewarded for his edifying labors, by sundry shares and bank bills; which he shrewdly took care to convert into cash, having as little faith in the system, as in the piety of his new convert. A more grave and moral community might have been outraged by this scandalous farce; but the Parisians laughed at it with their usual levity, and contented themselves with making it the subject of a number of songs and epigrams.

Law being now orthodox in his faith, took out letters of naturalization, and having thus surmounted the intervening obstacles, was elevated by the Regent to the post of Comptroller General. So accustomed had the community become to all juggles and transmutations in this hero of finance, that no one seemed shocked or astonished at his sudden elevation. On the contrary, being now considered perfectly established in place and power, he became more than ever the object of venal adoration. Men of rank and dignity thronged his antechamber, waiting patiently their turn for an audience; and titled dames demeaned themselves to take the front seats of the carriages of his wife and daughter, as if they had been riding with princesses of the blood royal. Law's head grew giddy with his elevation, and he began to aspire after aristocratical distinction. There was to be a court ball, at which several of the young noblemen were to dance in a ballet with the youthful king. Law requested that his son might be admitted into the ballet, and the Regent consented. The young scions of nobility, however, were indignant, and scouted the "intruding upstart." Their more worldly parents, fearful of displeasing the modern Midas, reprimanded them in vain. The stripplings had not yet imbibed the passion for gain, and still held to their high blood. The son of the banker received slights and annoyances on all sides, and the public applauded them for their spirit. A fit of illness came opportunely to relieve the youth from an honor which would have cost him a world of vexations and affronts.

In February, 1720, shortly after Law's instalment in office, a decree came out, uniting the bank to the India Company, by which last name the whole establishment was now known. The decree stated, that as the bank was royal, the king was bound to make good the value of its bills; that he committed to the company the government of the bank for fifty years, and sold to it fifty millions of stock belonging to him, for nine hundred millions; a simple advance of eighteen hundred per cent. The decree farther declared, in the king's name, that he would never draw on the bank, until the value of his drafts had first been lodged in it by his receivers general.

The bank, it was said, had by this time issued notes to the amount of one thousand millions; being more paper than all the banks of Europe were able to circulate. To aid its credit, the receivers of the revenue were directed to take bank notes of the sub-receivers. All payments, also, of one hundred livres and upward, were ordered to be made in bank notes. These compulsory measures for a short time gave a false credit to the bank, which proceeded to discount merchants' notes, to lend money on jewels, plate, and other valuables, as well as on mortgages.

Still farther to force on the system, an edict next appeared, forbidding any individual, or any corporate body, civil or religious, to hold in possession more than five hundred livres in current coin; that is to say, about seven louis-d'ors; the value of the louis-d'or in paper, being, at the time, seventy-two livres. All the gold and silver they might have, above this pittance, was to be brought to the royal bank, and exchanged either for shares or bills.

As confiscation was the penalty of disobedience to this decree, and informers were assured a share of the forfeitures, a bounty was in a manner held out to domestic spies and traitors; and the most odious scrutiny was awakened into the pecuniary affairs of families and individuals. The very confidence between friends and relatives was impaired, and all the domestic ties and virtues of society were threatened, until a general sentiment of indignation broke forth, that compelled the Regent to rescind the odious decree. Lord Stairs, the British ambassador, speaking of the system of espionage encouraged by this edict, observed that it was impossible to doubt that Law was a thorough Catholic, since he had thus established the *inquisition,* after having already proved *transubstantiation,* by changing specie into paper.

Equal abuses had taken place under the colonizing project. In his thousand expedients to amass capital, Law had sold parcels of land in Mississippi, at the rate of three thousand livers for a league square. Many capitalists had purchased estates large enough to constitute almost a principality; the only evil was, Law had sold a property which he could not deliver. The agents of police, who aided in recruiting the ranks cf the colonists, had been guilty of scandalous impositions. Under pretence of taking up mendicants and vagabonds, they had scoured the streets at night, seizing upon honest mechanics, or their sons, and hurrying them to their crimping-houses, for the sole purpose of extorting money from them as a ransom. The populace was roused to indignation by these abuses. The officers of police were mobbed in the exercise of their odious functions, and several of them were killed; which put an end to this flagrant abuse of power.

In March, a most extraordinary decree of the council fixed the price of shares of the India Company at nine thousand livres each. All ecclesiastical communities and hospitals were now prohibited from investing money at interest, in any thing but India stock. With all these props and stays, the system continued to totter. How could it be otherwise, under a despotic government, that could alter the value of property at every moment? The very compulsory measures that were adopted to establish the credit of the bank, hastened its fall; plainly showing there was a want of solid security. Law caused pamphlets to be published, setting forth, in eloquent language, the vast profits that must accrue to holders of the stock, and the impossibility of the king's ever doing it any harm. On the very back of these assertions, came forth an edict of the king, dated the 22d of May, wherein, under pretence of having reduced the value of his coin, it was declared necessary to reduce the value of his bank-notes one-half, and of the India shares from nine thousand to five thousand livres!

This decree came like a clap of thunder upon share-holders. They found one half of the pretended value of the paper in their hands annihilated in an instant; and what certainty had they with respect to the other half? The rich considered themselves ruined; those in humbler circumstances looked forward to abject beggary.

The parliament seized the occasion to stand forth as the protector of the public, and refused to register the decree. It gained the credit of compelling the Regent to retrace his step, though it is more probable he yielded to the universal burst of public astonishment and reprobation. On the 27th of May, the edict was revoked, and bank-bills were restored to their previous value. But the fatal blow had been struck; the delusion was at an end. Government itself had lost all public confidence, equally with the bank it had engendered, and which its own arbitrary acts had brought into discredit. "All Paris," says the Regent's mother, in her letters, "has been mourning at the cursed decree which Law has persuaded my son to make. I have received anonymous letters, stating that I have nothing to fear on my own account, but that my son shall be pursued with fire and sword."

The Regent now endeavored to avert the odium of his ruinous schemes from himself. He affected to have suddenly lost confidence in Law, and on the 29th of May, discharged him from his employ, as Comptroller General, and stationed a Swiss guard of sixteen men in his house. He even refused to see him, when, on the following day, he applied at the portal of the Palais Royal for admission: but having played off this farce before the public, he admitted him secretly the same night, by a private door, and continued as before to cooperate with him in his financial schemes.

On the first of June, the Regent issued a decree, permitting persons to have as much money as they pleased in their possession. Few, however, were in a state to benefit by this permission. There was a run upon the bank, but a royal ordinance immediately suspended payment, until farther orders. To relieve the public mind, a city stock was created, of twenty-five millions, bearing an interest of two and a half per cent., for which bank notes were taken in exchange. The bank notes thus withdrawn from circulation, were publicly burnt before the Hotel de

Ville. The public, however, had lost confidence in every thing and every body, and suspected fraud and collusion in those who pretended to burn the bills.

A general confusion now took place in the financial world. Families who had lived in opulence, found themselves suddenly reduced to indigence. Schemers who had been revelling in the delusion of princely fortunes, found their estates vanishing into thin air. Those who had any property remaining, sought to secure it against reverses. Cautious persons found there was no safety for property in a country where the coin was continually shifting in value, and where a despotism was exercised over public securities, and even over the private purses of individuals. They began to send their effects into other countries; when lo! on the 20th of June, a royal edict commanded them to bring back their effects, under penalty of forfeiting twice their value; and forbade them, under like penalty, from investing their money in foreign stocks. This was soon followed by another decree, forbidding any one to retain precious stones in his possession, or to sell them to foreigners: all must be deposited in the bank, in exchange for depreciating paper!

Execrations were now poured out, on all sides, against Law, and menaces of vengeance. What a contrast, in a short time, to the venal incense once offered up to him! "This person," writes the Regent's mother, "who was formerly worshipped as a god, is now not sure of his life. It is astonishing how greatly terrified he is. He is as a dead man; he is pale as a sheet, and it is said he can never get over it. My son is not dismayed, though he is threatened on all sides, and is very much amused with Law's terrors."

About the middle of July, the last grand attempt was made by Law and the Regent, to keep up the system, and provide for the immense emission of paper. A decree was fabricated, giving the India Company the entire monopoly of commerce, on condition that it would, in the course of a year, reimburse six hundred millions of livres of its bills, at the rate of fifty millions per month.

On the 17th, this decree was sent to parliament to be registered. It at once raised a storm of opposition in that assembly; and a vehement discussion took place. While that was going on, a disastrous scene was passing out of doors.

The calamitous effects of the system had reached the humblest concerns of human life. Provisions had risen to an enormous price; paper money was refused at all the shops; the people had not wherewithal to buy bread. It had been found absolutely indispensable to relax a little from the suspension of specie payments, and to allow small sums to be scantily exchanged for paper. The doors of the bank and the neighboring street were immediately thronged with a famishing multitude, seeking cash for bank-notes of ten livres. So great was the press and struggle, that several persons were stifled and crushed to death. The mob carried three of the bodies to the court-yard of the Palais Royal. Some cried for the Regent to come forth, and behold the effect of his system; others demanded the death of Law, the imposter, who had brought this misery and ruin upon the nation.

The moment was critical: the popular fury was rising to a tempest, when Le Blanc, the Secretary of State, stepped forth. He had previously sent for the military, and now only sought to gain time. Singling out six or seven stout fellows, who seemed to be the ringleaders of the mob: "My good fellows," said he, calmly, "carry away these bodies, and place them in some church, and then come back quickly to me for your pay." They immediately obeyed; a kind of funeral procession was formed; the arrival of troops dispersed those who lingered behind; and Paris was probably saved from an insurrection.

About ten o'clock in the morning, all being quiet, Law ventured to go in his carriage to the Palais Royal. He was saluted with cries and curses, as he passed along the streets; and he reached the Palais Royal in a terrible fright. The Regent amused himself with his fears, but retained him with him, and sent off his carriage, which was assailed by the mob, pelted with stones, and the glasses shivered. The news of this outrage was communicated to parliament in the midst of a furious discussion of the decree for the commercial monopoly. The first president, who had been absent for a short time, reentered, and communicated the tidings in a whimsical couplet:

> "Messieurs, Messieurs! bonne nouvelle!
> Le carrosse de Law est reduite en carrelle!"

> "Gentlemen, Gentlemen! good news!
> The carriage of Law is shivered to atoms!"

The members sprang up with joy: "And Law!" exclaimed they, "has he been torn to pieces?" The president was ignorant of the result of the tumult; whereupon the debate was cut short, the decree rejected, and the house adjourned; the members hurrying to learn the particulars. Such was the levity with which public affairs were treated, at that dissolute and disastrous period.

On the following day, there was an ordinance from the king, prohibit- ing all popular assemblage; and troops were stationed at various points, and in all public places. The regiment of guards was ordered to hold itself in readiness; and the musqueteers to be at their hotels, with their horses ready saddled. A number of small offices were opened, where people might cash small notes, though with great delay and difficulty. An edict was also issued, declaring that whoever should refuse to take bank notes in the course of trade, should forfeit double the amount!

The continued and vehement opposition of parliament to the whole delusive system of finance, had been a constant source of annoyance to the Regent; but this obstinate rejection of his last grand expedient of a commercial monopoly, was not to be tolerated. He determined to punish that intractable body. The Abbé Dubois and Law suggested a simple mode; it was to suppress the parliament altogether, being, as they observed, so far from useful, that it was a constant impediment to the march of public affairs. The Regent was half inclined to listen to their advice; but upon calmer consideration, and the advice of friends, he adopted a more moderate course. On the 20th of July, early in the morning, all the doors of the parliament-house were taken possession of by the troops. Others were sent to surround the house of the first president, and others to the houses of the various members; who were all at first in great alarm, until an order from the king was put into their hands, to render themselves at Pontoise, in the course of two days, to which place the parliament was thus suddenly and arbitrarily transferred.

This despotic act, says Voltaire, would at any other time have caused an insurrection; but one half of the Parisians were occupied by their ruin, and the other half by their fancied riches, which were soon to vanish. The president and members of parliament acquiesced in the mandate without a murmur; they even went as if on a party of pleasure, and made every preparation to lead a joyous life in their exile. The musqueteers, who held possession of the vacated parliament-house, a gay corps of fashionable young fellows, amused themselves with making songs and pasquinades, at the expense of the exiled legislators; and at length, to pass away time, formed themselves into a mock parliament; elected their presidents, kings, ministers, and advocates; took their seats in due form; arraigned a cat at their bar, in place of the Sieur Law, and after giving it a "fair trial," condemned it to be hanged. In this manner, public affairs and public institutions were lightly turned to jest.

As to the exiled parliament, it lived gaily and luxuriously at Pontoise, at the public expense; for the Regent had furnished funds, as usual, with a lavish hand. The first president had the mansion of the Duke de Bouillon put at his disposal, all ready furnished, with a vast and delightful garden on the borders of a river. There he kept open house to all the members of parliament. Several tables were spread every day, all furnished luxuriously and splendidly; the most exquisite wines and liquors, the choicest fruits and refreshments, of all kinds, abounded. A number of small chariots for one and two horses were always at hand, for such ladies and old gentlemen as wished to take an airing after din-

ner, and card and billiard tables for such as chose to amuse themselves
in that way until supper. The sister and the daughter of the first president
did the honors of his house, and he himself presided there with an air
of great ease, hospitality, and magnificence. It became a party of pleasure to drive from Paris to Pontoise, which was six leagues distant, and
partake of the amusements and festivities of the place. Business was
openly slighted; nothing was thought of but amusement. The Regent and
his government were laughed at, and made the subjects of continual
pleasantries; while the enormous expenses incurred by this idle and
lavish course of life, more than doubled the liberal sums provided. This
was the way in which the parliament resented their exile.

During all this time, the system was getting more and more involved.
The stock exchange had some time previously been removed to the
Place Vendome; but the tumult and noise becoming intolerable to the
residents of that polite quarter, and especially to the chancellor, whose
hotel was there, the Prince and Princess Carignan, both deep gamblers
in Mississippi stock, offered the extensive garden of their Hotel de Sois-
sons as a rallying-place for the worshippers of Mammon. The offer was
accepted. A number of barracks were immediately erected in the garden,
as offices for the stock-brokers, and an order was obtained from the
Regent, under pretext of police regulations, that no bargain should be
valid, unless concluded in these barracks. The rent of them immediately
mounted to a hundred livres a month for each, and the whole yielded
these noble proprietors an ignoble revenue of half a million of livres.

The mania for gain, however, was now at an end. A universal panic
succeeded. *"Saure qui peut!"* was the watch-word. Every one was
anxious to exchange falling paper for something of intrinsic and permanent value. Since money was not to be had, jewels, precious stones,
plate, porcelain, trinkets of gold and silver, all commanded any price, in
paper. Land was bought at fifty years' purchase, and he esteemed himself happy, who could get it even at this price. Monopolies now became
the rage among the noble holders of paper. The Duke de la Force
bought up nearly all the tallow, grease, and soap; others the coffee and
spices; others hay and oats. Foreign exchanges were almost impracticable. The debts of Dutch and English merchants were paid in this
fictitious money, all the coin of the realm having disappeared. All the
relations of debtor and creditor were confounded. With one thousand
crowns, one might pay a debt of eighteen thousand livres!

The Regent's mother, who once exulted in the affluence of bank paper,
now wrote in a very different tone: "I have often wished," said she, in
her letters, "that these bank-notes were in the depths of the infernal
regions. They have given my son more trouble than relief. Nobody in
France has a penny. * * * My son was once popular, but since the ar-

rival of this cursed Law, he is hated more and more. Not a week passes, without my receiving letters filled with frightful threats, and speaking of him as a tyrant. I have just received one, threatening him with poison. When I showed it to him, he did nothing but laugh."

In the mean time, Law was dismayed by the increasing troubles, and terrified at the tempest he had raised. He was not a man of real courage; and fearing for his personal safety, from popular tumult, or the despair of ruined individuals, he again took refuge in the palace of the Regent. The latter, as usual, amused himself with his terrors, and turned every new disaster into a jest; but he, too, began to think of his own security.

In pursuing the schemes of Law, he had no doubt calculated to carry through his term of government with ease and splendor; and to enrich himself, his connexions, and his favorites; and had hoped that the catastrophe of the system would not take place until after the expiration of the regency.

He now saw his mistake; that it was impossible much longer to prevent an explosion; and he determined at once to get Law out of the way, and then to charge him with the whole tissue of delusions of this paper alchymy. He accordingly took occasion of the recall of parliament in December, 1720, to suggest to Law the policy of his avoiding an encounter with that hostile and exasperated body. Law needed no urging to the measure. His only desire was to escape from Paris, and its tempestuous populace. Two days before the return of parliament, he took his sudden and secret departure. He travelled in a chaise bearing the arms of the Regent, and was escorted by a kind of safe-guard of servants, in the duke's livery. His first place of refuge was an estate of the Regent's, about six leagues from Paris, from whence he pushed forward to Bruxelles.

As soon as Law was fairly out of the way, the Duke of Orleans summoned a council of the regency, and informed them that they were assembled to deliberate on the state of the finances, and the affairs of the India Company. Accordingly La Houssaye, Comptroller General, rendered a perfectly clear statement, by which it appeared that there were bank bills in circulation to the amount of two milliards, seven hundred millions of livres, without any evidence that this enormous sum had been emitted in virtue of any ordinance from the general assembly of the India Company, which alone had the right to authorize such emissions.

The council was astonished at this disclosure, and looked to the Regent for explanation. Pushed to the extreme, the Regent avowed that Law had emitted bills to the amount of twelve hundred millions beyond what had been fixed by ordinances, and in contradiction to express prohibitions; that the thing being done, he, the Regent, had legalized or rather covered the transaction, by decrees ordering such emissions, which decrees he had *antedated*.

A stormy scene ensued between the Regent and the Duke de Bourbon, little to the credit of either, both having been deeply implicated in the cabalistic operations of the system. In fact, the several members of the council had been among the most venal "beneficiaries" of the scheme, and had interests at stake which they were anxious to secure. From all the circumstances of the case, I am inclined to think that others were more to blame than Law, for the disastrous effects of his financial projects. His bank, had it been confined to its original limits, and left to the control of its own internal regulations, might have gone on prosperously, and been of great benefit to the nation. It was an institution fitted for a free country; but unfortunately, it was subject to the control of a despotic government, that could, at its pleasure, alter the value of the specie within its vaults, and compel the most extravagant expansions of its paper circulation. The vital principle of a bank is security in the regularity of its operations, and the immediate convertibility of its paper into coin; and what confidence could be reposed in an institution, or its paper promises, when the sovereign could at any moment centuple those promises in the market, and seize upon all the money in the bank? The compulsory measures used, likewise, to force banknotes into currency, against the judgment of the public, was fatal to the system; for credit must be free and uncontrolled as the common air. The Regent was the evil spirit of the system, that forced Law on to an expansion of his paper currency far beyond what he had ever dreamed of. He it was that in a manner compelled the unlucky projector to devise all kinds of collateral companies and monopolies, by which to raise funds to meet the constantly and enormously increasing emissions of shares and notes. Law was but like a poor conjuror in the hands of a potent spirit that he has evoked, and that obliges him to go on, desperately and ruinously, with his conjurations. He only thought at the outset to raise the wind, but the Regent compelled him to raise the whirlwind.

The investigation of the affairs of the Company by the council, resulted in nothing beneficial to the public. The princes and nobles who had enriched themselves by all kinds of juggles and extortions, escaped unpunished, and retained the greater part of their spoils. Many of the "suddenly rich," who had risen from obscurity to a giddy height of imaginary prosperity, and had indulged in all kinds of vulgar and ridiculous excesses, awoke as out of a dream, in their original poverty, now made more galling and humiliating by their transient elevation.

The weight of the evil, however, fell on more valuable classes of society; honest tradesmen and artizans, who had been seduced away from the slow accumulations of industry, to the specious chances of speculation. Thousands of meritorious families, also, once opulent, had been reduced to indigence, by a too great confidence in government. There was a general derangement in the finances, that long exerted a baneful influence over the national prosperity; but the most disastrous effects of the system were upon the morals and manners of the nation. The faith of engagements, the sanctity of promises in affairs of business, were at an end. Every expedient to grasp present profit, or to evade present difficulty, was tolerated. While such deplorable laxity of principle was generated in the busy classes, the chivalry of France had soiled their pennons; and honor and glory, so long the idols of the Gallic nobility, had been tumbled to the earth, and trampled in the dirt of the stock-market.

As to Law, the originator of the system, he appears eventually to have profited but little by his schemes. "He was a quack," says Voltaire, "to whom the state was given to be cured, but who poisoned it with his drugs, and who poisoned himself." The effects which he left behind in France, were sold at a low price, and the proceeds dissipated. His landed estates were confiscated. He carried away with him barely enough to maintain himself, his wife, and daughter, with decency. The chief relique of his immense fortune was a great diamond, which he was often obliged to pawn. He was in England in 1721, and was presented to George the First. He returned shortly afterward, to the continent; shifting about from place to place, and died in Venice, in 1729. His wife and daughter, accustomed to live with the prodigality of princesses, could not conform to their altered fortunes, but dissipated the scanty means left to them, and sank into abject poverty. "I saw his wife," says Voltaire, "at Bruxelles, as much humiliated as she had been haughty and triumphant at Paris." An elder brother of Law remained in France, and was protected by the Duchess of Bourbon. His descendants acquitted themselves honorably, in various public employments; and one of them was the Marquis Lauriston, some time Lieutenant General and Peer of France.

SKETCHES IN PARIS IN 1825

FROM THE TRAVELLING NOTE-BOOK OF GEOFFREY CRAYON, GENT

THE PARISIAN HOTEL

A great hotel in Paris is a street set on end: the grand stair-case is the highway, and every floor or apartment a separate habitation. The one in which I am lodged may serve as a specimen. It is a large quadrangular pile, built round a spacious paved court. The ground floor is occupied by shops, magazines, and domestic offices. Then comes the *entre-sol*, with low ceilings, short windows, and dwarf chambers; then succeed a succession of floors, or stories, rising one above the other, to the number of Mahomet's heavens. Each floor is a mansion, complete within itself, with ante-chamber, saloons, dining and sleeping rooms, kitchen and other conveniencies. Some floors are divided into two or more suites of apartments. Each apartment has its main door of entrance, opening upon the stair-case, or landing-places, and locked like a street door. Thus several families and numerous single persons live under the same roof, totally independent of each other, and may live so for years, without holding more intercourse than is kept up in other cities by residents in the same street.

Like the great world, this little microcosm has its gradations of rank and style and importance. The *Premier,* or first floor with its grand saloons, lofty ceilings, and splendid furniture, is decidedly the aristocratical part of the establishment. The second floor is scarcely less aristocratical and magnificent; the other floors go on lessening in splendor as they gain in altitude, and end with the attics, the region of petty tailors, clerks, and sewing girls. To make the filling up of the mansion complete, every odd nook and corner is fitted up as a *joli petit apartement à garçon,* (a pretty little bachelor's apartment,) that is to say, some little dark inconvenient nestling-place for a poor devil of a bachelor.

The whole domain is shut up from the street by a great *porte-cochére,* or portal, calculated for the admission of carriages. This consists of two massy folding-doors, that swing heavily open upon a grand entrance, passing under the front of the edifice into the court-yard. On one side is a grand stair-case leading to the upper apartments. Immediately without the portal, is the porter's lodge, a small room with one or two bedrooms adjacent, for the accommodation of the *concierge,* or porter, and his family. This is one of the most important functionaries of the hotel. He is, in fact, the Cerberus of the establishment, and no one can pass in or out without his knowledge and consent. The *porte-cochére* in general is fastened by a sliding bolt, from which a cord or wire passes into the porter's lodge. Whoever wishes to go out, must speak to the porter, who draws the bolt. A visiter from without gives a single rap with the massive knocker; the bolt is immediately drawn, as if by an invisible hand; the door stands ajar, the visiter pushes it open, and enters. A face presents itself at the glass door of the porter's little chamber; the stranger pronounces the name of the person he comes to seek. If the person or family is of importance, occupying the first or second floor, the porter sounds a bell once or twice, to give notice that a visiter is at hand. The stranger in the mean time ascends the great stair-case, the highway common to all, and arrives at the outer door, equivalent to a street door, of the suite of rooms inhabited by his friends. Beside this hangs a bell-cord, with which he rings for admittance.

When the family or person inquired for is of less importance, or lives in some remote part of the mansion less easy to be apprized, no signal is given. The applicant pronounces the name at the porter's door, and is told, "*Montez au troisieme, au quatrième; sonnez à la porte à droite, ou à gauche;*" ("Ascend to the third or fourth story; ring the bell on the right or left hand door,") as the case may be.

The porter and his wife act as domestics to such of the inmates of the mansion as do not keep servants; making their beds, arranging their rooms, lighting their fires, and doing other menial offices, for which they receive a monthly stipend. They are also in confidential intercourse with the servants of the other inmates, and, having an eye on all the in-comers and out-goers, are thus enabled, by hook, and by crook, to learn the secrets and the domestic history of every member of the little territory within the *porte-cochére*.

The porter's lodge is accordingly a great scene of gossip, where all the private affairs of this interior neighborhood are discussed. The court-yard, also, is an assembling place in the evenings for the servants of the different families, and a sisterhood of sewing girls from the entre-sols and the attics, to play at various games, and dance to the music of their own songs, and the echoes of their feet; at which assemblages the porter's daughter takes the lead; a fresh, pretty, buxom girl, generally called "*La Petite,*" though almost as tall as a grenadier. These little evening gatherings, so characteristic of this gay country, are countenanced by the various families of the mansion, who often look down from their windows and balconies, on moonlight evenings, and enjoy the simple revels of their domestics. I must observe, however, that the hotel I am describing is rather a quiet, retired one, where most of the inmates are permanent residents from year to year, so that there is more of the spirit of neighborhood, than in the bustling, fashionable hotels in the gay parts of Paris, which are continually changing their inhabitants.

MY FRENCH NEIGHBOR

I often amuse myself by watching from my window (which by-the-by is tolerably elevated) the movements of the teeming little world below me; and as I am on sociable terms with the porter and his wife, I gather from them as they light my fire, or serve my breakfast, anecdotes of all my fellow lodgers. I have been somewhat curious in studying a little antique Frenchman, who occupies one of the *jolie chambers à garçon* already mentioned. He is one of those superannuated veterans who flourished before the revolution, and have weathered all the storms of Paris in conequence, very probably, of being fortunately too insignificant to attract attention. He has a small income, which he manages with the skill of a French economist: appropriating so much for his lodgings, so much for his meals; so much for his visits to St. Cloud and Versailles, and so much for his seat at the theatre. He has resided at the hotel for years, and always in the same chamber, which he furnishes at his own expense. The decorations of the room mark his various ages. There are some gallant pictures, which he hung up in his younger days; with a portrait of a lady of rank, whom he speaks tenderly of, dressed in the old French taste; and a pretty opera dancer, pirouetting in a hoop petticoat, who lately died at a good old age. In a corner of this picture is stuck a prescription for a rheumatism, and below it stands an easy-chair. He has a small parrot at the window, to amuse him when within doors, and a pug-dog to accompany him in his daily peregrinations. While I am writing, he is crossing the court to go out. He is attired in his best coat, of sky-blue, and is doubtless bound for the Tuilleries. His hair is dressed in the old style, with powdered ear-locks and a pig-tail. His little dog trips after him, sometimes on four legs, sometimes on three, and looking as if his leather small-clothes were too tight for him. Now the old gentleman stops to have a word with an old crony who lives in the entre-sol, and is just returning from his promenade. Now they take a pinch of snuff together; now they pull out huge red cotton handkerchiefs, (those "flags of abomination," as they have well been called,) and blow their noses most sonorously. Now they turn to make remarks upon their two little dogs, who are exchanging the morning's salutation; now they part, and my old gentleman stops to have a passing word with the porter's wife, and now he sallies forth, and is fairly launched upon the town for the day.

No man is so methodical as a complete idler, and none so scrupu-

lous in measuring and portioning out his time, as he whose time is
worth nothing. The old gentleman in question has his exact hour
for rising, and for shaving himself by a small mirror hung against his
casement. He sallies forth at a certain hour every morning, to take
his cup of coffee and his roll at a certain cafe, where he reads the
papers. He has been a regular admirer of the lady who presides at
the bar, and always stops to have a little *badinage* with her, *en passant*.
He has his regular walks on the Boulevards and in the Palais Royal,
where he sets his watch by the petard fired off by the sun at mid-day.
He has his daily resort in the Garden of the Tuilleries, to meet with
a knot of veteran idlers like himself, who talk on pretty much the
same subjects whenever they meet. He has been present at all the
sights and shows and rejoicings of Paris for the last fifty years: has
witnessed the great events of the revolution; the guillotining of the
king and queen; the coronation of Bonaparte; the capture of Paris,
and the restoration of the Bourbons. All these he speaks of with
the coolness of a theatrical critic; and I question whether he has not
been gratified by each in its turn; not from any inherent love of
tumult, but from that insatiable appetite for spectacle, which prevails
among the inhabitants of this metropolis. I have been amused with
a farce, in which one of these systematic old triflers is represented.
He sings a song detailing his whole day's round of insignificant occupations, and goes to bed delighted with the idea that his next day
will be an exact repetition of the same routine:

>"Je me couche le soir,
>Enchanté de pouvoir
>Recommencer mon train
>Le lendemain
>Matin."

THE ENGLISHMAN AT PARIS

In another part of the hotel, a handsome suite of rooms is occupied by an old English gentleman, of great probity, some understanding, and very considerable crustiness, who has come to France to
live economically. He has a very fair property, but his wife, being
of that blessed kind compared in Scripture to the frutiful vine, has
overwhelmed him with a family of buxom daughters, who hang clus-
tering about him, ready to be gathered by any hand. He is seldom
to be seen in public, without one hanging on each arm, and smiling
on all the world, while his own mouth is drawn down at each corner
like a mastiff's with internal growling at every thing about him. He
adheres rigidly to English fasion in dress, and trudges about in long

gaiters and broad-brimmed hat; while his daughters almost over-shadow him with feathers, flowers, and French bonnets.

He contrives to keep up an atmosphere of English habits, opinions, and prejudices, and to carry a semblance of London into the very heart of Paris. His mornings are spent at Galignani's news-room, where he forms one of a knot of inveterate quidnuncs, who read the same articles over a dozen times in a dozen different papers. He generally dines in company with some of his own countrymen, and they have what is called a "comfortable sitting" after dinner, in the English fashion, drinking wine, discussing the news of the London papers, and canvassing the French character, the French metropolis, and the French revolution, ending with a unanimous admission of English courage, English morality, English cookery, English wealth, the magnitude of London, and the ingratitude of the French.

His evenings are chiefly spent at a club of his countrymen, where the London papers are taken. Sometimes his daughters entice him to the theatres, but not often. He abuses French tragedy, as all fustian and bombast, Talma as a ranter, and Duchesnois as a mere termagant. It is true his ear is not sufficiently familiar with the language to understand French verse, and he generally goes to sleep during the performance. The wit of the French comedy is flat and pointless to him. He would not give one of Munden's wry faces, or Liston's inexpressible looks, for the whole of it.

He will not admit that Paris has any advantage over London. The Seine is a muddy rivulet in comparison with the Thames; the West End of London surpasses the finest parts of the French capital; and on some one's observing that there was a very thick fog out of doors: "Pish!" said he, crustily, "it is nothing to the fogs we have in London!"

He has infinite trouble in bringing his table into any thing like conformity to English rule. With his liquors, it is true, he is tolerably successful. He procures London porter, and a stock of port and sherry, at considerable expense; for he observes that he cannot stand those cursed thin French wines: they dilute his blood so much as to give him the rheumatism. As to their white wines, he stigmatizes them as mere substitutes for cider; and as to claret, why "it would be port if it could." He has continual quarrels with his French cook, whom he renders wretched by insisting on his conforming to Mrs. Glass; for it is easier to convert a Frenchman from his religion than his cookery. The poor fellow, by dint of repeated efforts, once brought himself to serve up *ros bif* sufficiently raw to suit what he considered the cannibal taste of his master; but then he could not refrain, at the last moment, adding some exquisite sauce, that put the old gentleman in a fury.

He detests wood-fires, and has procured a quantity of coal; but not having a grate, he is obliged to burn it on the hearth. Here he sits poking and stirring the fire with one end of a tongs, while the room is as murky as a smithy; railing at French chimneys, French masons, and French architects; giving a poke, at the end of every sentence, as though he were stirring up the very bowels of the delinquents he is anathematizing. He lives in a state militant with inanimate objects around him; gets into high dudgeon with doors and casements, because they will not come under English law, and has implacable feuds with sundry refractory pieces of furniture. Among these is one in patricular with which he is sure to have a high quarrel every time he goes to dress. It is a *commode*, one of those smooth, polished, plausible pieces of French furniture, that have the perversity of five hundred devils. Each drawer has a will of its own; will open or not, just as the whim takes it, and sets lock and key at defiance. Sometimes a drawer will refuse to yield to either persuasion or force, and will part with both handles rather than yield; another will come out in the most coy and coquettish manner imaginable; elbowing along, zig-zag; on corner retreating as the other advances; making a thousand difficulties and objections at every move; until the old gentleman, out of all patience, gives a sudden jerk, and brings drawer and contents into the middle of the floor. His hostility to this unlucky piece of furniture increases every day, as if incensed that it does not grow better. He is like the fretful, invalid, who cursed his bed, that the longer he lay, the harder it grew. The only benefit he has derived from the quarrel is, that it has furnished him with a crusty joke, which he utters on all occasions. He swears that a French *commode* is the most *incommodious* thing in existence, and that although the nation cannot make a joint-stool that will stand steady, yet they are always talking of every thing's being *perfectionée*.

His servants understand his humor, and avail themselves of it. He was one day disturbed by a pertinacious rattling and shaking at one of the doors, and bawled out in an angry tone to know the cause of the disturbance. "Sir," said the footman, testily, "it's this confounded French lock!" "Ah!" said the old gentleman, pacified by this hit at the nation, "I thought there was something French at the bottom of it."

ENGLISH AND FRENCH CHARACTER

As I am a mere looker-on in Europe, and hold myself as much as possible aloof from its quarrels and prejudices, I feel something like one overlooking a game, who, without any great skill of his own, can occasionally percieve the blunders of much abler players. This neutrality of feeling enables me to enjoy the contrasts of character presented in this time of general peace; when the various people of Europe, who have so long been sundered by wars, are brought together, and placed side by side in this great gathering place of nations. No greater contrast, however, is exhibited, than that of the French and English. The peace has deluged this gay capital with English visitors, of all ranks and conditions. They throng every place of curiosity and amusement, fill the public gardens, the galleries, the caffés, salons, theatres; always herding together, never associating with the French. The two nations are like two threads of different colours, tangled together, but never blended.

In fact they present a continual antithesis, and seem to value themselves upon being unlike each other, yet each have their peculiar merits, which should entitle them to each other's esteem. The French intellect is quick and active. It flashes its way into a subject with the rapidity of lightning; seizes upon remote conclusions with a sudden bound, and its deductions are almost intuitive. The English intellect is less rapid, but more persevering; less sudden, but more sure in its deductions. The quickness and mobility of the French enable them to find enjoyment in the multiplicity of sensations. They speak and act more from immediate impressions, than from reflection and meditation. They are therefore more social and communicative; more fond of society and of places of public resort and amusement. An Englishman is more reflective in his habits. He lives in the world of his own thoughts, and seems more self-existent and self-dependent, He loves the quiet of his own apartment; even when abroad, he in a manner makes a little solitude around him, by his silence and reserve: he moves about shy and solitary, and, as it were, buttoned up, body and soul.

The French are great optimists, they seize upon every good as it flies, and revel in the passing pleasure. The Englishman is too apt to neglect the present good in preparing against the possible evil. However adversities may lower, let the sun shine but for a moment, and forth sallies the mercurial Frenchman, in holyday dress and holyday spirits, gay as a butterfly, as thou his sunshine were perpetual; but let the sun beam never so brightly, so there be but a cloud in the horizon, the wary Englishman ventures forth distrustfully, with his umbrella in his hand.

The Frenchman has a wonderful facility at turning small things to advantage. No one can be gay and luxurious on smaller means, no one requires less expense to be happy. He practices a kind of gilding in his style of living, and hammers out every guinea into gold leaf. The Englishman on the contrary is expensive in his habits and expensive in his enjoyments. He values every thing, whether useful or ornamental, by what it costs. He has no satisfaction in show, unless it be solid and complete. Every thing goes with him by the square foot. What-ever display he makes, the depth is sure to equal the surface. The Frenchman's habitation like himself, is open, cheerful, bustling, and noisy. He lives in a part of a great hotel with wide portal; paved court, a spacious dirty stone staircase, and a family on every floor. All is clatter and chatter. He is good-humored and talkative with his servants; sociable with his neighbors, and complaisant to all the world. Any body has access to himself and his apartments; his very bed-room is open to visitors, whatever may be its state of confusion; and all this not from any peculiarly hospitable feeling, but from that communicative habit which predominates over his character.

The Englishman, on the contrary, ensconces himself in a snug brick mansion, which he has all to himself; locks the front door; puts broken bottles along his walls, and spring-guns and man-traps in his gardens; shrowds himself with trees and window-curtains; exults in his quiet and privacy, and seems disposed to keep out noise, day-light, and com-pany. His house, like himself, has a reserved, inhospitable exterior, yet whoever gains admittance is apt to find a warm heart and warm fire-side within.

The French excel in wit; the English in humour; the French have gayer fancy, the English richer imagination. The former are full of sensibility; easily moved, and prone to sudden and great excitement; but their excitement is not durable; the English are more phlegmatic; not so readily affected; but capable of being aroused to great enthusiasm. The faults of these opposite temperaments are, that the vivacity of the French is apt to sparkle up and be frothy, the gravity of the English to settle down and grow muddy. When the two characters can be fixed in a medium, the French kept from effervescence and the English from stagnation, both will be found excellent.

This contrast of character may also be noticed in the great concerns of the two nations. The ardent Frenchman is all for military renown: he fights for glory, that is to say for success in arms. For provided the national flag be victorious, he cares little about the expense, the injustice, or the inutility of the war. It is wonderful how the poorest Frenchman will revel on a triumphant bulletin; a great victory is meat and drink to him; and at the sight of a military sovereign, bringing home captured cannon and captured standards, he throws up his greasy cap in the air, and is ready to jump out of his wooden shoes for joy.

John Bull, on the contrary, is a reasoning, considerate person. If he does wrong, it is in the most rational way imaginable. He fights because the good of the world requires it. He is a moral person, and makes war upon his neighbor for the maintenance of peace and good order, and sound principles. He is a money-making personage, and fights for the prosperity of commerce and manufactures. Thus the two nations have been fighting time out of mind for glory and good. The French, in pursuit of glory, have had their capital twice taken, and John, in pursuit of good, has run himself over head and ears in debt.

THE TUILLERIES AND WINDSOR CASTLE

I have sometimes fancied I could discover national characteristics in national edifices. In the Chateau of the Tuilleries, for instance, I perceive the same jumble of contrarieties that marks the French character; the same whimsical mixture of the great and the little; the splendid and the paltry, the sublime and the grotesque. On visiting this famous pile, the first thing that strikes both eye and ear is military display. The courts glitter with steel-clad soldiery, and resound with tramp of horse, the roll of drum, and the bray of trumpet. Dismounted guardmen patrol its arcades with loaded carbines, jingling spurs, and clanking sabres. Gigantic grenadiers are posted about its stair-cases; young officers of the guards loll from the balconies, or lounge in groups upon the terraces; and the gleam of bayonet from window to window, shows that centinels are pacing up and down the corridors and ante-chambers. The first floor is brilliant with the splendors of a court. French taste has tasked itself in adorning the sumptuous suites of apartments; nor are the gilded chapel and splendid theatre forgotten, where Piety and Pleasure are next-door neighbors, and harmonize together with perfect French *bienseance.*

Mingled up with all this regal and military magnificence, is a world of whimsical and make-shift detail. A great part of the huge edifice is cut up into little chambers and nestling-places for retainers of the court, dependants on retainers, and hangers-on of dependants. Some are squeezed into narrow entre-sols, those low, dark, intermediate slices of apartments between floors, the inhabitants of which seem shoved in edge ways, like books between narrow shelves; others are perched, like swallows, under the eaves; the high roofs, too, which are as tall and steep as a French cocked-hat, have rows of little dormer windows, tier above tier, just large enough to admit light and air for some dormitory, and to enable its occupant to peep out at the sky. Even to the very ridge of the roof, may be seen, here and there, one of these air-holes, with a stove pipe beside it, to carry off the smoke from the handful of fuel with which its weasen-faced tenant simmers his *demi-tasse* of coffee.

On approaching the palace from the Pont Royal, you take in, at a glance, all the various strata of inhabitants; the garreteer in the roof; the retainer in the entre-sol; the courtiers at the casements of the royal apartments; while, on the ground floor, a steam of savory odours, and a score or two of cooks, in white caps, bobbing their heads about the windows, betray that scientific and all-important laboratory, the Royal Kitchen.

Go into the grand ante-chamber of the royal apartments on Sunday and see the mixture of Old and New France: the old emigres, returned with the Bourbons, little, withered, spindle-shanked old noblemen, clad in court dresses; that figured in these saloons before the revolution, and have been carefully treasured up during their exile; with the solitaires and *ailes de pigeon* of former days: and the court swords strutting out behind, like pins stuck through dry beetles. See them haunting the scenes of their former splendor, in hopes of a restitution of estates, like ghosts haunting the vicinity of buried treasure: while around them you see young France, grown up in the fighting school of Napoleon, equipped *en militaire,* tall, hardy frank, vigorous, sun-burnt, fierce-whiskered, with tramping boots, towering crests, and glittering breast-plates.

It is incredible the number of ancient and hereditary feeders on royalty said to be housed in this establishment. Indeed all the royal palaces abound with noble families returned from exile, and who have nestling-places allotted them while they await the restoration of their estates, or the much-talked of law, indemnity. Some of them have fine quarters, but poor living. Some families have but five or six hundred francs a year, and all their retinue consists of a servant woman. With all this they maintain their old aristocratical *hauteur,* look down with vast contempt upon the opulent families which have risen since the revolution; stygmatize them all as *parvenus,* or upstarts, and refuse to visit them.

In regarding the exterior of the Tuilleries, with all its outward signs of internal populousness, I have often thought what a rare sight it would be to see it suddenly unroofed, and all its nooks and corners laid open to the day. It would be like turning up the stump of an old tree; and dislodging the world of grubs, and ants, and beetles lodged beneath. Indeed there is a scandalous anecdote current, that, in the time of one of the petty plots, when petards were exploded under the windows of the Tuilleries, the police made a sudden investigation of the palace at four o'clock in the morning; when a scene of the most whimsical confusion ensued. Hosts of supernumerary inhabitants were found foisted into the huge edifice: every rat-hole had its occupant, and places which had been considered as tenanted only by spiders, were found crowded with a surreptitious population. It is added that many ludicrous accidents occurred; great scampering and slamming of doors and whisking away in night-gowns and slippers; and several persons, who were found by accident in their neighbors' chambers, evinced indubitable astonishment at the circumstance.

As I have fancied I could read the French character in the National Palace of the Tuilleries, so I have pictured to myself some of the traits of John Bull in his royal abode of Winsor Castle. The Tuilleries, outwardly a peaceful palace, is in effect a swaggering military hold; while, the old castle, on the contrary, in spits of its bullying look, is completely under petticoat government. Every corner and nook is built up into some snug, cosy nestling place, some "procreant cradle," not tenanted by meagre expectants or whiskered warriors, but by sleek place-men; knowing realizers of present pay and present pudding, who seem placed there not to kill and destroy, but to breed and multiply. Nursery maids and children shine with rosy faces at the windows, and swarm about the courts and terraces. The very soldiery have a pacific look, and, when off duty, may be seen loitering about the place with the nursery maids; not making love to them in the gay gallant style of the French soldiery, but, with infinite bonhommie; aiding them to take care of the broods of children.

Though the old castle is in decay, every thing about it thrives; the very crevices of the walls are tenanted by swallows, rooks, and pigeons; all sure of quiet lodgment; the ivy strikes its roots deep in the fissures, and flourishes about the mouldering tower.* Thus it is with honest John; according to his own account, he is ever going to ruin, yet every thing that lives on him, thrives and waxes fat. He would fain be a soldier and swagger like his neighbours, but his domestic, quiet-loving, uxorious nature continually gets the upper hand; and, though he may mount his helmet and gird on his sword, yet he is apt to sink into the plodding, pains-taking father of a family; with a troop of children at his heels, and his women-kind hanging on each arm.

THE FIELD OF WATERLOO

I have spoken heretofore with some levity of the contrast that exists between the English and French character; but it deserves more serious consideration. They are the two great nations of modern times most diametrically opposed, and most worthy of each other's rivalry; essentially distinct in their characters, excelling in opposite qualities, and reflecting lustre on each other by their very opposition. In nothing is this contrast more strikingly evinced than in their military conduct. For ages have they been contending, and for ages have they crowded each other's history with acts of splendid heroism. Take the Battle

* The above sketch was written before the thorough repairs and magnificent additions made of late years to Windsor Castle.

of Waterloo, for instance, the last and most memorable trial of their rival prowess. Nothing could surpass the brilliant daring on the one side, and the steadfast enduring on the other. The French cavalry broke like waves on the compact squares of English infantry. They were seen galloping round those serried walls of men, seeking in vain for an entrance; tossing their arms in the air, in the heat of their enthusiasm, and braving the whole front of battle. The British troops, on the other hand, forbidden to move or fire, stood firm and enduring. Their columns were ripped up by cannonry; whole rows were swept down at a shot: the survivors closed their ranks, and stood firm. In this way many columns stood through the pelting of the iron tempest without firing a shot; without any action to stir their blood, or excite their spirits. Death thinned their ranks, but could not shake their souls.

A beautiful instance of the quick and generous impulses to which the French are prone, is given in the case of a French cavalier, in the hottest of the action, charging furiously upon a British officer, but perceiving in the moment of assault that his adversary had lost his sword-arm, dropping the point of his sabre, and courteously riding on. Peace be with that generous warrior, whatever were his fate! If he went down in the storm of battle, with the foundering fortunes of his chieftain, may the turf of Waterloo grow green above his grave!—and happier far would be the fate of such a spirit, to sink amidst the tempest, unconscious of defeat, than to survive, and mourn over the blighted laurels of his country.

In this way the two armies fought through a long and bloody day. The French with enthusiastic valor, the English with cool, inflexible courage, until Fate, as if to leave the question of superiority still undecided between two such adversaries, brought up the Prussians to decide the fortunes of the field.

It was several years afterward, that I visited the field of Waterloo. The ploughshare had been busy with its obvious labors, and the frequent harvest had nearly obliterated the vestiges of war. Still the blackened ruins of Hoguemont stood, a monumental pile, to mark the violence of this vehement struggle. Its broken walls, pierced by bullets, and shattered by explosions, showed the deadly strife that had taken place within; when Gaul and Britain, hemmed in between narrow walls, hand to hand and foot to foot, fought from garden to court-yard, from court-yard to chamber, with intense and concentrated rivalship. Columns of smoke towered from this vortex of battle as from a volcano: "it was," said my guide, "like a little hell upon earth." Not far off, two or three broad spots of rank, unwholesome green still marked the places where these rival warriors, after their fierce and fitful struggle, slept quietly together in the lap of their

common mother earth. Over all the rest of the field, peace had resumed its sway. The thoughtless whistle of the peasant floated on
the air, instead of the trumpet's clangor; the team slowly labored up
the hill-side, once shaken by the hoofs of rushing squadrons; and
wide fields of corn waved peacefully over the soldiers' graves, as
summer seas dimple over the place where the tall ship lies buried.

To the foregoing desultory notes on the French military character,
let me append a few traits which I picked up verbally in one of the
French provinces. They may have already appeared in print, but I have
never met with them.

At the breaking out of the revolution, when so many of the old
families emigrated, a descendant of the great Turenne, by the name
of De Latour D'Auvergne, refused to accompany his relations, and
entered into the Republican army. He served in all the campaigns
of the revolution, distinguished himself by his valor, his accomplishments, and his generous spirit, and might have risen to fortune and
to the highest honors. He refused, however, all rank in the army,
above that of captain, and would receive no recompense for his
achievements but a sword of honor. Napoleon, in testimony of his merits,
gave him the title of Premier Grenadier de France, (First Grenadier of
France,) which was the only title he would ever bear. He was killed in
Germany, at the battle of Neuberg. To honor his memory, his place
was always retained in his regiment, as if he still occupied it; and
whenever the regiment was mustered, and the name of De Latour
D'Auvergne was called out, the reply was: "Dead on the field of honor!"

PARIS AT THE RESTORATION

Paris presented a singular aspect just after the downfall of Napoleon,
and the restoration of the Bourbons. It was filled with a restless, roaming population, a dark sallow race, with fierce moustaches, black cravats,
and feverish, menacing looks; men suddenly thrown out of employ by
the return of peace; officers cut short in their career, and cast loose with
scanty means, many of them in utter indigence, upon the world: the
broken elements of armies. They haunted the places of public resort,
like restless unhappy spirits, taking no pleasure, hanging about like
lowering clouds that linger after a storm, and giving a singular air of
gloom to this otherwise gay metropolis.

The vaunted courtesy of the old school, the smooth urbanity that
prevailed in former days of settled government and long-established

aristocracy; had disappeared amidst the savage republicanism of the revolution, and the military furor of the empire: recent reverses had stung the national vanity to the quick; and English travelers, who crowded to Paris on the return of peace, expecting to meet with a gay, good-humoured, complaisant populace, such as existed in the time of the "Sentimental Journey," were surprized at finding them irritable and fractious, quick at fancying affronts, and not unapt to offer insults. They accordingly inveighed with heat and bitterness at the rudeness they experienced in the French Metropolis: yet what better had they to expect? Had Charles II been reinstated in his Kingdom by the valor of French troops; had he been wheeled triumphantly to London over the trampled bodies and trampled standards of England's bravest sons; had a French general dictated to the English capital, and a French army been quartered in Hyde Park; had Paris poured forth its motley population, and the wealthy bourgeoisie of every French trading town swarmed to London; crowding its squares; filling its streets with their equipages; thronging its fashionable hotels and places of amusements; elbowing its impoverished nobility out of their palaces and opera-boxes, looking down on the humiliated inhabitants as a conquered people; in such a reverse of the case, what degree of courtesy would the populace of London have been apt to exercise toward their visitors?*

On the contrary, I have always admired the degree of magnanimity exhibited by the French on the occupation of their capital by the English. When we consider the military ambition of this nation, its love of glory, the splendid height to which its renown in arms had recently been carried, and with these, the tremendous reverses it had just undergone, its armies shattered, annihilated, its capital captured, garrisoned, and over run, and that too, by its ancient rival the English, toward whom it had cherished for centuries a jealous and almost religious hostility; could we have wondered, of the tiger spirit of this fiery people had broken out in bloody feuds and deadly quarrels; and that they had sought to rid themselves in any way, of their invaders? But it is cowardly nations only, those who dare not wield the sword, that revenge themselves with the lurking dagger. There were no assassinations in Paris. The French had fought valiantly, desperately, in the field; but, when valour was no longer of avail, they submitted like gallant men to a fate they could not withstand. Some instances of insult from the populace were experienced by English

---

* The above remarks were suggested by a conversation with the late Mr. CANNING, whom the author met in Paris, and who expressed himself in the most liberal way concerning the magnanimity of the French on the occupation of their capital by strangers.

visitors; some personal recontres, which led to duels, did take place; but these smacked of open and honorable hostility. No instances of lurking and perfidious revenge occurred, and the British soldier patrolled the streets of Paris safe from treacherous assault.

If the English met with hardships and repulse in social intercourse, it was, in some degree a proof that the people are more sincere than has been represented. The emigrants who had just returned were not yet reinstated. Society was constituted of those who had flourished under the late regimé; the newly ennobled, the recently enriched, who felt their prosperity and their consequence endangered by this change of things. The broken down officer who saw his glory tarnished, his fortune ruined, his occupation gone, could not be expected to look with complacency upon the authors of his downfall. The English visitor, flushed with health, and wealth, and victory, could little enter into the feelings of the blighted warrior, scarred with a hundred battles, an exile from the camp, broken in constitution by the wars, impoverished by the peace, and cast back, a needy stranger in the splendid, but captured metropolis of his country.

> Oh! who can tell what heroes feel
> When all but life and honor's lost!

And here let me notice the conduct of the French soldiery on the dismemberment of the Army of the Loire, when two hundred thousand men were suddenly thrown out of employ; men who had been brought up to the camp, and scarce knew any other home. Few in civil, peaceful life, are aware of the severe trial to the feelings that takes place on the dissolution of a regiment. There is a fraternity in arms. The community of dangers, hardships, enjoyments; the participation in battles and victories; the companionship in adventures at a time of life when men's feelings are most fresh, susceptible, and ardent, all these bind the members of a regiment strongly together. To them the regiment is friends, family, home. They identify themselves with its fortunes, its glories, its disgraces. Imagine this romantic tie suddenly dissolved; the regiment broken up; the occupation of its members gone; their military pride mortified; the career of glory closed behind them; that of obscurity, dependence, want, neglect, perhaps beggary before them. Such was the case with the soldiers of the army of the Loire. They were sent off in squads with officers, to the principal towns where they were to be disarmed and discharged. In this way they passed through the country with arms in their hands, often exposed to slights and scoffs, to hunger and various hardships and privations; but they conducted themselves magnanimously, without any of those out-breaks of violence and wrong that so often attends the dismemberment of armies.

The few years that have elapsed since the time above alluded to, have already had their effect. The proud and angry spirits which then roamed about Paris unemployed, have cooled down, and found occupation. The national character begins to recover its old channels, though worn deeper by recent torrents. The natural urbanity of the French begins to find its way, like oil, to the surface, though there still remains a degree of roughness and bluntness of manner, partly real, and partly affected by such as imagine it to indicate force and frankness. The events of the last thirty years have rendered the French a more reflecting people. They have acquired greater independence of mind and strength of judgement, together with a portion of that prudence which results from experiencing the dangerous consequences of excesses. However that period may have been stained by crimes, and filled with extravagances, the French have certainly come out of it a greater nation than before. One of their own philosophers observes, that in one or two generations the nation will probably combine the ease and elegance of the old character with force and solidity. They were light, he says, before the revolution; then wild and savage; they have become more thoughtful and reflective. It is only old Frenchmen, now-a-days, that are gay and trivial; the young are very serious personages.

P.S. In the course of a morning's walk about the time the above remarks were written, I observed the Duke of Wellington, who was on a brief visit to Paris. He was alone, simply attired in a blue frock; with an umbrella under his arm, and his hat drawn over his eyes, sauntering across the Place Vendome, close by the Column of Napoleon. He gave a glance up at the column as he passed, and continued his loitering way up the Rue de la Paix; stopping occasionally to gaze in at the shop-windows; elbowed now and then by other gazers, who little suspected that the quiet, lounging individual they were jostling so unceremoniously, was the conqueror who had twice entered their capital victoriously; had controlled the destinies of the nation, and eclipsed the glory of the military idol, at the base of whose column he was thus negligently sauntering.

Some years afterwards I was at an evening's entertainment given by the Duke at Apsley House, to William IV. The Duke had manifested his admiration of his great adversary, by having portraits of him in different parts of the house. At the bottom of the grand staircase, stood the colossal statue of the Emperor by Canova. It was of marble, in the antique style, with one arm partly extended, holding a figure of Victory. Over this arm the ladies, in tripping up stairs to the ball, had thrown their shawls. It was a singular office for the statue of Napoleon to perform in the mansion of the Duke of Wellington!

"Imperial Caesar dead and turned to clay," etc., etc.

A CONTENTED MAN!

In the garden of the Tuilleries there is a sunny corner under the wall of a terrace which fronts the South. Along the wall is a range of benches commanding a view of the walks and avenues of the garden. This genial nook is a place of great resort in the latter part of autumn and in fine days in winter, as it seems to retain the flavour of departed summer. On a calm, bright morning it is quite alive with nursery maids and their playful little charges. Hither also resort a number of ancient ladies and gentlemen, of the old school who, with laudable thrift in small pleasures and small expenses, for which the French are to be noted, come here to enjoy sunshine and save firewood. Here may often be seen some cavalier of the old school, when the sunbeams have warmed his blood into something like a glow, fluttering about like a frostbitten moth thawed before the fire, putting forth a feeble show of gallantry among the antiquated dames, and, now and then eying the buxom nursery maids with what might almost be mistaken for an air of libertinism.

Among the habitual frequenters of this place I had often remarked an old gentleman whose dress was decidedly antirevolutional. He wore the three cornered cocked hat of the *ancien regime* his hair was frizzed over each ear into *ailes de pigeon,* a style strongly savouring of bourbonism, and a queue stuck out behind, the loyalty of which was not to be disputed. His dress though ancient had an air of decayed gentility and I observed that he took his snuff out of an elegant, though old fashioned gold box. He appeared to be the most popular man on the walk. He had a compliment for every old lady, he kissed every child, and he patted every little dog on the head, for children and little dogs are very important members of society in France. I must observe, however, that he seldom kissed a child without, at the same time, pinching the nursery maid's cheek; a Frenchman of the old school never forgets his devoirs to the sex.

I had taken a liking to this old gentleman. There was an habitual expression of benevolence in his face, which I have very frequently remarked in these reliques of the politer days of France. The constant interchange of those thousand little courtesies which imperceptibly sweeten life, have a happy effect upon the features and spread a mellow evening charm over the wrinkles of old age.

Where there is a favourable predisposition one soon forms a kind of tacit intimacy by often meeting on the same walks. Once or twice I accommodated him with a bench, after which we touched hats on passing each other, at length we got so far as to take a pinch of snuff together out of his box, which is equivalent to eating salt together in the east; from that time our acquaintance was established.

I now became his frequent companion in his morning promenades and derived much amusement from his good humoured remarks on men and manners. One morning as we were strolling through an alley of the Tuilleries with the Autumnal breeze whirling the yellow leaves about our path, my companion fell into a peculiarly communicative vein, and gave me several particulars of his history. He had once been wealthy and possessed of a fine estate in the country and a noble hotel in Paris; but the revolution, which effected so many disastrous changes, stripped him of every thing. He was secretly denounced by his own steward during a sanguinary period of the revolution, and a number of the bloodhounds of the Convention were sent to arrest him. He received private intelligence of their approach in time to effect his escape. He landed in England without money or friends, but considered himself singularly fortunate in having his head upon his shoulders; several of his neighbours having been gullotined as a punishment for being rich.

When he reached London he had but a Louis in his pocket and no prospect of getting another. He ate a solitary dinner on beefsteak and was almost poisoned by port wine, which from its colour he had mistaken for claret. The dingy look of the chop house and of the little mahogany coloured box in which he ate his dinner, contrasted sadly with the gay saloons of Paris. Every thing looked gloomy and disheartening. Poverty stared him in the face; he turned over the few shillings he had of change; did not know what was to become of him and— went to the theatre.

He took his seat in the pit, listened attentively to a tragedy of which he did not understand a word, and which seemed made up of fighting and stabbing and scene shifting, and began to feel his spirits sinking within him; when, casting his eyes into the orchestra, what was his surprize to recognize an old friend and neighbor in the very act of extorting music from a huge Violincello.

As soon as the evening's performance was over he tapped his friend on the shoulder; they kissed each other on each cheek, and the musician took him home and shared his lodgings with him. He had learnt music as an accomplishment, by his friend's advice he now turned to it as a means of support. He procured a violin, offered himself for the orchestra, was received, and again considered himself one of the most fortunate men upon earth.

Here therefore he lived for many years during the ascendancy of the terrible Napoleon. He found several emigrants living like himself by the exercise of their talents. They associated together, talked of France and of old times, and endeavoured to keep up a semblance of Parisian life in the centre of London.

They dined at a miserable cheap French restaurateur in the neighborhood of Leicester square, where they were served with a caricature of French cookery, they took their promenade in St. James' Park and endeavoured to fancy it the Tuilleries; in short they made shift to accommodate themselves to every thing but an English Sunday. Indeed the old gentleman seemed to have nothing to say against the English, whom he affirmed to be *brave gens,* and he mingled so much among them, that, at the end of twenty years, he could speak their language almost well enough to be understood.

The downfall of Napoleon was another epoch in his life. He had considered himself a fortunate man to make his escape penniless out of France, and he considered himself fortunate to be able to return penniless into it. It is true that he found his parisian Hotel had passed through several hands during the vicissitudes of the times, so as to be beyond the reach of recovery; but then he had been noticed benignantly by government and had a pension of several hundred francs, upon which, with careful management, he lived independently, and, as far as I could judge, happily.

As his once splendid hotel was now occupied as a *hotel garni* he hired a small chambre in the attic; it was but, as he said, changing his bed room up two pair of stairs, he was still in his own house. His room was decorated with pictures of several beauties of former times, with whom he professed to have been on favorable terms: among them was a favorite opera dancer who had been the admiration of Paris at the breaking out of the revolution. She had been a protege of my friend, and one of the few of his youthful favorites who had survived the lapse of time and its various vicissitudes. They had renewed their acquaintance and she now and then visited him, but the beautiful Psyche, once the fashion of the day and the idol of the parterre was now a shrivelled little old woman, warped in the back and with a hooked nose.

The old gentleman was a devout attendant upon levees; he was most zealous in his loyalty and could not speak of the royal family without a burst of enthusiasm, for he still felt towards them as his companions in exile. As to his poverty he made light of it, and indeed had a good-humoured way of consoling himself for every cross and privation. If he had lost his chateau in the country, he had half a dozen royal palaces as it were at his command. He had Versailles and St. Cloud for his country resorts and the shady alleys of the Tuilleries and the Luxembourg for his town recreation. Thus all his promenades and relaxations were magnificent yet cost nothing. When I walk through these fine gardens, said he, I have only to fancy myself the owner of them and they are mine. All these gay crowds are my visitors and I defy the grand signor himself to display a greater variety of beauty. Nay what is better, I have not the trouble of entertaining them. My estate is a perfect *sans souci*, where every one does as he pleases and no one troubles the owner. All Paris is my theatre and presents me with a continual spectacle. I have a table spread for me in every street and thousands of waiters ready to fly at my bidding. When my servants, have waited upon me I pay them, discharge them and there's an end; I have no fears of their wronging or pilfering me when my back is turned. Upon the whole said the old gentleman, with a smile of infinite good humour, when I think upon the various risks I have run and the manner in which I have escaped them; when I recollect all that I have suffered, and consider all that I at present enjoy, I cannot but look upon myself as a man of singular good fortune.

Such was the brief history of this practical philosopher, and it is a picture of many a Frenchman ruined by the Revolution. The French appear to have a greater facility than most men in accommodating themselves to the reverses of life, and of extracting honey out of the bitter things of this world. The first shock of calamity is apt to overwhelm them, but when it is once past, their natural buoyancy of feeling soon brings them to the surface. This may be called the result of levity of character, but it answers the end of reconciling us to misfortune, and if it be not true philosophy, it is something almost as efficacious. Ever since I have heard the story of my little Frenchman, I have treasured it up in my heart; and I thank my stars I have at length found, what I had long considered as not to be found on earth—a contented man.

———

P.S. There is no calculating on human happiness. Since writing the foregoing, the law of indemnity has been passed, and my friend restored to a great part of his fortune. I was absent from Paris at the time, but on my return hastened to congratulate him. I found him magnificently lodged on the first floor of his hotel. I was ushered, by a servant in livery, through splendid saloons, to a cabinet richly furnished, where I found my little Frenchman reclining on a couch. He received me with his usual cordiality; but I saw the gaiety and benevolence of his countenance had fled; he had an eye full of care and anxiety.

I congratulated him on his good fortune. "Good fortune?" echoed he; "bah! I have been plundered of a princely fortune, and they gave me a pittance as an indemnity."

Alas! I found my late poor and contented friend one of the richest and most miserable men in Paris. Instead of rejoicing in the ample competency restored to him, he is daily repining at the superfluity withheld. He no longer wanders in happy idleness about Paris, but is a repining attendant in the anti-chambers of ministers. His loyalty has evaporated with his gaiety; he screws his mouth when the Bourbons are mentioned, and even shrugs his shoulders when he hears the praises of the king. In a word, he is one of the many philosophers undone by the law of indemnity, and his case is desperate, for I doubt whether even another reverse of fortune, which should restore him to poverty, could make him again a happy man.

BROEK
THE DUTCH PARADISE

THE DUTCH PARADISE

It has long been a matter of discussion and controversy among the pious and the learned, as to the situation of the terrestrial paradise whence our first parents were exiled. This question has been put to rest by certain of the faithful in Holland, who have decided in favor of the village of BROEK, about six miles from Amsterdam. It may not, they observe, correspond in all respects to the description of the Garden of Eden, handed down from days of yore, but it comes nearer to their ideas of a perfect paradise than any other place on earth.

This eulogium induced me to make some inquiries as to this favoured spot, in the course of a sojourn at the City of Amsterdam, and the information I procured fully justified the enthusiastic praises I had heard. The village of Broek is situated in Waterland, in the midst of the greenest and richest pastures of Holland; I may say, of Europe. These pastures are the source of its wealth, for it is famous for its dairies, and for those oval cheeses which regale and perfume the whole civilized world. The population consists of about six hundred persons, comprising several families which have inhabited the place since time immemorial; and have waxed rich on the products of their meadows. They keep all their wealth among themselves; intermarrying, and keeping all strangers at a wary distance. They are a "hard money" people, and remarkable for turning the penny the right way. It is said to have been an old rule established by one of the primitive financiers and legislators of Broek, that no one should leave the village with more than six guilders in his pocket, or return with less than ten; a shrewd regulation, well worthy the attention of modern political economists, who are so anxious to fix the balance of trade.

What, however, renders Broek so perfect an elysium, in the eyes of all true Hollanders, is the matchless height to which the spirit of cleanliness is carried here. It amounts almost to a religion among the inhabitants, who pass the greater part of their time rubbing and scrubbing, and painting and varnishing: each housewife vies with her neighbor in her devotion to the scrubbing-brush, as zealous Catholics do in their devotion to the cross; and it is said, a notable housewife of the place in days of yore, is held in pious remembrance, and almost canonized as a saint, for having died of pure exhaustion and chagrin, in an ineffectual attempt to scour a black man white.

These particulars awakened my ardent curiosity to see a place which I pictured to myself the very fountain-head of certain hereditary habits and customs prevalent among the descendants of the original Dutch settlers of my native state. I accordingly lost no time in performing a pilgrimage to Broek.

Before I reached the place, I beheld symptoms of the tranquil character of its inhabitants. A little clump-built boat was in full sail along the lazy bosom of a canal, but its sail consisted of the blades of two paddles stood on end, while the navigator sat steering with a third paddle in the stern, crouched down like a toad, with a slouched hat drawn over his eyes. I presumed him to be some nautical lover, on the way to his mistress. After proceeding a little farther, I came in sight of the harbor or port of destination of this drowsy navigator. This was the Broeken-Meer, an artificial basin, or sheet of olive-green water, tranquil as a mill-pond. On this the village of the Broek is situated, and the borders are laboriously decorated with flower-beds, box-trees clipped into all kinds of ingenious shapes and fancies, and little "lust" houses, or pavilions.

I alighted outside of the village, for no horse nor vehicle is permitted to enter its precincts, lest it should cause defilement of the well-scoured pavements. Shaking the dust off my feet, therefore, I prepared to enter, with due reverence and circumspection, this *sanctum sanctorum* of Dutch cleanliness. I entered by a narrow street, paved with yellow bricks, laid edgewise, and so clean that one might eat from them. Indeed, they were actually worn deep, not by the tread of feet, but by the friction of the scrubbing-brush.

The houses were built of wood, and all appeared to have been freshly painted, of green, yellow, and other bright colors. They were separated from each other by gardens and orchards, and stood at some little distance from the street, with wide areas or court-yards, paved in mosaic, with variegated stones, polished by frequent rubbing. The areas were divided from the street by curiously-wrought railings, or balustrades, of iron, surmounted with brass and copper balls, scoured into dazzling effulgence. The very trunks of the trees in front of the houses were by the same process made to look as if they had been varnished. The porches, doors, and window-frames of the houses were of exotic woods, curiously carved, and polished like costly furniture. The front doors are never opened, excepting on christenings, marriages, or funerals: on all ordinary occasions, visitors enter by the back door. In former times, persons when admitted had to put on slippers, but this oriental ceremony is no longer insisted upon.

A poor devil Frenchman, who attended upon me as ciceroné, boasted with some degree of exultation, of a triumph of his countrymen over the stern regulations of the place. During the time that Holland was overrun with armies of the French republic, a French general, surrounded by his whole état major, who had come from Amsterdam to view the wonders of Broek, applied for admission at one of these taboo'd portals. The reply was, that the owner never received any one who did not come introduced by some friend. "Very well," said the general: "take my compliments to your master, and tell him I will return here to-morrow with a company of soldiers, '*pour parler raison avec mon ami Hollandais.*'" Terrified at the idea of having a company of soldiers billeted upon him, the owner threw open his house, entertained the general and his retinue with unwonted hospitality; though it is said it cost the family a month's scrubbing and scouring, to restore all things to exact order, after this military invasion. My vagabond informant seemed to consider this one of the greatest victories of the republic.

I walked about the place in mute wonder and admiration. A dead stillness prevailed around, like that in the deserted streets of Pompeii. No sign of life was to be seen, excepting now and then a hand, and a long pipe, and an occasional puff of smoke, out of the window of some "lust-haus" overhanging a miniature canal; and on approaching a little nearer, the periphery in profile of some robustious burgher.

Among the grand houses pointed out to me, were those of Claes Bakker, and Cornelius Bakker, richly carved and gilded, with flower-gardens and clipped shrubberies; and that of the Great Ditmus, who, my poor devil cicerone informed me, in a whisper, was worth two millions; all these were mansions shut up from the world, and only kept to be cleaned. After having been conducted from one wonder to another of the village, I was ushered by my guide into the grounds and gardens of Mynheer Broekker, another mighty cheese-manufacturer, worth eighty thousand guilders a year. I had repeatedly been struck with the similarity of all that I had seen in this amphibious little village, to the buildings and landscapes on Chinese platters and tea-pots; but here I found the similarity complete; for I was told that these gardens were modelled upon Van Bramm's description of those of Yuen min Yuen, in China. Here were serpentine walks, with trellised borders; winding canals, with fanciful Chinese bridges; flower beds resembling huge baskets, with the flower of "love lies bleeding" falling over to the ground. But mostly had the fancy of Mynheer Broekker been displayed about a stagnant little lake, on which a corpulent little pinnace lay at anchor. On the border was a cottage, within which were a wooden man and woman seated at table, and a wooden dog beneath, all the size of life: on pressing a spring, the woman commenced spinning, and the dog barked furiously. On the lake were wooden swans, painted to the life: some floating, others on the nest among the rushes; while a wooden sportsman, crouched among the bushes, was preparing his gun to take deadly aim. In another part of the garden was a dominie in his clerical robes, with wig, pipe, and cocked hat; and mandarins with nodding heads, amid red lions, green tigers, and blue hares. Last of all, the heathen deities, in wood and plaster, male and female, naked and bare-faced as usual, and seeming to stare with wonder at finding themselves in such strange company.

My shabby French guide, while he pointed out all these mechanical marvels of the garden, was anxious to let me see that he had too polite a taste to be pleased by them. At every new nick-nack he would screw down his mouth, shrug up his shoulders, take a pinch of snuff and exclaim: *"Ma foi, Monsieur, ces Hollandais sont forts pour ces betises la!"*

To attempt to gain admission to any of these stately abodes was out of the question having no company of soldiers to enforce a solicitation. I was fortunate enough, however, through the aid of my guide, to make my way into the kitchen of the illustrious Ditmus, and I question whether the parlor would have proved more worthy of observation. The cook, a little wiry, hook-nosed woman, worn thin by incessant action and friction, was bustling about among her kettles and sauce-pans, with the scullion at her heels, both clattering in wooden shoes, which were as clean and white as the milk-pails; rows of vessels, of brass and copper, regiments of pewter dishes, and portly porringers, gave resplendent evidence of the intensity of their cleanliness; the very trammels and hangers in the fire-place were highly scoured, and the burnished face of the good Saint Nicholas shone forth from the iron plate of the chimney-back.

Among the decorations of the kitchen, was a printed sheet of wood-cuts, representing the various holiday customs of Holland, with explanatory rhymes. Here I was delighted to recognize the jollities of New-Year's day; the festivities of Paäs and Pinkster, and all the other merry-makings handed down in my native place from the earliest times of New-Amsterdam, and which had been such bright spots in the year, in my childhood. I eagerly made myself master of this precious document, for a trifling consideration, and bore it off as a memento of the place; though I question if, in so doing, I did not carry off with me the whole current literature of Broek.

I must not omit to mention, that this village is the paradise of cows as well as men: indeed you would almost suppose the cow to be as much an object of worship here, as the bull was among the ancient Egyptians; and well does she merit it, for she is in fact the patroness of the place. The same scrupulous cleanliness, however, which pervades every thing else, is manifested in the treatment of this venerated animal. She is not permitted to perambulate the place, but in winter, when she forsakes the rich pasture, a well-built house is provided for her, well painted, and maintained in the most perfect order. Her stall is of ample dimensions; the floor is scrubbed and polished; her hide is daily curried and brushed, and sponged to her heart's content, and her tail is daintily tucked up to the ceiling, and decorated with a ribband!

On my way back through the village, I passed the house of the prediger, or preacher; a very comfortable mansion, which led me to augur well of the state of religion in the village. On inquiry, I was told that for a long time the inhabitants lived in a great state of indifference as to religious matters: it was in vain that their preachers endeavored to arouse their thoughts as to a future state: the joys of heaven, as commonly depicted, were but little to their taste. At length a dominie appeared among them, who struck out in a different vein. He depicted the New Jerusalem as a place all smooth and level; with beautiful dykes, and ditches, and canals; and houses all shining with paint and varnish, and glazed tiles; and where there should never come horse, nor ass, nor cat, nor dog, nor anything that could make noise or dirt; but there should be nothing but rubbing and scrubbing, and washing and painting, and gilding and varnishing, for ever and ever, amen! Since that time, the good housewives of Broek have all turned their faces Zion-ward.

GUESTS FROM GIBBET-ISLAND

A LEGEND OF COMMUNIPAW

FOUND AMONG THE KNICKERBOCKER PAPERS AT WOLFERT'S ROOST

Whoever has visited the ancient and renowned village of Communipaw, may have noticed an old stone building, of most ruinous and sinister appearance. The doors and window-shutters are ready to drop from their hinges; old clothes are stuffed in the broken panes of glass, while legions of half-starved dogs prowl about the premises, and rush out and bark at every passer by; for your beggarly house in a village is most apt to swarm with profligate and ill-conditioned dogs. What adds to the sinister appearance of this mansion, is a tall frame in front, not a little resembling a gallows, and which looks as if waiting to accommodate some of the inhabitants with a well-merited airing. It is not a gallows, however, but an ancient sign-post; for this dwelling, in the golden days of Communipaw, was one of the most orderly and peaceful of village taverns, where public affairs were talked and smoked over. In fact, it was in this very building that Oloffe the Dreamer, and his companions, concerted that great voyage of discovery and colonization, in which they explored Buttermilk Channel, were nearly shipwrecked in the strait of Hell-gate, and finally landed on the island of Manhattan, and founded the great city of New-Amsterdam.

Even after the province had been cruelly wrested from the sway of their High Mightinesses, by the combined forces of the British and the Yankees, this tavern continued its ancient loyalty. It is true, the head of the Prince of Orange disappeared from the sign; a strange bird being painted over it, with the explanatory legend of "DIE WILDE GANS," or The Wild Goose; but this all the world knew to be a sly riddle of the landlord, the worthy Teunis Van Gieson, a knowing man in a small way, who laid his finger beside his nose and winked, when any one studied the signification of his sign, and observed that his goose was hatching, but would join the flock whenever they flew over the water; an enigma which was the perpetual recreation and delight of the loyal but fat-headed burghers of Communipaw.

Under the sway of this patriotic, though discreet and quiet publican, the tavern continued to flourish in primeval tranquillity, and was the resort of true-hearted Nederlanders, from all parts of Pavonia; who met here quietly and secretly, to smoke and drink the downfall of Briton and Yankee, and success to Admiral Van Tromp.

The only drawback on the comfort of the establishment, was a

147

nephew of mine host, a sister's son, Yan Yost Vanderscamp by name, and a real scamp by nature. This unlucky whipster showed an early propensity to mischief, which he gratified in a small way, by playing tricks upon the frequenters of the Wild Goose; putting gunpowder in their pipes, or squibs in their pockets, and astonishing them with an explosion, while they sat nodding round the fire-place in the bar-room; and if perchance a worthy burgher from some distant part of Pavonia lingered until dark over his potation, it was odds but young Vander-scamp would slip a briar under his horse's tail, as he mounted, and send him clattering along the road, in neck-or-nothing style, to the infinite astonishment and discomfiture of the rider.

It may be wondered at, that mine host of the Wild Goose did not turn such a graceless varlet out of doors; but Teunis Van Gieson was an easy-tempered man, and, having no child of his own, looked upon his nephew with almost parental indulgence. His patience and good nature were doomed to be tried by another inmate of his mansion. This was a cross-grained curmudgeon of a negro, named Pluto, who was a kind of enigma in Communipaw. Where he came from, nobody knew. He was found one morning, after a storm, cast like a sea-monster on the strand, in front of the Wild Goose, and lay there, more dead than alive. The neighbors gathered round, and speculated on this production of the deep; whether it were fish or flesh, or a compound of both, commonly yclept a merman. The kind-hearted Teunis Van Giesen, seeing that he wore the human form, took him into his house, and warmed him into life. By degrees, he showed signs of intelligence, and even uttered sounds very much like language, but which no one in Communipaw could understand. Some thought him a negro just from Guinea, who had either fallen overboard, or escaped from a slave-ship. Nothing, however, could ever draw from him any account of his origin. When questioned on the subject, he merely pointed to Gibbet-Island, a small rocky islet, which lies in the open bay, just opposite Communi-paw, as if that were his native place, though every body knew it had never been inhabited.

In the process of time, he acquired something of the Dutch language, that is to say, he learnt all its vocabulary of oaths and maledictions, with just words sufficient to string them together, "Donder en blick-sem!" (thunder and lightning,) was the gentlest of his ejaculations. For years he kept about the Wild Goose, more like one of those famil-iar spirits, or household goblins, we read of, than like a human being. He acknowledged allegiance to no one, but performed various domestic offices, when it suited his humor; waiting occasionally on the guests; grooming the horses, cutting wood, drawing water; and all this with-out being ordered. Lay any command on him, and the stubborn sea-urchin was sure to rebel. He was never so much at home, however, as when on the water, plying about in skiff or canoe, entirely alone, fishing, crabbing, or grabbing for oysters, and would bring home quantities for the larder of the Wild Goose, which he would throw down at the kitchen door, with a growl. No wind nor weather deterred him from launching forth on his favorite element: indeed, the wilder the weather, the more he seemed to enjoy it. If a storm was brewing, he was sure to put off from shore; and would be seen far out in the bay, his light skiff dancing like a feather on the waves, when sea and sky were in a turmoil, and the stoutest ships were fain to lower their sails. Sometimes, on such occasions, he would be absent for days together. How he weathered the tempest, and how and where he subsisted, no one could divine, nor did any one venture to ask, for all had an almost superstitious awe of him. Some of the Communipaw oystermen declared they had more than once seen him suddenly disappear, canoe and all, as if plunged beneath the waves, and after a while come up again, in quite a different part of the bay; whence they concluded that he could live under water like a notable species of wild duck, commonly called the Hell-diver. All began to consider him in the light of foul-weather bird, like the Mother Carey's Chicken, or Stormy Petrel; and whenever they saw him putting far out in his skiff, in cloudy weather, made up their minds for a storm.

The only being for whom he seemed to have any liking, was Yan Yost Vanderscamp, and him he liked for his very wickedness. He in a manner took the boy under his tutelage, prompted him to all kinds of mischief, aided him in every wild harum-scarum freak, until the lad became the complete scape-grace of the village; a pest to his uncle, and to every one else. Nor were his pranks confined to the land; he soon learned to accompany old Pluto on the water. Together these worthies would cruise about the broad bay, and all the neighboring straits and rivers; poking around in skiffs and canoes; robbing the set nets of the fishermen; landing on remote coasts, and laying waste orchards and water-melon patches; in short, carrying on a complete system of piracy, on a small scale. Piloted by Pluto, the youthful Vanderscamp soon became acquainted with all the bays, rivers, creeks, and inlets of the watery world around him; could navigate from the Hook to Spiting-devil on the darkest night, and learned to set even the terrors of Hell-gate at defiance.

At length, negro and boy suddenly disappeared, and days and weeks elapsed, but without tidings of them. Some said they must have run away and gone to sea; others jocosely hinted, that old Pluto, being no other than his namesake in disguise, had spirited away the boy to the nether regions. All, however, agreed on one thing, that the village was well rid of them.

In the process of time, the good Teunis Van Gieson slept with his fathers, and the tavern remained shut up, waiting for a claimant, for the next heir was Yan Yost Vanderscamp, and he had not been heard of for years. At length, one day, a boat was seen pulling for shore, from a long, black, rakish-looking schooner, that lay at anchor in the bay. The boat's crew seemed worthy of the craft from which they debarked. Never had such a set of noisy, roistering, swaggering varlets landed in peaceful Communipaw. They were outlandish in garb and demeanor, and were headed by a rough, burly, bully ruffian, with fiery whiskers, a copper nose, a scar across his face, and a great Flaunderish beaver slouched on one side of his head, in whom, to their dismay, the quiet inhabitants were made to recognise their early pest, Yan Yost Vanderscamp. The rear of this hopeful gang was brought up by old Pluto, who had lost an eye, grown grizzly-headed, and looked more like a devil than ever. Vanderscamp renewed his acquaintance with the old burghers, much against their will, and in a manner not at all to their taste. He slapped them familiarly on the back, gave them an iron grip of the hand, and was hail fellow well met. According to his own account, he had been all the world over; had made money by bags full; had ships in every sea, and now meant to turn the Wild Goose into a country seat, where he and his comrades, all rich merchants from foreign parts, might enjoy themselves in the interval of their voyages.

Sure enough, in a little while there was a complete metamorphose of the Wild Goose. From being a quiet, peaceful Dutch public house, it became a most riotous, uproarious private dwelling; a complete rendezvous for boisterous men of the seas, who came here to have what they called a "blow out" on dry land, and might be seen at all hours, lounging about the door, or lolling out of the windows; swearing among themselves, and cracking rough jokes on every passer by. The house was fitted up, too, in so strange a manner: hammocks slung to the walls, instead of bedsteads; odd kinds of furniture, of foreign fashion; bamboo couches, Spanish chairs; pistols, cutlasses, and blunderbusses, suspended on every peg; silver crucifixes on the mantle-pieces, silver candle-sticks and porringers on the tables, contrasting oddly with the pewter and Delf ware of the original establishment. And then the strange amusements of these sea-monsters! Pitching Spanish dollars, instead of quoits; firing blunderbusses out of the window; shooting at a mark, or at any unhappy dog, or cat, or pig, or barn-door fowl, that might happen to come within reach.

The only being who seemed to relish their rough waggery, was old

Pluto; and yet he led but a dog's life of it; for they practised all kinds of manual jokes upon him; kicked him about like a foot-ball; shook him by his grizly mop of wool, and never spoke to him without coupling a curse by way of adjective to his name, and consigning him to the infernal regions. The old fellow, however, seemed to like them the better, the more they cursed him, though his utmost expression of pleasure never amounted to more than the growl of a petted bear, when his ears are rubbed.

Old Pluto was the ministering spirit at the orgies of the Wild Goose; and such orgies as took place there! Such drinking, singing, whooping, swearing; with an occasional interlude of quarrelling and fighting. The noisier grew the revel, the more old Pluto plied the potations, until the guests would become frantic in their merriment, smashing every thing to pieces, and throwing the house out of the windows. Sometimes, after a drinking bout, they sallied forth and scoured the village, to the dismay of the worthy burghers, who gathered their women within doors, and would have shut up the house. Vanderscamp, however, was not to be rebuffed. He insisted on renewing acquaintance with his old neighbors, and on introducing his friends, the merchants, to their families; swore he was on the look-out for a wife, and meant, before he stopped, to find husbands for all their daughters. So, will-ye nill-ye, sociable he was; swaggered about their best parlors, with his hat on one side of his head; sat on the good wife's nicely-waxed mahogany table, kicking his heels against the carved and polished legs; kissed and tousled the young vrouws; and, if they frowned and pouted, gave them a gold rosary, or a sparkling cross, to put them in good humor again.

Sometimes nothing would satisfy him, but he must have some of his old neighbors to dinner at the Wild Goose. There was no refusing him, for he had the complete upper hand of the community, and the peaceful burghers all stood in awe of him. But what a time would the quiet and worthy men have, among these rake-hells, who would delight to astound them with the most extravagant gunpowder tales, embroidered with all kinds of foreign oaths; clink the can with them; pledge them in deep potations; bawl drinking songs in their ears; and occasionally fire pistols over their heads, or under the table, and then laugh in their faces, and ask them how they liked the smell of gunpowder.

Thus was the little village of Communipaw for a time like the unfortunate wight possessed with devils; until Vanderscamp and his brother merchants would sail on another trading voyage, when the Wild Goose would be shut up, and every thing relapse into quiet, only to be disturbed by his next visitation.

The mystery of all these proceedings gradually dawned upon the

tardy intellects of Communipaw. These were the times of the notorious
Captain Kidd when the American harbors were the resorts of piratical
adventures of all kinds, who, under pretext of mercantile voyages, scoured
the West Indies, made plundering descents upon the Spanish main,
visited even the remote Indian Seas, and then came to dispose of their
booty; have their feasts and fit out new expeditions, in the English
colonies.

Vanderscamp had served in this hopeful school, and having risen
to importance among the buccaneers, had pitched upon his native
village and early home, as a quiet, out of the way, unsuspected place,
where he and his comrades while anchored at New York might have
their feasts, and concert their plans without molestation.

At length the attention of the British government was called to these
piratical enterprises that were becoming so frequent and outrageous.
Vigorous measures were taken to check and punish them. Several of
the most noted freebooters were caught and executed, and three of
Vanderscamp's chosen comrades, the most riotous swash bucklers of the
Wild Goose, were hanged in chains, on Gibbet Island, in full sight
of their favorite resort. As to Vanderscamp himself, he and his man
Pluto again disappeared, and it was hoped by the people of Communipaw that he had fallen in some foreign brawl, or been swung on some
foreign gallows.

For a time, therefore, the tranquility of the village was restored; the
worthy Dutchmen once more smoked their pipes in peace, eyeing with
peculiar complacency their old pests and terrors the pirates dangling
and drying in the sun on Gibbet Island.

This perfect calm was doomed at length to be ruffled. The fiery per-
secution of the pirates gradually subsided. Justice was satisfied with
the examples that had been made, and there was no more talk of
Kidd and the other heroes of like kidney. On a calm summer evening
a boat, somewhat heavily laden, was seen pulling into Communipaw.
What was the surprize and disquiet of the inhabitants to see Yan Yost
Vanderscamp at the helm and his man Pluto tugging at the oar. Vanderscamp, however, was apparently an altered man. He brought home with
him a wife, who seemed to be a shrew, and to have the upper hand of
him. He no longer was the swaggering bully ruffian, but affected the
regular merchant, and talked of retiring from business and settling
down quietly to pass the rest of his days in his native place.

The Wild goose mansion was again opened, but with diminished
splendor and no riot. It is true Vanderscamp had frequent nautical
visitors and the sound of revelry was occasionally overheard in his
house, but every thing seemed to be done under the rose, and old Pluto
was the only servant that officiated at these orgies. The visitors indeed

were by no means of the turbulent stamp of their predecessors; but quiet mysterious traders, full of nods and winks and hyeroglyphic signs with whom to use their cant phraze "every thing was smug." Their ships came to anchor at night in the lower bay, and, on a private signal, Vanderscamp would launch his boat, and, accompanied solely by his man Pluto, would make them mysterious visits. Sometimes boats pulled in at night, in front of the Wild Goose, and various articles of merchandize were landed in the dark and spirited away, no body knew whither. One of the more curious of the inhabitants kept watch and caught a glimpse of the features of some of these night visitors, by the casual glance of a lantern, and declared that he recognized more than one of the free booting frequenters of the Wild goose in former times; whence he concluded that Vanderscamp was at his old game, and that this mysterious merchandize was nothing more nor less than piratical plunder.

The more charitable opinion, however, was, that Vanderscamp and his comrades, having been driven from their old line of business by the "oppressions of government," had resorted to smuggling to make both ends meet. Be that as it may; I come now to the extraordinary fact, which is the butt end of this story. It happened late one night that Yan Yost Vanderscamp was returning across the broad bay in his light skiff, rowed by his man Pluto. He had been carousing on board of a vessel, newly arrived, and was somewhat obfuscated in intellect, by the liquor he had imbibed. It was a still sultry night; a heavy mass of lurid clouds was rising in the west, with the low muttering of distant thunder. Vanderscamp called on Pluto to pull lustily that they might get home before the gathering storm. The old negro made no reply, but shaped his course so as to skirt the rocky shores of Gibbet Island. A faint creaking over head caused Vanderscamp to cast up his eyes, when, to his horror he beheld the bodies of his three pot companions and brothers in iniquity dangling in the moon light, their rags fluttering and their chains creaking as they were slowly swung back ward and forward by the rising breeze.

"What do you mean you blockhead," cried Vanderscamp, "by pulling so close to the island."

"I thought you'd be glad to see your old friends once more," growled the negro. "You were never afraid of a living man, what do you fear from the dead!"

"Who's afraid!" hiccupped Vanderscamp, partly heated by liquor, partly nettled by the jeer of the negro— "Who's afraid! Hang me but I would be glad to see them once more, alive or dead, at the Wild goose. Come my lads in the wind," continued he, taking a draught and flourishing the bottle above his head, "here's fair weather to you in the

other world; and if you should be walking the rounds to night, odds
fish but I'll be happy if you will drop in to supper."

A dismal creaking was the only reply. The wind blew loud and shrill,
and as it whistled round the gallows and among the bones, sounded
as if they were laughing and gibbering in the air. Old Pluto chuckled
to himself, and now pulled for home. The storm burst over the voyagers
while they were yet far from shore. The rain fell in torrents, the thunder
crashed and pealed and the lightning kept up an incessant blaze. It
was stark midnight before they landed at Communipaw.

Dripping and shivering Vanderscamp crawled homeward. He was
completely sobered by the storm; the water soaked from without, having
diluted and cooled the liquor within. Arrived at the Wild Goose, he
knocked timidly and dubiously at the door, for he dreaded the reception
he was to experience from his wife. He had reason to do so. She met
him at the threshold, in a precious ill humor.

"Is this a time," she said, "to keep people out of their beds, and to
bring home company, to turn the house upside down?"

" 'Company?' said Vanderscamp, meekly; 'I have brought no company
with me, wife."

"No indeed! they have got here before you, but by your invitation;
and blessed looking company they are, truly!"

Vanderscamp's knees smote together, "For the love of heaven, where
are they, wife?"

"Where?—why in the blue room, up stairs, making themselves as much
at home as if the house were their own."

Vanderscamp made a desperate effort, scrambled up to the room,
and threw open the door. Sure enough, there at a table, on which burned
a light as blue as brimstone, sat the three guests from Gibbet-Island,
with halters round their necks, and bobbing their cups together, as if
they were hob-or-nobbing, and trolling the old Dutch freebooter's glee,
since translated into English:

> "For three merry lads be we,
> And three merry lads be we;
> I on the land, and thou on the sand,
> And Jack on the gallows-tree."

Vanderscamp saw and heard no more. Starting back with horror, he
missed his footing on the landing place, and fell from the top of the
stairs to the bottom. He was taken up speechless, and either from the
fall or the fright, was buried in the yard of the little Dutch church at
Bergen, on the following Sunday.

From that day forward, the fate of the Wild Goose was sealed. It was pronounced a *haunted house,* and avoided accordingly. No one inhabited it but Vanderscamp's shrew of a widow, and old Pluto, and they were considered but little better than its hobgoblin visitors. Pluto grew more and more haggard and morose, and looked more like an imp of darkness than a human being. He spoke to no one, but went about muttering to himself; or, as some hinted, talking with the devil, who, though unseen, was ever at his elbow. Now and then he was seen pulling about the bay alone, in his skiff, in dark weather, or at the approach of night-fall; nobody could tell why, unless on an errand to invite more guests from the gallows. Indeed it was affirmed that the Wild Goose still continued to be a house of entertainment for such guests, and that on stormy nights, the blue chamber was occasionally illuminated, and sounds of diabolical merriment were overheard, mingling with the howling of the tempest. Some treated these as idle stories, until on one such night, it was about the time of the equinox, there was a horrible uproar in the Wild Goose, that could not be mistaken. It was not so much the sound of revelry, however, as strife, with two or three piercing shrieks, that pervaded every part of the village. Nevertheless, no one thought of hastening to the spot. On the contrary, the honest burghers of Communipaw drew their night-caps over their ears, and buried their heads under the bed-clothes, at the thoughts of Vanderscamp and his gallows companions.

The next morning, some of the bolder and more curious undertook to reconnoitre. All was quiet and lifeless at the Wild Goose. The door yawned wide open, and had evidently been open all night, for the storm had beaten into the house. Gathering more courage from the silence and apparent desertion, they gradually ventured over the threshold. The house had indeed the air of having been possessed by devils. Everything was topsy turvy; trunks had been broken open, and chests of drawers and corner cup-boards turned inside out, as in a time of general sack and pillage; but the most woeful sight was the widow of Yan Yost Vanderscamp, extended a corpse on the floor of the blue chamber, with the marks of a deadly gripe on the wind-pipe.

All now was conjecture and dismay at Communipaw: and the disappearance of old Pluto, who was no where to be found, gave rise to all kinds of wild surmises. Some suggested that the negro had betrayed the house to some of Vanderscamp's buccaneering associates, and that they had decamped together with the booty; others surmised that the negro was nothing more nor less than a devil incarnate, who had now accomplished his ends and made off with his dues.

Events, however, vindicated the negro from this last imputation. His skiff was picked up drifting about the bay bottom upward, as if wrecked in a tempest; and his body was found, shortly afterward by some Communipaw fishermen stranded among the rocks of Gibbet island, near the foot of the pirates' gallows. The fishermen shook their heads and observed that old Pluto had ventured once too often, to invite guests from Gibbet Island.

THE EARLY EXPERIENCES OF RALPH RINGWOOD

NOTED DOWN FROM HIS CONVERSATIONS: BY GEOFFREY CRAYON, GENT.*

"I am a Kentuckian by residence and choice, but a Virginian by birth. The cause of my first leaving the 'Ancient Dominion,' and emigrating to Kentucky, was a jackass! You stare, but have a little patience, and I'll soon show you how it came to pass. My father, who was of one of the old Virginian families, resided in Richmond. He was a widower, and his domestic affairs were managed by a house-keeper of the old school, such as used to administer the concerns of opulent Virginian households. She was a dignitary that almost rivalled my father in importance, and seemed to think every thing belonged to her; in fact she was so considerate in her economy, and so careful of expense, as sometimes to vex my father; who would swear she was disgracing him by her meanness. She always appeared with that ancient insignia of house-keeping trust and authority, a great bunch of keys jingling at her girdle. She superintended the arrangements of the table at every meal, and saw that the dishes were all placed according to her primitive notions of symmetry. In the evening she took her stand and served out tea with a mingled respectfulness and pride of station, truly exemplary. Her great ambition was to have every thing in order, and that the establishment under her sway should be cited as a model of good house-keeping. If any thing went wrong, poor old Barbara would take it to heart, and sit in her room and cry; until a few chapters in the Bible would quiet her spirits, and make all calm again. The Bible, in fact, was her constant resort in time of trouble. She opened it indiscriminately, and whether she chanced among the Lamentations of Jeremiah, the Canticles of Solomon, or the rough enumeration of the tribes in Deuteronomy, a chapter was a chapter, and operated like balm to her soul. Such was our good old house-keeper Barbara; who was destined, unwittingly, to have a most important effect upon my destiny.

"It came to pass, during the days of my juvenility, while I was yet what is termed 'an unlucky boy,' that a gentleman of our neighborhood,

---

* RALPH RINGWOOD, though a fictitious name, is a real personage: the late Governor Duval of Florida. I have given some anecdotes of his early and eccentric career in, as nearly as I can recollect, the very words in which he related them. They certainly afforded strong temptations to the embellishments of fiction; but I thought them so strikingly characteristic of the individual, and of the scenes and society into which his peculiar humors carried him, that I preferred giving them in their original simplicity.   G.C.

a great advocate for experiments and improvements of all kinds, took it into his head that it would be an immense public advantage to introduce a breed of mules, and accordingly imported three jacks to stock the neighborhood. This in a part of the country where the people cared for nothing but blood horses! Why, Sir! they would have considered their mares disgraced, and their whole stud dishonored, by such a misalliance. The whole matter was a town-talk, and a town scandal. The worthy amalgamator of quadrupeds found himself in a dismal scrape: so he backed out in time, abjured the whole doctrine of amalgamation, and turned his jacks loose to shift for themselves upon the town common. There they used to run about and lead an idle, good-for-nothing, holiday life, the happiest animals in the country.

"It so happened, that my way to school lay across the common. The first time that I saw one of these animals, it set up a braying and frightened me confoundedly. However, I soon got over my fright, and seeing that it had something of a horse look, my Virginian love for any thing of the equestrian species predominated, and I determined to back it. I accordingly applied at a grocer's shop, procured a cord that had been round a loaf of sugar, and made a kind of halter; then summoning some of my school-fellows, we drove master Jack about the common until we hemmed him in an angle of a 'worm fence.' After some difficulty, we fixed the halter round his muzzle, and I mounted. Up flew his heels, away I went over his head, and off he scampered. However, I was on my legs in a twinkling, gave chase, caught him and remounted. By dint of repeated tumbles, I soon learned to stick to his back, so that he could no more cast me than he could his own skin. From that time, master Jack and his companions had a scampering life of it, for we all rode them between school hours, and on holiday afternoons; and you may be sure school boys' nags are never permitted to suffer the grass to grow under their feet. They soon became so knowing, that they took to their heels at sight of a school-boy; and we were generally much longer in chasing than we were in riding them.

"Sunday approached, on which I projected an equestrian excursion on one of these long-eared steeds. As I knew the jacks would be in great demand on Sunday morning, I secured one over night, and conducted him home, to be ready for an early outset. But where was I to quarter him for the night? I could not put him in the stable: our old black groom George was as absolute in that domain as Barbara was within doors, and would have thought his stable, his horses, and himself disgraced, by the introduction of a jackass. I recollected the smoke-house; an outbuilding appended to all Virginian establishments for the smoking of hams, and other kinds of meat. So I got the key, put master Jack in, locked the door, returned the key to its place, and went to bed, intending to release my prisoner at an early hour, before any of the family were awake. I was so tired, however, by the exertions I had made in catching the donkey, that I fell into a sound sleep, and the morning broke without my waking.

"Not so with dame Barbara, the house-keeper. As usual, to use her own phrase, 'she was up before the crow put his shoes on,' and bustled about to get things in order for breakfast. Her first resort was to the smoke-house. Scarce had she opened the door, when master Jack, tired of his confinement, and glad to be released from darkness, gave a loud bray, and rushed forth. Down dropped old Barbara; the animal trampled over her, and made off for the common. Poor Barbara! She had never before seen a donkey, and having read in the Bible that the Devil went about like a roaring lion seeking whom he might devour, she took it for granted that this was Beelzebub himself. The kitchen was soon in a hubbub; the servants hurried to the spot. There lay old Barbara in fits; as fast as she got out of one, the thoughts of the devil came over her, and she fell into another, for the good soul was devoutly superstitious.

"As ill luck would have it, among those attracted by the noise, was a little cursed fidgetty, crabbed uncle of mine; one of those uneasy spirits, that cannot rest quietly in their beds in the morning, but must be up early, to bother the household. He was only a kind of half-uncle, after all, for he had married my father's sister: yet he assumed great authority on the strength of this left-handed relationship, and was a universal intermeddler, and family pest. This prying little busy-body soon ferreted out the truth of the story, and discovered, by hook and by crook, that I was at the bottom of the affair, and had locked up the donkey in the smoke-house. He stopped to inquire no farther, for he was one of those testy curmudgeons, with whom unlucky boys are always in the wrong. Leaving old Barbara to wrestle in imagination with the Devil, he made for my bed-chamber, where I still lay wrapped in rosy slumbers, little dreaming of the mischief I had done, and the storm about to break over me.

"In an instant, I was awakened by a shower of thwacks, and started up in wild amazement. I demanded the meaning of this attack, but received no other reply than that I had murdered the house-keeper; while my uncle continued whacking away during my confusion. I seized a poker, and put myself on the defensive. I was a stout boy for my years, while my uncle was a little wiffet of a man; one that in Kentucky we would not call even an 'individual;' nothing more than a 'remote circumstance.' I soon, therefore, brought him to a parley, and learned the whole extent of the charge brought against me. I confessed to the donkey and the smoke-house, but pleaded not guilty of the murder of the house-keeper. I soon found out that old Barbara was still alive. She continued under the doctor's hands, however, for several days; and whenever she had an ill turn, my uncle would seek to give me another flogging. I appealed to my father, but got no redress. I was considered an 'unlucky boy,' prone to all kinds of mischief; so that prepossessions were against me, in all cases of appeal.

"I felt stung to the soul at all this. I had been beaten, degraded, and treated with slighting when I complained. I lost my usual good spirits and good humor; and, being out of temper with every body, fancied every body out of temper with me. A certain wild, roving spirit of freedom, which I believe is as inherent in me as it is in the partridge, was brought into sudden activity by the checks and restraints I suffered. 'I'll go from home,' thought I, 'and shift for myself.' Perhaps this notion was quickened by the rage for emigrating to Kentucky, which was at that time prevalent in Virginia. I had heard such stories of the romantic beauties of the country; of the abundance of game of all kinds, and of the glorious independent life of the hunters who ranged its noble forests, and lived by the rifle; that I was as much agog to get there, as boys who live in sea-ports are to launch themselves among the wonders and adventures of the ocean.

"After a time, old Barbara got better in mind and body, and matters were explained to her; and she became gradually convinced that it was not the Devil she had encountered. When she heard how harshly I had been treated on her account, the good old soul was extremely grieved, and spoke warmly to my father in my behalf. He had himself remarked the change in my behaviour, and thought punishment might have been carried too far. He sought, therefore, to have some conversation with me, and to soothe my feelings; but it was too late. I frankly told him the course of mortification that I had experienced, and the fixed determination I had made to go from home.

" 'And where do you mean to go?'

" 'To Kentucky.'

" 'To Kentucky! Why you know nobody there.'

" 'No matter: I can soon make acquaintances.'

" 'And what will you do when you get there?'

" 'Hunt!'

" 'My father gave a long, low whistle, and looked in my face with a serio-comic expression. I was not far in my teens, and to talk of setting off alone for Kentucky, to turn hunter, seemed doubtless the idle prattle of a boy. He was little aware of the dogged resolution of my character; and his smile of incredulity but fixed me more obstinately in my purpose. I assured him I was serious in what I said, and would certainly set off for Kentucky in the Spring.

"Month after month passed away. My father now and then adverted slightly to what had passed between us; doubtless for the purpose of sounding me. I always expressed the same grave and fixed determination. By degrees he spoke to me more directly on the subject; endeavoring earnestly but kindly to dissuade me. My only reply was, 'I had made up my mind.'

"Accordingly, as soon as the Spring had fairly opened, I sought him one day in his study, and informed him I was about to set out for Kentucky, and had come to take my leave. He made no objection, for he had exhausted persuasion and remonstrance, and doubtless thought it best to give way to my humor, trusting that a little rough experience would soon bring me home again. I asked money for my journey. He went to a chest, took out a long green silk purse, well filled, and laid it on the table. I now asked for a horse and servant.

" 'A horse!' said my father, sneeringly: 'why, you would not go a mile without racing him, and breaking your neck; and as to a servant, you cannot take care of yourself, much less of him.'

" 'How am I to travel, then?'

" 'Why I suppose you are man enough to travel on foot.'

" 'He spoke jestingly, little thinking I would take him at his word; but I was thoroughly piqued in respect to my enterprise; so I pocketed the purse; went to my room, tied up three or four shirts in a pocket-handkerchief, put a dirk in my bosom, girt a couple of pistols round my waist, and felt like a knight-errant armed cap-à-pie, and ready to rove the world in quest of adventures.

" 'My sister (I had but one) hung round me and wept, and entreated me to stay. I felt my heart swell in my throat; but I gulped it back to its place, and straightened myself up: I would not suffer myself to cry. I at length disengaged myself from her, and got to the door.

" 'When will you come back?' cried she.

" 'Never, by heavens!' cried I, 'until I come back a member of congress from Kentucky. I am determined to show that I am not the tail-end of the family.'

" 'Such was my first out-set from home. You may suppose what a greenhorn I was, and how little I knew of the world I was launching into.'

" 'I do not recollect any incident of importance, until I reached the borders of Pennsylvania. I had stopped at an inn to get some refreshment; as I was eating in a back room. I overheard two men in the bar-room conjecture who and what I could be. One determined, at length, that I was a run-away apprentice, and ought to be stopped, to which the other assented. When I had finished my meal, and paid for it, I went out at the back door, lest I should be stopped by my supervisors. Scorning, however, to steal off like a culprit, I walked round to the front of the house. One of the men advanced to the front door. He wore his hat on one side, and had a consequential air that nettled me.

"'Where are you going, youngster?' demanded he.

"'That's none of your business!' replied I, rather pertly.

"'Yes but it is, though! You have run away from home, and must give an account of yourself.'

"'He advanced to seize me, when I drew forth a pistol. 'If you advance another step, I'll shoot you!'

"'He sprang back as if he had trodden upon a rattle-snake, and his hat fell off in the movement.

"'Let him alone!' cried his companion; 'he's a foolish, mad-headed boy, and don't know what he's about. He'll shoot you, you may rely on it.'

"'He did not need any caution in the matter; he was afraid even to pick up his hat: so I pushed forward on my way, without molestation. This incident, however, had its effect upon me. I became fearful of sleeping in any house at night, lest I should be stopped. I took my meals in the houses, in the course of the day, but would turn aside at night, into some wood or ravine, make a fire, and sleep before it. This I considered was true hunter's style, and I wished to inure myself to it.

"At length I arrived at Brownsville, leg-weary and way-worn, and in a shabby plight, as you may suppose, having been 'camping out' for some nights past. I applied at some of the inferior inns, but could gain no admission. I was regarded for a moment with a dubious eye, and then informed they did not receive foot-passengers. At last I went boldly to the principal inn. The landlord appeared as unwilling as the rest to receive a vagrant boy beneath his roof; but his wife interfered, in the midst of his excuses, and half elbowing him aside:

"'Where are you going, my lad?' said she.

"'To Kentucky.'

"'What are you going there for?'

"'To hunt.'

"She looked earnestly at me for a moment or two. 'Have you a mother living?' said she, at length.

"'No, madam: she has been dead for some time.'

"'I thought so!' cried she, warmly. 'I knew if you had a mother living, you would not be here.' From that moment the good woman treated me with a mother's kindness.

I remained several days beneath her roof, recovering from the fatigue of my journey. While here, I purchased a rifle, and practised daily at a mark, to prepare myself for a hunter's life. When sufficiently recruited in strength, I took leave of my kind host and hostess, and resumed my journey.

"At Wheeling I embarked in a flat-bottomed family boat, technically called a broad-horn, a prime river conveyance in those days. In this ark for two weeks I floated down the Ohio. The river was as yet in all its wild beauty. Its loftiest trees had not been thinned out. The forest overhung the water's edge, and was occasionally skirted by immense cane-brakes. Wild animals of all kinds abounded. We heard them rushing through the thickets, and splashing in the water. Deer and bears would frequently swim across the river; others would come down to the bank, and gaze at the boat as it passed. I was incessantly on the alert with my rifle; but some how or other, the game was never within shot. Sometimes I got a chance to land and try my skill on shore. I shot squirrels, and small birds, and even wild turkeys; but though I caught glimpses of deer bounding away through the woods, I never could get a fair shot at them.

"In this way we glided in our broad-horn past Cincinnati, the 'Queen of the West' as she is now called; then a mere group of log cabins; and the site of the bustling city of Louisville, then designated by a solitary house. As I said before, the Ohio was as yet a wild river; all was forest, forest, forest! Near the confluence of Green River with the Ohio, I landed, bade adieu to the broad-horn, and struck for the interior of Kentucky. I had no precise plan; my only idea was to make for one of the wildest parts of the country. I had relatives in Lexington, and other settled places, to whom I thought it probable my father would write concerning me: so as I was full of manhood and independence, and resolutely bent on making my way in the world without assistance or control, I resolved to keep clear of them all.

"In the course of my first day's trudge, I shot a wild turkey, and slung it on my back for provisions. The forest was open and clear from under-wood. I saw deer in abundance, but always running, running. It seemed to me as if these animals never stood still.

"At length I came to where a gang of half-starved wolves were feasting on the carcass of a deer which they had run down; and snarling and snapping, and fighting like so many dogs. They were all so ravenous and intent upon their prey, that they did not notice me, and I had time to make my observations. One, larger and fiercer than the rest, seemed to claim the larger share, and to keep the others in awe. If any one came too near him while eating, he would fly off, seize and shake him, and then return to his repast. 'This' thought I, 'must be the captain; if I can kill him, I shall defeat the whole army.' I accordingly took aim, fired, and down dropped the old fellow. He might be only shamming dead; so I loaded and put a second ball through him. He never budged; all the rest ran off, and my victory was complete.

"It would not be easy to describe my triumphant feelings on this great achievement. I marched on with renovated spirit; regarding myself as absolute lord of the forest. As night drew near, I prepared for camping. My first care was to collect dry wood and make a roaring fire to cook and sleep by, and to frighten off wolves, and bears, and panthers. I then began to pluck my turkey for supper. I had camped out several times in the early part of my expedition; but that was in comparatively more settled and civilized regions; where there were no wild animals of consequence in the forest. This was my first camping out in the real wilderness; and I was soon made sensible of the loneliness and wildness of my situation.

"In a little while, a concert of wolves commenced: there might have been a dozen or two, but it seemed to me as if there were thousands. I never heard such howling and whining. Having prepared my turkey, I divided it into two parts, thrust two sticks into one of the halves, and planted them on end before the fire, the hunter's mode of roasting. The smell of roast meat quickened the appetites of the wolves, and their concert became truly infernal. They seemed to be all around me, but I could only now and then get a glimpse of one of them, as he came within the glare of the light.

"I did not much care for the wolves, who I knew to be a cowardly race, but I had heard terrible stories of panthers, and began to fear their stealthy prowlings in the surrounding darkness. I was thirsty, and heard a brook bubbling and tinkling along at no great distance, but absolutely dared not go there, lest some panther might lie in wait, and spring upon me. By and by a deer whistled. I had never heard one before, and thought it must be a panther. I now felt uneasy lest he might climb the trees, crawl along the branches over head, and plump down upon me; so I kept my eyes fixed on the branches, until my head ached. I more than once thought I saw fiery eyes glaring down from among the leaves. At length I thought of my supper, and turned to see if my half-turkey was cooked. In crowding so near the fire, I had pressed the meat into the flames, and it was consumed. I had nothing to do but toast the other half, and take better care of it. On that half I made my supper, without salt or bread. I was still so possessed with the dread of panthers, that I could not close my eyes all night, but lay watching the trees until day-break, when all my fears were dispelled with the darkness; and as I saw the morning sun sparkling down through the branches of the trees, I smiled to think how I suffered myself to be dismayed by sounds and shadows: but I was a young woodsman, and a stranger in Kentucky.

"Having breakfasted on the remainder of my turkey, and slaked my thirst at the bubbling stream, without farther dread of panthers, I resumed my wayfaring with buoyant feelings. I again saw deer, but as usual running, running! I tried in vain to get a shot at them, and began to fear I never should. I was gazing with vexation after a herd in full scamper, when I was startled by a human voice. Turning round, I saw a man at a short distance from me, in a hunting-dress.

" 'What are you after, my lad?' cried he

" 'Those deer;' replied I, pettishly; 'but it seems as if they never stand still.'

" 'Upon that he burst out laughing. 'Where are you from?' said he.

" 'From Richmond.'

" 'What! In old Virginny?'

" 'The same.'

" 'And how on earth did you get here?'

" 'I landed at Green River from a broad-horn.'

" 'And where are your companions?'

" 'I have none.'

" 'What?—all alone!'

" 'Yes.'

" 'Where are you going?'

" 'Any where.'

" 'And what have you come here for?'

" 'To hunt.'

" 'Well,' said he, laughingly, 'you'll make a real hunter; there's no mistaking that!'

" 'Have you killed any thing?'

" 'Nothing but a turkey; I can't get within shot of a deer: they are always running.'

" 'Oh, I'll tell you the secret of that. You're always pushing forward, and starting the deer at a distance, and gazing at those that are scampering; but you must step as slow, and silent, and cautious as a cat, and keep your eyes close around you, and lurk from tree to tree, if you wish to get a chance at deer. But come, go home with me. My name is Bill Smithers; I live not far off: stay with me a little while, and I'll teach you how to hunt.'

"I gladly accepted the invitation of honest Bill Smithers. We soon reached his habitation; a mere log hut, with a square hole for a window, and a chimney made of sticks and clay. Here he lived, with a wife and child. He had 'girdled' the trees for an acre or two around, preparatory to clearing a space for corn and potatoes. In the mean time he maintained his family entirely by his rifle, and I soon found him to be a first-rate huntsman. Under his tutelage I received my first effective lessons in 'woodcraft.'

"The more I knew of a hunter's life, the more I relished it. The country, too, which had been the promised land of my boyhood, did not, like most promised lands, disappoint me. No wilderness could be more beautiful than this part of Kentucky, in those times. The forests were open and spacious, with noble trees, some of which looked as if they had stood for centuries. There were beautiful prairies, too, diversified with groves and clumps of trees, which looked like vast parks, and in which you could see the deer running, at a great distance. In the proper season, these prairies would be covered in many places with wild strawberries, where your horses' hoofs would be dyed to the fet-lock. I thought there could not be another place in the world equal to Kentucky—and I think so still.

"After I had passed ten or twelve days with Bill Smithers, I thought it time to shift my quarters, for his house was scarce large enough for his own family, and I had no idea of being an incumbrance to any one. I accordingly made up my bundle, shouldered my rifle, took a friendly leave of Smithers and his wife, and set out in quest of a Nimrod of the wilderness, one John Miller, who lived alone, nearly forty miles off, and who I hoped would be well pleased to have a hunting companion.

"I soon found out that one of the most important items in woodcraft, in a new country, was the skill to find one's way in the wilderness. There were no regular roads in the forests, but they were cut up and perplexed by paths leading in all directions. Some of these were made by the cattle of the settlers, and were called 'stock-tracks,' but others had been made by the immense droves of buffaloes which roamed about the country, from the flood until recent times. These were called buffalo-tracks, and traversed Kentucky from end to end, like high-ways. Traces of them may still be seen in uncultivated parts, or deeply worn in the rocks where they crossed the mountains. I was a young woodsman, and sorely puzzled to distinguish one kind of track from the other, or to make out my course through this tangled labyrinth. While thus perplexed, I heard a distant roaring and rushing sound; a gloom stole over the forest: on looking up, when I could catch a stray glimpse of the sky, I beheld the clouds rolled up like balls, the lower part as black as ink. There was now and then an explosion, like a burst of cannonry afar off, and the crash of a falling tree. I had heard of hurricanes in the woods, and surmised that one was at hand. It soon came crashing its way; the forest writhing, and twisting, and groaning before it. The hurricane did not extend far on either side, but in a manner ploughed a furrow through the woodland; snapping off or up-rooting trees that had stood for centuries, and filling the air with whirling branches. I was directly in its course, and took my stand behind an immense poplar, six feet in diameter. It bore for a time the full fury of the blast, but at length began to yield. Seeing it falling, I scrambled nimbly, round the trunk like a squirrel. Down it went, bearing down another tree with it. I crept under the trunk as a shelter, and was protected from other trees which fell around me, but was sore all over, from the twigs and branches driven against me by the blast.

"This was the only incident of consequence that occurred on my way to John Miller's, where I arrived on the following day, and was received by the veteran with the rough kindness of a backwoodsman. He was a gray-haired man, hardy and weather-beaten, with a blue wart, like a great bead, over one eye, whence he was nicknamed by the hunters, 'Blue-bead Miller.' He had been in these parts from the earliest settlements, and had signalized himself in the hard conflicts with the Indians, which gained Kentucky the appellation of 'the Bloody Ground.' In one of these fights he had had an arm broken; in another he had narrowly escaped, when hotly pursued, by jumping from a precipice thirty feet high into a river.

"Miller willingly received me into his house as an inmate, and seemed pleased with the idea of making a hunter of me. His dwelling was a small log-house, with a loft or garret of boards, so that there was ample room for both of us. Under his instruction, I soon made a tolerable proficiency in hunting. My first exploit, of any consequence, was killing a bear. I was hunting in company with two brothers, when we came upon the track of Bruin, in a wood, where there was an undergrowth of canes and grape-vines. He was scrambling up a tree, when I shot him through the breast: he fell to the ground, and lay motionless. The brothers sent in their dog, who seized the bear by the throat. Bruin raised one arm, and gave the dog a hug that crushed his ribs. One yell, and all was over. I don't know which was first dead, the dog or the bear. The two brothers sat down and cried like children over their unfortunate dog. Yet they were mere rough huntsmen, almost as wild and untameable as Indians: but they were fine fellows.

"By degrees I became known, and somewhat of a favorite among the hunters of the neighborhood; that is to say, men who lived within a circle of thirty or forty miles, and came occasionally to see John Miller, who was a patriarch among them. They lived widely apart, in log-huts and wigwams, almost with the simplicity of Indians, and well nigh as destitute of the comforts and inventions of civilized life. They seldom saw each other; weeks, and even months would elapse, without their visiting. When they did meet, it was very much after the manner of Indians; loitering about all day, without having much to say, but becoming communicative as evening advanced, and sitting up half the night before the fire, telling hunting stories, and terrible tales of the fights of the Bloody Ground.

"Sometimes several would join in a distant hunting expedition, or rather campaign. Expeditions of this kind lasted from November until

April; during which we laid up our stock of summer provisions. We shifted our hunting-camps from place to place, according as we found the game. They were generally pitched near a run of water, and close by a cane-brake, to screen us from the wind. One side of our lodge was open towards the fire. Our horses were hoppled and turned loose in the cane-bakes, with bells round their necks. One of the party staid at home to watch the camp, prepare the meals, and keep off the wolves; the others hunted. When a hunter killed a deer at a distance from the camp, he would open it and take out the entrails; then climbing a sapling, he would bend it down, tie the deer to the top, and let it spring up again, so as to suspend the carcass out of reach of the wolves. At night he would return to the camp, and give an account of his luck. The next morning early he would get a house out of the cane-brake and bring home his game. That day he would stay at home to cut up the carcass, while the others hunted.

"Our days were thus spent in silent and lonely occupations. It was only at night that we would gather together before the fire, and be sociable. I was a novice, and used to listen with open eyes and ears to the strange and wild stories told by the old hunters, and believed every thing I heard. Some of their stories bordered upon the supernatural. They believed that their rifles might be spell-bound, so as not to be able to kill a buffalo, even at arm's length. This super-stition they had derived from the Indians, who often think the white hunters have laid a spell upon their rifles. Miller partook of this super-stition, and used to tell of his rifle's having a spell upon it; but it often seemed to me to be a shuffling way of accounting for a bad shot. If a hunter grossly missed his aim, he would ask, 'Who shot last with this rifle?'—and hint that he must have charmed it. The sure mode to disenchant the gun, was to shoot a silver bullet out of it.

"By the opening of Spring we would generally have quantities of bear's-meat and venison salted, dried, and smoked, and numerous packs of skins. We would then make the best of our way home from our distant hunting-grounds; transporting our spoils, sometimes in canoes along the rivers, sometimes on horse-back over land, and our return would often be celebrated by feasting and dancing, in true backwoods style. I have given you some idea of our hunting; let me now give you a sketch of our frolicking.

"It was on our return from a winter's hunting in the neighborhood of Green River, when we received notice that there was to be a grand frolic at Bob Mosely's, to greet the hunters. This Bob Mosely was a prime fellow throughout the country. He was an indifferent hunter, it is true, and rather lazy, to boot; but then he could play the fiddle, and that was enough to make him of consequence. There was no other man within a hundred miles that could play the fiddle, so there was no having a regular frolic without Bob Mosely. The hunters, therefore, were always ready to give him a share of their game in exchange for his music, and Bob was always ready to get up a carousal, whenever there was a party returning from a hunting expedition. The present frolic was to take place at Bob Mosely's own house, which was on the Pigeon Roost Fork of the Muddy, which is a branch of Rough Creek, which is a branch of Green River.

"Every body was agog for the revel at Bob Mosely's; and as all the fashion in the neighborhood was to be there, I thought I must brush up for the occasion. My leathern hunting-dress, which was the only one I had, was somewhat the worse for wear, it is true, and considerably japanned with blood and grease; but I was up to hunting expedients. Getting into a periogue, I paddled off to a part of the Green River where there was sand and clay, that might serve for soap; then taking off my dress, I scrubbed and scoured it, until I thought it looked very well. I then put it on the end of a stick, and hung it out of the periogue to dry, while I stretched myself very comfortably on the green bank of the river. Unluckily a flaw struck the periogue, and tipped over the stick: down went my dress to the bottom of the river, and I never saw it more. Here was I, left almost in a state of nature. I managed to make a kind of Robinson Crusoe garb of undressed skins, with the hair on, which enabled me to get home with decency; but my dream of gayety and fashion was at an end; for how could I think of figuring in high life at the Pigeon Roost, equipped like a mere Orson?

"Old Miller, who really began to take some pride in me, was confounded when he understood that I did not intend to go to Bob Mosely's; but when I told him my misfortune, and that I had no dress: 'By the powers,' cried he, 'but you *shall* go, and you shall be the best dressed and the best mounted lad there!'

"He immediately set to work to cut out and make up a hunting-shirt, of dressed deer-skin, gaily fringed at the shoulders, and leggins of the same, fringed from hip to heel. He then made me a rakish raccoon-cap, with a flaunting tail to it; mounted me on his best horse; and I may say, without vanity, that I was one of the smartest fellows that figured on that occasion, at the Pigeon-Roost Fork of the Muddy.

"It was no small occasion, either, let me tell you. Bob Mosely's house was a tolerably large bark shanty, with a clap-board roof; and there were assembled all the young hunters and pretty girls of the country, for many a mile round. The young men were in their best hunting-dresses, but not one could compare with mine; and my raccoon-cap, with its flowing tail, was the admiration of every body. The girls were

mostly in doe-skin dresses; for there was no spinning and weaving
as yet in the woods; nor any need of it. I never saw girls that seemed
to me better dressed; and I was somewhat of a judge, having seen
fashions at Richmond. We had a hearty dinner, and a merry one; for
there was Jemmy Kiel, famous for raccoon hunting, and Bob Tarleton,
and Wesley Pigman, and Joe Taylor, and several other prime fellows
for a frolic, that made all ring again, and laughed, that you might have
heard them a mile.

"After dinner, we began dancing, and were hard at it, when, about
three o'clock in the afternoon, there was a new arrival—two daughters of old Simon Schultz; two young ladies that affected fashion and
late hours. Their arrival had nearly put an end to all our merriment.
I must go a little round about in my story, to explain to you how
that happened.

"As old Schultz, the father, was one day looking in the cane-
brakes for his cattle, he came upon the track of horses. He knew
they were none of his, and that none of his neighbors had horses about
that place. They must be stray horses; or must belong to some traveller
who had lost his way, as the track led no where. He accordingly
followed it up, until he came to an unlucky pedlar, with two or three
pack-horses, who had been bewildered among the cattle-tracks, and
had wandered for two or three days among woods and cane-brakes,
until he was almost famished.

"Old Schultz brought him to his house; fed him on venison, bear's
meat, and hominy, and at the end of a week put him in prime condition. The pedlar could not sufficiently express his thankfulness; and
when about to depart, inquired what he had to pay? Old Schultz
stepped back, with surprise. 'Stranger,' said he, 'you have been welcome under my roof. I've given you nothing but wild meat and hominy,
because I had no better, but have been glad of your company. You are
welcome to stay as long as you please; but by Zounds! if any one
offers to pay Simon Schultz for food, he affronts him!' So saying, he
walked out in a huff.

"The pedlar admired the hospitality of his host, but could not reconcile it to his conscience to go away without making some recompense.
There were honest Simon's two daughters, two strapping, red-haired
girls. He opened his packs and displayed riches before them of which
they had no conception; for in those days there were no country stores
in those parts, with their artificial finery and trinketry; and this was
the first pedlar that had wandered into that part of the wilderness.
The girls were for a time completely dazzled, and knew not what to
choose: but what caught their eyes most, were two looking-glasses,
about the size of a dollar, set in gilt tin. They had never seen the like

before, having used no other mirror than a pail of water. The pedlar presented them these jewels, without the least hesitation: nay, he gallantly hung them round their necks by red ribbands, almost as fine as the glasses themselves. This done, he took his departure, leaving them as much astonished as two princesses in a fairy tale, that have received a magic gift from an enchanter.

"It was with these looking-glasses, hung round their necks as lockets, by red ribbands, that old Schultz's daughters made their appearance at three o'clock in the afternoon, at the frolic at Bob Mosely's, on the Pigeon-Roost Fork of the Muddy.

"By the powers, but it was an event! Such a thing had never before been seen in Kentucky. Bob Tarleton, a strapping fellow, with a head like a chestnut-burr, and a look like a boar in an apple orchard, stepped up, caught hold of the looking-glass of one of the girls, and gazing at it for a moment, cried out: 'Joe Taylor, come here! come here! I'll be darn'd if Patty Schultz aint got a locket that you can see your face in, as clear as in a spring of water!'

"In a twinkling all the young hunters gathered round old Schultz's daughters. I, who knew what looking-glasses were, did not budge. Some of the girls who sat near me were excessively mortified at finding themselves thus deserted. I heard Peggy Pugh say to Sally Pigman, 'Goodness knows, it's well Schultz's daughters is got them things round their necks, for it's the first time the young men crowded round them!'

"I saw immediately the danger of the case. We were a small community, and could not afford to be split up by feuds. So I stepped up to the girls, and whispered to them: 'Polly,' said I, 'those lockets are powerful fine, and become you amazingly; but you don't consider that the country is not advanced enough in these parts for such things. You and I understand these matters, but these people don't. Fine things like these may do very well in the old settlements, but they won't answer at the Pigeon-Roost Fork of the Muddy. You had better lay them aside for the present, or we shall have no peace.'

"Polly and her sister luckily saw their error; they took off the lockets, laid them aside, and harmony was restored: otherwise, I verily believe there would have been an end of our community. Indeed, notwithstanding the great sacrifice they made on this occasion, I do not think old Schultz's daughters were ever much liked afterwards among the young women.

"This was the first time that looking-glasses were ever seen in the Green River part of Kentucky!'

"I had now lived some time with old Miller, and had become a tolerably expert hunter. Game, however, began to grow scarce. The buffalo had gathered together, as if by universal understanding, and had crossed the Mississippi, never to return. Strangers kept pouring into the country, clearing away the forests, and building in all directions. The hunters began to grow restive. Jemmy Kiel, the same of whom I have already spoken for his skill in raccoon catching, came to me one day: 'I can't stand this any longer,' said he; 'we're getting too thick here. Simon Schultz crowds me so, that I have no comfort of my life.'

" 'Why how you talk!' said I; 'Simon Schultz lives twelve miles off.'

" 'No matter; his cattle run with mine, and I've no idea of living where another man's cattle can run with mine. That's too close neighborhood; I want elbow-room. This country, too, is growing too poor to live in; there's no game; so two or three of us have made up our minds to follow the buffalo to the Missouri, and we should like to have you of the party. Other hunters of my acquaintance talked in the same manner. This set me thinking; but the more I thought, the more I was perplexed. I had no one to advise with: old Miller and his associates knew of but one mode of life, and I had no experience in any other: but I had a wider scope of thought. When out hunting alone, I used to forget the sport, and sit for hours together on the trunk of a tree, with rifle in hand, buried in thought, and debating with myself: 'Shall I go with Jemmy Kiel and his company, or shall I remain here? If I remain here, there will soon be nothing left to hunt; but am I to be a hunter all my life? Have not I something more in me, than to be carrying a rifle on my shoulder, day after day, and dodging about after bears, and deer, and other brute beasts? My vanity told me I had; and I called to mind my boyish boast to my sister, that I would never return home, until I returned a member of congress from Kentucky; but was this the way to fit myself for such a station?'

"Various plans passed through my mind, but they were abandoned almost as soon as formed. At length I determined on becoming a lawyer. True it is, I knew almost nothing. I had left school before I had learnt beyond the 'rule of three.' 'Never mind,' said I to myself, resolutely; 'I am a terrible fellow for hanging on to any thing, when I've once made up my mind; and if a man has but ordinary capacity, and will set to work with heart and soul, and stick to it, he can do almost any thing.' With this maxim, which has been pretty much my main-stay throughout life, I fortified myself in my determination to attempt the law. But how was I to set about it? I must quit this forest life, and go to one or other of the towns, where I might be able to study, and to attend the courts. This too required funds. I examined into the state of my finances. The purse given me by my father had remained untouched, in the bottom of an old chest up in the loft, for money was scarcely needed in these parts. I had bargained away the skins acquired in hunting, for a horse and various other matters, on which, in case of need, I could raise funds. I therefore thought I could make shift to maintain myself until I was fitted for the bar.

"I informed my worthy host and patron, old Miller, of my plan. He shook his head at my turning my back upon the woods, when I was in a fair way of making a first-rate hunter; but he made no effort to dissuade me. I accordingly set off in September, on horseback, intending to visit Lexington, Frankfort, and other of the principal towns, in search of a favorable place to prosecute my studies. My choice was made sooner than I expected. I had put up one night in Bardstown, and found, on inquiry, that I could get comfortable board and accommodation in a private family for a dollar and half a week. I liked the place, and resolved to look no farther. So the next morning I prepared to turn my face homeward, and take my final leave of forest life.

"I had taken my breakfast, and was waiting for my horse, when, in pacing up and down the piazza, I saw a young girl seated near a window, evidently a visiter. She was very pretty; with auburn hair, and blue eyes, and was dressed in white. I had seen nothing of the kind since I had left Richmond; and at that time I was too much of a boy to be much struck by female charms. She was so delicate and dainty-looking, so different from the hale, buxom, brown girls of the woods; and then her white dress!—it was perfectly dazzling! Never was poor youth more taken by surprise, and suddenly bewitched. My heart yearned to know her; but how was I to accost her? I had grown wild in the woods, and had none of the habitudes of polite life. Had she been like Peggy Pugh, or Sally Pigman, or any other of my leathern-dressed belles of the Pigeon Roost, I should have approached her without dread; nay, had she been as fair as Schultz's daughters, with their looking-glass lockets, I should not have hesitated: but that white dress, and those auburn ringlets, and blue eyes, and delicate looks, quite daunted, while they fascinated me. I don't know what put it into my head, but I thought, all at once, that I would kiss her! It would take a long acquaintance to arrive at such a boon, but I might seize upon it by sheer robbery. Nobody knew me here. I would just step in, snatch a kiss, mount my horse, and ride off. She would not be the worse for it; and that kiss—oh! I should die if I did not get it!

"I gave no time for the thought to cool, but entered the house, and stepped lightly into the room. She was seated with her back to the door, looking out at the window, and did not hear my approach. I tapped her chair, and as she turned and looked up, I snatched as sweet a kiss as ever was stolen, and vanished in a twinkling. The next moment I was on horseback, galloping homeward; my very ears tingling at what I had done.

"On my return home, I sold my horse, and turned every thing to cash;

and found, with the remains of the paternal purse, that I had nearly four
hundred dollars; a little capital, which I resolved to manage with the
strictest economy.

"It was hard parting with old Miller, who had been like a father to me:
it cost me, too, something of a struggle to give up the free, independent
wild-wood life I had hitherto led; but I had marked out my course, and
have never been one to flinch or turn back.

"I footed it sturdily to Bardstown; took possession of the quarters for
which I had bargained, shut myself up, and set to work with might and
main, to study. But what a task I had before me! I had every thing to
learn; not merely law, but all the elementary branches of knowledge. I
read and read, for sixteen hours out of the four-and-twenty; but the
more I read, the more I became aware of my own ignorance, and shed
bitter tears over my deficiency. It seemed as if the wilderness of knowledge expanded and grew more perplexed as I advanced. Every height
gained, only revealed a wider region to be traversed, and nearly filled
me with despair. I grew moody, silent, and unsocial, but studied on
doggedly and incessantly. The only person with whom I held any conversation, was the worthy man in whose house I was quartered. He
was honest and well-meaning, but perfectly ignorant, and I believe would
have liked me much better, if I had not been so much addicted to reading. He considered all books filled with lies and impositions, and seldom
could look into one, without finding something to rouse his spleen. Nothing put him into a greater passion, than the assertion that the world
turned on its own axis every four-and-twenty hours. He swore it was an
outrage upon common sense. 'Why, if it did,' said he, 'there would not
be a drop of water in the well, by morning, and all the milk and cream
in the dairy would be turned topsy turvy! And then to talk of the earth
going round the sun! 'How do they know it?' I've seen the sun rise
every morning, and set every evening, for more than thirty years. They
must not talk to me about the earth's going round the sun!'

"At another time he was in a perfect fret at being told the distance between the sun and moon. 'How can any one tell the distance!' cried he.
'Who surveyed it? who carried the chain? By Jupiter! they only talk this
way before me to annoy me. But then there's some people of sense who
give in to this cursed humbug! There's Judge Broadnax, now, one of the
best lawyers we have; isn't it surprising he should believe in such stuff?
Why, Sir, the other day I heard him talk of the distance from a star he
called Mars to the sun! He must have got it out of one or other of those
confounded books he's so fond of reading; a book some impudent fellow has written, who knew nobody could swear the distance was more or
less.'

"For my own part, feeling my own deficiency in scientific lore, I never ventured to unsettle his conviction that the sun made his daily circuit round the earth; and for aught I said to the contrary, he lived and died in that belief.

"I had been about a year at Bardstown, living thus studiously and reclusely, when, as I was one day walking the street, I met two young girls, in one of whom I immediately recalled the little beauty whom I had kissed so impudently. She blushed up to the eyes, and so did I; but we both passed on without farther sign of recognition. This second glimpse of her, however, caused an odd fluttering about my heart. I could not get her out of my thoughts for days. She quite interfered with my studies. I tried to think of her as a mere child, but it would not do: she had improved in beauty, and was tending toward womanhood; and then I myself was but little better than a stripling. However, I did not attempt to seek after her, or even to find out who she was, but returned doggedly to my books. By degrees she faded from my thoughts, or if she did cross them occasionally, it was only to increase my despondency; for I feared that with all my exertions, I should never be able to fit myself for the bar, or enable myself to support a wife.

"One cold stormy evening I was seated, in dumpish mood, in the bar-room of the inn, looking into the fire, and turning over uncomfortable thoughts, when I was accosted by some one who had entered the room without my perceiving it. I looked up, and saw before me a tall and, as I thought, pompous-looking man, arrayed in small clothes and knee-buckles, with powdered head, and shoes nicely blacked and polished; a style of dress unparalleled in those days, in that rough country. I took a pique against him from the very portliness of his appearance, and stateliness of his manner, and bristled up as he accosted me. He demanded if my name was not Ringwood.

"I was startled, for I supposed myself perfectly incog.; but I answered in the affirmative.

" 'Your family, I believe, lives in Richmond.'

"My gorge began to rise. 'Yes, Sir,' replied I, sulkily, 'my family does live in Richmond.'

" 'And what, may I ask, has brought you into this part of the country?'

" 'Zounds, Sir?' cried I, starting on my feet, 'what business is it of yours? How dare you to question me in this manner?'

"The entrance of some persons prevented a reply; but I walked up and down the bar-room, fuming with conscious independence and insulted dignity, while the pompous-looking personage, who had thus trespassed upon my spleen, retired without proffering another word.

"The next day, while seated in my room, some one tapped at the door, and, on being bid to enter, the stranger in the powdered head, small-clothes, and shining shoes and buckles, walked in with ceremonious courtesy.

"My boyish pride was again in arms; but he subdued me. He was formal, but kind and friendly. He knew my family, and understood my situation, and the dogged struggle I was making. A little conversation, when my jealous pride was once put to rest, drew every thing from me. He was a lawyer of experience, and of extensive practice, and offered at once to take me with him, and direct my studies. The offer was too advantageous and gratifying not to be immediately accepted. From that time I began to look up. I was put into a proper track, and was enabled to study to a proper purpose. I made acquaintance, too, with some of the young men of the place, who were in the same pursuit, and was encouraged at finding that I could 'hold my own' in argument with them. We instituted a debating club, in which I soon became prominent and popular. Men of talents, engaged in other pursuits, joined it, and this diversified our subjects, and put me on various tracks of inquiry. Ladies, too, attended some of our discussions, and this gave them a polite tone, and had an influence on the manners of the debaters. My legal patron also may have had a favorable effect on correcting any roughness contracted in my hunter's life. He was calculated to bend me in an opposite direction, for he was of the old school; quoted Chesterfield on all occasions, and talked of Sir Charles Grandison, who was his beau ideal. It was Sir Charles Grandison, however, Kentuckyized.

"I had always been fond of female society. My experience, however, had hitherto been among the rough daughters of the backwoodsman; and I felt an awe of young ladies in 'store clothes,' and delicately brought up. Two or three of the married ladies of Bardstown, who had heard me at the debating club, determined that I was a genius, and undertook to bring me out. I believe I really improved under their hands; became quiet where I had been shy or sulky, and easy where I had been impudent.

"I called to take tea one evening with one of these ladies, when to my surprise, and somewhat to my confusion, I found with her the identical blue-eyed little beauty whom I had so audaciously kissed. I was formally introduced to her, but neither of us betrayed any sign of previous acquaintance, except blushing to the eyes. While tea was getting ready, the lady of the house went out of the room to give some directions, and left us alone.

"Heavens and earth, what a situation! I would have given all the pittance I was worth, to have been in the deepest dell of the forest. I felt the necessity of saying something in excuse of my former rudeness, but I could not conjure up an idea, nor utter a word. Every moment matters were growing worse. I felt at one time tempted to do as I had done when I robbed her of the kiss: bolt from the room, and take to flight; but I was chained to the spot, for I really longed to gain her good will.

"At length I plucked up courage, on seeing that she was equally confused with myself, and walking desperately up to her, I exclaimed:

"'I have been trying to muster up something to say to you, but I cannot. I feel that I am in a horrible scrape. Do have pity on me, and help me out of it!'

"A smile dimpled about her mouth, and played among the blushes of her cheek. She looked up with a shy but arch glance of the eye, that expressed a volume of comic recollection; we both broke into a laugh, and from that moment all went on well.

"A few evenings afterward, I met her at a dance, and prosecuted the acquaintance. I soon became deeply attached to her; paid my court regularly; and before I was nineteen years of age, had engaged myself to marry her. I spoke to her mother, a widow lady, to ask her consent. She seemed to demur; upon which, with my customary haste, I told her there would be no use in opposing the match, for if her daughter chose to have me, I would take her, in defiance of her family, and the whole world.

"She laughed, and told me I need not give myself any uneasiness; there would be no unreasonable opposition. She knew my family, and all about me. The only obstacle was, that I had no means of supporting a wife, and she had nothing to give with her daughter.

"No matter; at that moment every thing was bright before me. I was in one of my sanguine moods. I feared nothing, doubted nothing. So it was agreed that I should prosecute my studies, obtain a license, and as soon as I should be fairly launched in business, we would be married.

"I now prosecuted my studies with redoubled ardor, and was up to my ears in law, when I received a letter from my father, who had heard of me and my whereabouts. He applauded the course I had taken, but advised me to lay a foundation of general knowledge, and offered to defray my expenses, if I would go to college. I felt the want of a general education, and was staggered with this offer. It militated somewhat against the self-dependent course I had so proudly, or rather conceitedly, marked out for myself, but it would enable me to enter more advantageously upon my legal career. I talked over the matter with the lovely girl to whom I was engaged. She sided in opinion with my father, and talked so disinterestedly, yet tenderly, that if possible, I loved her more than ever. I reluctantly, therefore, agreed to go to college for a couple of years, though it must necessarily postpone our union.

"Scarcely had I formed this resolution, when her mother was taken ill, and died, leaving her without a protector. This again altered all my plans. I felt as if I could protect her. I gave up all idea of collegiate studies; persuaded myself that by dint of industry and application I might overcome the deficiencies of education, and resolved to take out a license as soon as possible.

"That very autumn I was admitted to the bar, and within a month afterward, was married. We were a young couple; she not much above sixteen, I not quite twenty; and both almost without a dollar in the world. The establishment which we set up was suited to our circumstances: a log-house, with two small rooms; a bed, a table, a half dozen chairs, a half dozen knives and forks, a half dozen spoons; every thing by half dozens; a little delft ware; every thing in a small way: we were so poor, but then so happy!

"We had not been married many days, when court was held at a county town, about twenty-five miles distant. It was necessary for me to go there, and put myself in the way of business: but how was I to go? I had expended all my means on our establishment; and then, it was hard parting with my wife, so soon after marriage. However, go I must. Money must be made, or we should soon have the wolf at the door. I accordingly borrowed a horse, and borrowed a little cash, and rode off from my door, leaving my wife standing at it, and waving her hand after me. Her last look, so sweet and beaming, went to my heart. I felt as if I could go through fire and water for her.

"I arrived at the county town, on a cool October evening. The inn was crowded, for the court was to commence on the following day. I knew no one, and wondered how I, a stranger, and a mere youngster, was to make my way in such a crowd, and to get business. The public room was thronged with the idlers of the country, who gather together on such occasions. There was some drinking going forward, with much noise, and a little altercation. Just as I entered the room, I saw a rough bully of a fellow, who was partly intoxicated, strike an old man. He came swaggering by me, and elbowed me as he passed. I immediately knocked him down, and kicked him into the street. I needed no better introduction. In a moment I had a dozen rough shakes of the hand, and invitations to drink, and found myself quite a personage in this rough assembly.

"The next morning the court opened. I took my seat among the lawyers, but felt as a mere spectator, not having a suit in progress or prospect, nor having any idea where business was to come from. In the course of the morning, a man was put at the bar, charged with passing counterfeit money, and was asked if he was ready for trial. He answered in the negative. He had been confined in a place where there were no lawyers, and had not had an opportunity of consulting any. He was told to choose counsel from the lawyers present, and to be ready for trial on the following day. He looked round the court, and selected me. I was thunder-struck. I could not tell why he should make such a choice. I, a beardless youngster; unpractised at the bar; perfectly unknown. I felt diffident yet delighted, and could have hugged the rascal.

"Before leaving the court, he gave me one hundred dollars in a bag, as a retaining fee. I could scarcely believe my senses; it seemed like a dream. The heaviness of the fee spoke but lightly in favor of his innocence, but that was no affair of mine. I was to be advocate, not judge, nor jury. I followed him to jail, and learned from him all the particulars of his case; thence I went to the clerk's office, and took minutes of the indictment. I then examined the law on the subject, and prepared my brief in my room. All this occupied me until midnight, when I went to bed, and tried to sleep. It was all in vain. Never in my life was I more wide awake. A host of thoughts and fancies kept rushing through my mind: the shower of gold that had so unexpectedly fallen into my lap; the idea of my poor little wife at home, that I was to astonish with my good fortune! But then the awful responsibility I had undertaken!—to speak for the first time in a strange court; the expectations the culprit had evidently formed of my talents; all these, and a crowd of similar notions, kept whirling through my mind. I tossed about all night, fearing the morning would find me exhausted and incompetent; in a word, the day dawned on me, a miserable fellow!

"I got up feverish and nervous. I walked out before breakfast, striving to collect my thoughts, and tranquillize my feelings. It was a bright morning; the air was pure and frosty. I bathed my forehead and my hands in a beautiful running stream; but I could not allay the fever heat that raged within. I returned to breakfast, but could not eat. A single cup of coffee formed my repast. It was time to go to court, and I went there with a throbbing heart. I believe if it had not been for the thoughts of my little wife, in her lonely log house, I should have given back to the man his hundred dollars, and relinquished the cause. I took my seat, looking, I am convinced, more like a culprit than the rogue I was to defend.

When the time came for me to speak, my heart died within me. I rose embarrassed and dismayed, and stammered in opening my cause. I went on from had to worse, and felt as if I was going down hill. Just then the public prosecutor, a man of talents, but somewhat rough in his practice, made a sarcastic remark on something I had said. It was like an electric spark, and ran tingling through every vein in my body. In an instant my diffidence was gone. My whole spirit was in arms. I answered with promptness and bitterness, for I felt the cruelty of such an attack upon a novice in my situation. The public prosecutor made a kind of apology: this, from a man of his redoubted powers, was a vast concession. I renewed my argument with a fearless glow; carried the case through triumphantly, and the man was acquitted.

"This was the making of me. Every body was curious to know who this new lawyer was, that had thus suddenly risen among them, and bearded the attorney-general at the very outset. The story of my debut at the inn, on the preceding evening, when I had knocked down a bully, and kicked him out of doors, for striking an old man, was circulated, with favorable exaggerations. Even my very beardless chin and juvenile countenance were in my favor, for people gave me far more credit than I really deserved. The chance business which occurs in our country courts came thronging upon me. I was repeatedly employed in other causes; and by Saturday night, when the court closed, and I had paid my bill at the inn, I found myself with an hundred and fifty dollars in silver, three hundred dollars in notes, and a horse that I afterward sold for two hundred dollars more.

"Never did miser gloat on his money with more delight. I locked the door of my room; piled the money in a heap upon the table; walked round it; sat with my elbows on the table, and my chin upon my hands, and gazed upon it. Was I thinking of the money? No! I was thinking of my little wife at home. Another sleepless night ensued; but what a night of golden fancies, and splendid air-castles! As soon as morning dawned, I was up, mounted the borrowed horse with which I had come to court, and led the other, which I had received as a fee. All the way I was delighting myself with the thoughts of the surprise I had in store for my little wife; for both of us had expected nothing but that I should spend all the money I had borrowed, and should return in debt.

"Our meeting was joyous, as you may suppose: but I played the part of the Indian hunter, who, when he returns from the chase, never for a time speaks of his success. She had prepared a snug little rustic meal for me, and while it was getting ready, I seated myself at an old-fashioned desk in one corner, and began to count over my money, and put it away. She came to me before I had finished, and asked who I had collected the money for.

"'For myself, to be sure,' replied I, with affected coolness; 'I made it at court.'

"She looked me for a moment in the face, incredulously. I tried to keep countenance, and to play Indian, but it would not do. My muscles began to twitch; my feelings all at once gave way. I caught her in my arms; laughed, cried, and danced about the room, like a crazy man. From that time forward, we never wanted for money.

"I had not been long in successful practice, when I was surprised one day by a visit from my woodland patron, old Miller. The tidings of my prosperity had reached him in the wilderness, and he had walked one hundred and fifty miles on foot to see me. By that time I had improved my domestic establishment, and had all things comfortable about me. He looked around him with a wondering eye, at what he considered luxuries and superfluities; but supposed they were all right, in my altered circumstances. He said he did not know, upon the whole, but that I had acted for the best. It is true, if game had continued plenty, it would have been a folly for me to quit a hunter's life; but hunting was pretty nigh done up in Kentucky. The buffalo had gone to Missouri; the elk were nearly gone also; deer, too, were growing scarce; they might last out his time, as he was growing old, but they were not worth setting up life upon. He had once lived on the borders of Virginia. Game grew scarce there; he followed it up across Kentucky, and now it was again giving him the slip; but he was too old to follow it farther.

"He remained with us three days. My wife did every thing in her power to make him comfortable; but at the end of that time, he said he must be off again to the woods. He was tired of the village, and of having so many people about him. He accordingly returned to the wilderness, and to hunting life. But I fear he did not make a good end of it; for I understand that a few years before his death, he married Sukey Thomas, who lived at the White Oak Run."

THE SEMINOLES

From the time of the chimerical cruisings of Old Ponce de Leon in search of the Fountain of Youth; the avaricious expedition of Pamphilo de Narvaez in quest of Gold; and the chivalrous enterprise of Hernando de Soto, to discover and conquer a second Mexico, the natives of Florida have been continually subjected to the invasions and encroachments of white men. They have resisted them perseveringly but fruitlessly, and are now battling amidst swamps and morasses, for the last foothold of their native soil, with all the ferocity of dispair. Can we wonder at the bitterness of a hostility that has been handed down from father to son for upward of three centuries, and exasperated by the wrongs and miseries of each succeeding generation! The very name of the savages with whom we are fighting, betokens their fallen and homeless condition. Formed of the wrecks of once powerful tribes, and driven from their ancient seats of prosperity and dominion, they are known by the name of the Seminoles, or "Wanderers."

Bartram, who travelled through Florida in the latter part of the last century, speaks of passing through a great extent of ancient Indian fields, now silent and deserted, over grown with forests, orange groves, and rank vegetation, the site of the ancient Alachua, the capital of a famous and powerful tribe, who in days of old could assemble thousands at ball-play and other athletic exercises "are these then happy fields and green plains." "Almost every step we take," adds he, "over these fertile heights, discovers the remains and traces of ancient human habitations and cultivation."

We are told that about the year 1763, when Florida was ceded by the Spaniards to the English, the Indians generally retired from the towns and the neighborhood of the whites, and burying themselves in the deep forests, intricate swamps and hommocks, and vast savannas of the interior, devoted themselves to a pastoral life, and the rearing of horses and cattle. These are the people that received the name of the Seminoles, or Wanderers, which they still retain.

Bartram gives a pleasing picture of them at the time he visited them in their wilderness; where their distance from the abodes of white men gave them a transient quiet and security. "This handful of people," says he, "possesses a vast territory, all East and the greatest part of West Florida, which being naturally cut and divided into thousands of islets, knolls and eminences, by the inumerable rivers, lakes, swamps, vast savannahs, and ponds, form so many secure retreats and temporary dwelling-places that effectually guard them from any sudden invasions or attacks from their enemies; and being such a swampy, hommocky country, furnishes such a plenty and variety of supplies for the nourishment of varieties of animals, that I can venture to assert, that no part of the globe so abounds with wild game, or creatures fit for the food of man.

"Thus they enjoy a superabundance of the necessaries and conveniences of life, with the security of person and property, the two great concerns of mankind. The hides of deer, bears, tigers, and wolves, together with honey, wax, and other productions of the country, purchase their clothing equipage, and domestic utensils from the whites. They seem to be free from want or desires. No cruel enemy to dread; nothing to give them disquietude, *but the gradual encroachments of the white people*. Thus contented and undisturbed, they appear as blithe and free as the birds of the air, and like them as volatile and active, tuneful and vociferous. The visage, action, and deportment of the Seminoles form the most striking picture of happiness in this life; joy, contentment, love, and friendship, without guile or affectation, seem inherent in them, or predominent in their vital principle, for it leaves them with but the last breath of life. They are fond of games and gambling, and amuse themselves, like children, in relating extravagant stories, to cause surprize and mirth."*

The same writer gives an engaging picture of his treatment by these savages.

"Soon after entering the forests, we were met in the path by a small company of Indians, smiling and beckoning to us long before we joined them. This was a family of Talahasochte, who had been out on a hunt, and were returning home loaded with barbacued meat, hides, and honey. Their company consisted of the man, his wife and children, well mounted on fine horses, with a number of pack-horses. The man offered us a fawn-skin of honey which I accepted and at parting presented him with some fish-hooks sewing-needles, etc."

"On our return to camp in the evening. we were saluted by a party of young Indian warriors, who had pitched their tents on a green eminence near the lake, at a small distance from our camp, under a little grove of Oaks and Palms. This company consisted of seven young Seminoles, under the conduct of a young prince or chief of Talahasochte, a town southward in the isthmus. They were all dressed and painted with singular elegance, and richly ornamented with silver plates, chains, etc., after the Seminole mode, with waving plumes of feathers on their crests. On our coming up to them, they arose and shook hands; we alighted and sat a while with them by their cheerful fire.

* Bartram's "Travels in North America."

"The young prince informed our chief that he was in pursuit of a young fellow who had fled from the town, carrying off with him one of his favorite young wives. He said, merrily, he would have the ears of both of them before he returned. He was rather above the middle stature, and the most perfect human figure I ever saw; of an amiable, engaging countenance, air, and deportment; free and familiar in conversation, yet retaining a becoming gracefulness and dignity. We arose, took leave of them, and crossed a little vale covered with a charming green turf, already illuminated by the soft light of the full moon.

"Soon after joining our companions at camp, our neighbors, the prince and his associates, paid us a visit. We treated them with the best fare we had, having till this time preserved our spirituous liquors. They left us with perfect cordiality and cheerfulness, wishing us a good repose, and retired to their own camp. Having a band of music with them, consisting of a drum, flutes, and a rattle-gourd, they entertained us during the night with their music, vocal and instrumental. There is a languishing softness and melancholy air in the Indian convivial songs, especially of the amorous class, irresistibly moving attention, and exquisitely pleasing, especially in their soliary recesses, when all nature is silent."

Travellers who have been among them, in more recent times, before they had embarked in their present desperate struggle, represent them in much the same light; as leading a pleasant, indolent life, in a climate that required little shelter or clothing, and where the spontaneous fruits of the earth furnished subsistance without toil. A cleanly race, delighting in bathing, passing much of their time under the shade of their trees, with heaps of oranges and other fine fruits for their refreshment; talking, laughing, dancing and sleeping. Every chief had a fan hanging to his side, made of feathers of the wild turkey, the beautiful pink-coloured crane, or the scarlet flamingo. With this he would sit and fan himself with great stateliness, while the young people danced before him. The women joined in the dances with the men, excepting the war-dances. They wore strings of tortoise-shells and pebbles round their legs, which rattled in cadence to the music. They were treated with more attention among the Seminoles than among most Indian tribes.

ORIGIN OF THE WHITE, THE RED, AND THE BLACK MEN.

A SEMINOLE TRADITION

When the Floridas were erected into a territory of the United States, one of the earliest cares of the Governor, WILLIAM P. DUVAL, was directed to the instruction and civilization of the natives. For this purpose he called a meeting of the chiefs, in which he informed them of the wish of their Great Father at Washington that they should have schools and teachers among them, and that their children should be instructed like the children of white men. The chiefs listened with their customary silence and decorum to a long speech, setting forth the advantages that would accrue to them from this measure, and when he had concluded, begged the interval of a day to deliberate on it.

On the following day, a solemn convocation was held, at which one of the chiefs addressed the governor in the name of all the rest. "My brother," said he, "we have been thinking over the proposition of our Great Father at Washington, to send teachers and set up schools among us. We are very thankful for the interest he takes in our welfare; but after much deliberation, have concluded to decline his offer. What will do very well for white men, will not do for red men. I know you white men say we all come from the same father and mother, but you are mistaken. We have a tradition handed down from our forefathers, and we believe it, that the Great Spirit, when he undertook to make men, made the black man; it was his first attempt, and pretty well for a beginning; but he soon saw he had bungled; so he determined to try his hand again. He did so, and made the red man. He liked him much better than the black man, but still *he* was not exactly what he wanted. So he tried once more, and made the white man; and then he was satisfied. You see, therefore, that you were made last, and that is the reason I call you my youngest brother.

"When the Great Spirit had made the three men, he called them together and showed them three boxes. The first was filled with books, and maps, and papers; the second with bows and arrows, knives and tomahawks; the third with spades, axes, hoes, and hammers. 'These, my sons,' said he, 'are the means by which you are to live; choose among them according to your fancy.'

"The white man, being the favorite, had the first choice. He passed by the box of working-tools without notice; but when he came to the weapons for war and hunting, he stopped and looked hard at them. The red man trembled, for he had set his heart upon that box. The white man, however, after looking upon it for a moment, passed on, and chose the box of books and papers. The red man's turn came next; and you may be sure he seized with joy upon the bows and arrows, and tomahawks. As to the black man, he had no choice left, but to put up with the box of tools.

"From this it is clear that the Great Spirit intended the white man should learn to read and write; to understand all about the moon and stars; and to make every thing, even rum and whiskey. That the red man should be a first-rate hunter, and a mighty warrior, but he was not to learn any thing from books, as the Great Suirit had not given him any: nor was he to make rum and whiskey, lest he should kill himself with drinking. As to the black man, as he had nothing but working tools, it was clear he was to work for the white and red man, which he has continued to do.

"We must go according to the wishes of the Great Spirit, or we shall get into trouble. To know how to read and write, is very good for white men, but very bad for red men. It makes white men better, but red men worse. Some of the Creeks and Cherokees learnt to read and write, and they are the greatest rascals among all the Indians. They went on to Washington, and said they were going to see their Great Father, to talk about the good of the nation. And when they got there, they all wrote upon a little piece of paper, without the nation at home knowing any thing about it. And the first thing the nation at home knew of the matter, they were called together by the Indian agent, who showed them a little piece of paper, which he told them was a treaty, which their brethren had made in their name, with their Great Father at Washington. And as they knew not what a treaty was, he held up the little piece of paper, and they looked under it, and lo! it covered a great extent of country, and they found that their brethren, by knowing how to read and write, had sold their houses, and their lands, and the graves of their fathers; and that the white man, by knowing how to read and write, had gained them. Tell our Great Father at Washington, therefore, that we are very sorry we cannot receive teachers among us; for reading and writing, though very good for white men, is a very bad for Indians."

THE CONSPIRACY OF NEAMATHLA

AN AUTHENTIC SKETCH

In the autumn of 1823, Governor DUVAL, and other commissioners on the part of the United States, concluded a treaty with the chiefs and warriors of the Florida Indians, by which the latter, for certain considerations, ceded all claims to the whole territory, excepting a district in the eastern part, to which they were to remove, and within which they were to reside for twenty years. Several of the chiefs signed the treaty with great reluctance; but none opposed it more strongly than Neamathla, principal chief of the Mickasookies, a fierce and warlike people many of them Creeks by origin, who lived about the Mickasookie lake. Neamathla had always been active in those depredations on the frontiers of Georgia, which had brought vengeance and ruin on the Seminoles. He was a remarkable man; upward of sixty years of age, about six feet high, with a fine eye, and a strongly-marked countenance, over which he possessed great command. His hatred of the white men appeared to be mixed with contempt; on the common people he looked down with infinite scorn. He seemed unwilling to acknowledge any superiority of rank or dignity in Governor Duval, claiming to associate with him on terms of equality, as two great chieftains. Though he had been prevailed upon to sign the treaty, his heart revolted at it. In one of his frank conversations with Governor Duval, he observed: "This country belongs to the red man; and if I had the number of warriors at my command that this nation once had, I would not leave a white man on my lands. I would exterminate the whole. I can say this to you, for you can understand me: You are a man; but I would not say it to your people. They'd cry out I was a savage, and would take my life. They cannot appreciate the feelings of a man that loves his country."

As Florida had but recently been erected into a territory, every thing as yet was in rude and simple style. The Governor, to make himself acquainted with the Indians, and to be near at hand to keep an eye upon them, fixed his residence at Tallahassee, near the Fowel towns inhabited by the Mickasookies. His government palace for a time was a mere log house, and he lived on hunters' fare. The village of Neamathla was but about three miles off, and thither the governor occassionally rode to visit the old chieftain. In one of these visits, he found Neamathla seated in his wig wam, in the centre of the village, surrounded by his warriors. The governor had brought him some liquor as a present, but it mounted quickly into his brain, and rendered him quite boastful and belligerent. The theme ever uppermost in his mind. was the treaty with the whites. "It was true," he said, "the red men had made such a treaty, but the white men had not acted up to it. The red men had received none of the money, and the cattle that had been promised them: the treaty, therefore, was at an end, and they did not mean to be bound by it."

Governor Duval calmly represented to him that the time appointed in the treaty for the payment and delivery of the money and the cattle had not yet arrived. This the old chieftain knew full well, but he chose, for the moment, to pretend ignorance. He kept on drinking and talking his voice growing louder and louder, until it resounded all over the village. He held in his hand a long knife, with which had been rasping tobacco; this he kept flourishing backward and forward, as he talked, by way of giving effect to his words, brandishing it at times within an inch of the Governor's throat. He concluded his tirade by repeating, that the country belonged to the red men, and that, sooner than give it up, his bones and the bones of his people should bleach upon its soil."

Duval knew that the object of all this bluster was to see whether he could be intimidated. He kept his eye, therefore, fixed steadily on the chief, and, the moment he concluded with his menace, siezed him by the bosom of his hunting shirt, and, clinching his other fist:

"I've heard what you have said," replied he, "You have made a treaty, yet you say your bones shall bleach before you comply with it. As sure as there is a sun in heaven, your bones *shall* bleach, if you do not fulfill every article of that treaty! I'll let you know that I am *first* here, and will see that you do your duty."

Upon this, the old chieftain threw himself back, burst into a fit of laughing, and declared that all he had said was in joke. The Governor suspected, however, that there was a grave meaning at the bottom of this jocularity.

For two months, every thing went on smoothly; the Indians repaired daily to the log-cabin palace of the governor, at Tallahassee, and appeared perfectly contented. All at once they ceased their visits, and for three or four days not one was to be seen. Governor Duval began to apprehend that some mischief was brewing. On the evening of the fourth day, a chief named Yellow-Hair, a resolute, intelligent fellow, who had always evinced an attachment for the Governor, entered his cabin about twelve o'clock at night, and informed him, that between four and five hundred warriors, painted and decorated, were assembled to hold a secret war-talk at Neamathla's town. He had slipped off to give intelligence, at the risk of his life, and hastened back lest his absence should be discovered.

Governor Duval passed an anxious night after this intelligence. He knew the talent and the daring character of Neamathla; he recollected the threats he had thrown out, he reflected that about eighty white families were scattered widely apart, over a great extent of country, and might be swept away at once, should the Indians, as he feared, determine to clear the country. That he did not exaggerate the dangers of the case, has been proved by the horrid scenes of Indian warfare which have since desolated that devoted region. After a night of sleepless cogitation, Duval determined on a measure suited to this prompt and resolute character. Knowing the admiration of the savages for personal courage, he determined, by a sudden surprize, to endeavour to overawe and check them. It was hazarding much; but where so many lives were in jeopardy, he felt bound to incur the hazard.

Accordingly, on the next morning, he set off on horseback, attended merely by a white man, who had been reared among the Seminoles, and understood their language and manners, and who acted as interpreter. They struck into an Indian "trail" leading to Neamathla's village. After proceeding about half a mile, Governor Duval informed the interpreter of the object of his expedition. The latter, though a bold man, paused and remonstrated. The Indians among whom they were going were among the most desperate and discontented of the nation. Many of them were veteran warriors, impoverished and exasperated by defeat, and ready to set their lives at any hazard. He said that, if they were holding a war council, it must be with desperate intent, and it would be certain death to intrude among them.

Duval made light of his apprehensions, he said he was perfectly well acquainted with the Indian character, and should certainly proceed. So saying, he rode on. When within half a mile of the village, the interpreter adressed him again in such tremulous tone, that Duval turned and looked him in the face. He was deadly pale, and once more urged the governor to return, as they would certainly be massacred if they proceeded.

Duval repeated his determination to go on, but advised the other to return, lest his pale face should betray fear to the Indians, and they might take advantage of it. The interpreter replied that he would rather die a thousand deaths than have it said he had deserted his leader when in peril.

Duval then told him he must translate faithfully all he should say to the Indians, without softening a word.

The interpreter promised faithfully to do so, adding that he well knew, when they were once in the town, nothing but boldness could save them.

They now rode into the village, and advanced to the council-house. This was rather a group of four houses, forming a square, in the center of which was the great council-fire. The houses were open in front, toward the fire, and closed in the rear. At each corner of the square, there was an interval between the houses, for ingress and egress. In these houses sat the old man, and the chiefs: the young men were gathered round the fire. Neamathla presided at the council, elevated on a higher seat than the rest.

Governor Duval entered by one of the corner intervals, and rode boldly into the centre of the square. The young men made way for him; an old man who was speaking paused in the midst of his harangue. In an instant thirty or forty rifles were cocked and levelled. Never had Duval heard so loud a click of triggers: it seemed to strike to his heart. He gave one glance at the Indians, and turned off with an air of contempt. He did not dare, he says, to look again, lest it might affect his nerves; and on the firmness of his nerves every thing depended.

The chief threw up his arm. The rifles were lowered. Duval breathed more freely; he felt disposed to leap from his horse, but restrained himself, and dismounted leisurely. He then walked deliberately up to Neamathla, and demanded, in an authoritative tone, what were his motives for holding that council. The moment he made this demand, the orator sat down. The chief made no reply, but hung his head in apparent confusion. After a moment's pause, Duval proceeded:

"I am well aware of the meaning of this war-council, and deem it my duty to warn you against prosecuting the schemes you have been devising. If a single hair of a white man in this country falls to the ground; I will hang you and your chiefs on the trees around your council-house. You cannot pretend to withstand the power of the whitemen. You are in the palm of the hand of your Great Father at Washington, who can crush you like an egg-shell. You may kill me: I am but one man; but recollect, white men are numerous as the leaves on the trees. Remember the fate of your warriors whose bones are whitening in battle-fields. Remember your wives and children who perished in swamps. Do you want to provoke more hostilities? Another war with the white men, and there will not be a Seminole left to tell the story of his race."

Seeing the effect of his words, he concluded by appointing a day for the Indians to meet him at St Marks, and give an account of their conduct. He then rode off, without giving them time to recover from their surprise. That night he rode forty miles to Apalachicola river, to the tribe of the same name, who were in feud with the Seminoles. They promptly put two hundred and fifty warriors at his disposal, whom he ordered to be at St. Marks at the appointed day. He sent our runners, also, and mustered one hundred of the militia to repair to the same place; together with a number of regulars from the army. All his arrangements were successful.

Having taken these measures, he returned to Tallahassee, to the neighborhood of the conspirators, to show them that he was not afraid. Here he ascertained, through Yellow-Hair, that nine towns were disaffected, and had been concerned in the conspiracy. He was careful to inform himself, from the same source, of the names of the warriors in each of those towns who were most popular, though poor, and destitute of rank and command.

When the appointed day was at hand for the meeting at St. Marks, Governor Duval set off with Neamathla, who was at the head of eight or nine hundred warriors, but who feared to venture into the fort without him. As they entered the fort, and saw troops and militia drawn up there, and a force of Apalachicola soldiers stationed on the opposite bank of the river, they thought they were betrayed, and were about to fly; but Duval assured them they were safe, and, that when the talk was over, they might go home unmolested.

A grand talk was now held, in which the late conspiracy was discussed. As he had foreseen Neamathla and the other old chiefs threw all the blame upon the young men. "Well," replied Duval, "With us white men, when we find a man incompetent to govern those under him, we put him down, and appoint another in his place. Now as you all acknowledge you cannot manage your young men, we must put chiefs over them who can."

So saying, he deposed Neamathla first, appointing another in his place; and so on with all the rest; taking care to substitute the warriors who had been pointed out to him as poor and popular; putting medals round their necks, and investing them with great ceremony. The Indians were sur- prized and delighted at finding the appointments fall upon the very men they would themselves have chosen; and hailed them with acclamations. The warriors thus unexpectedly elevated to command, and clothed with dignity, were secured to the interests of the governor, and sure to keep an eye on the disaffected. As to the great chief Neamathla, he left the country in disgust; and returned to the Creek nation, who elected him a chief of one of their towns. Thus by the resolute spirit and prompt sagac- ity of one man, a dangerous conspiracy was completely defeated. Gov- ernor Duval was afterwards enabled to remove the whole nation, through his own personal influence, without the aid of the General Govern- ment.

Note.—The foregoing anecdotes concerning the Seminoles, were gathered in conversation with Governor Duval (the original of Ralph Ringwood).

THE COUNT VAN HORN

During the minority of Louis XV, while the Duke of Orleans was regent of France, a young Flemish nobleman, the Count Antoine Joseph Van Horn, made his sudden appearance in Paris, and by his character, conduct, and the subsequent disasters in which he became involved, created a great sensation in the high circles of the proud aristocracy. He was about twenty-two years of age, tall, finely formed, with a pale romantic countenance, and eyes of remarkable brilliancy and wildness.

He was one of the most ancient and highly-esteemed families of European nobility, being of the line of the Princes of Horn and Overique, sovereign Counts of Hautekerke, and hereditary grand Veneurs of the empire. The family took its name from the little town and seigneurie of Horn in Brabant; and was known as early as the eleventh century among the little dynasties of the Netherlands, and since that time, by a long line of illustrious generations. At the peace of Utrecht, when the Netherlands passed under subjection to Austria, the House of Van Horn came under the domination of the Emperor. At the time we treat of two of the branches of this ancient house were extinct; the third and only surviving branch was represented by the reigning Prince, Maximilian Emanuel Van Horn, twenty-four years of age, who resided in honorable and courtly style on his hereditary domains of Baussigny in the Netherlands, and his brother the Count Antoine Joseph, who is the subject of this memoir.

The ancient house of Van Horn, by the intermarriage of its various branches with the noble families of the continent had become widely connected and interwoven with the high aristocracy of Europe; the Count Antoine, therefore, could claim relationship to many of the proudest names in Paris. In fact, he was grandson, by the mother's side, of the Prince de Ligne, and even might boast of affinity to the Regent (the Duke of Orleans) himself. There were circumstances, however, connected with his sudden appearance in Paris and his previous story, that placed him in what is termed "a false position;" a word of baleful significance in the fashionable vocabulary of France.

The young Count had been a captain in the service of Austria, but had been cashiered for irregular conduct, and for disrespect to Prince Louis of Baden, Commander-in-chief. To check him in his wild career, and bring him to sober reflections, his brother the prince caused him to be arrested, and sent to the old castle of Van Wert, in the domains of Horn. This was the same castle in which, in former times,

John Van Horn, Stadtholder of Gueldres, had imprisoned his father; a circumstance which has furnished Rembrandt with the subject of an admirable painting. The Governor of the Castle was one Van Wert, grandson of the famous John Van Wert, the hero of many a popular song and legend. It was the intention of the prince that his brother should be held in honorable durance, for his object was to sober and improve, not to punish and afflict him. Van Wert, however, was a stern, harsh man; of violent passions. He treated the youth in a manner that prisoners and offenders were treated in the strong holds of the robber counts of Germany in old times; confined him in a dungeon, and inflicted on him such hardships and indignities, that the irritable temperament of the young Count was roused to continual fury, which ended in insanity. For six months was the unfortunate youth kept in this horrible state, without his brother the Prince being informed of his melancholy condition, or of the cruel treatment to which he was subjected. At length, one day, in a paroxysm of frenzy, the Count knocked down two of his gaolers with a beetle, escaped from the castle of Van Wert, and eluded all pursuit; and after roving about in a state of distraction, made his way to Baussigny, and appeared like a spectre before his brother.

The prince was shocked at his wretched emaciated appearance and, his lamentable state of mental alienation. He received him with the most compassionate tenderness; lodged him in his own room; appointed three servants to attend and watch over him day and night; and endeavoured, by the most soothing and affectionate assiduity, to atone for the past act of rigor with which he reproached himself. When he learned, however, the manner in which his unfortunate brother had been treated in confinement, and the course of brutalities that had led to his mental malady, he was aroused to indignation. His first step was to cashier Van Wert from his command. That violent man set the prince at defiance, and attempted to maintain himself in his government and his castle, by instigating the peasants, for several leagues round, to revolt. His insurrection might have been formidable against the power of a petty prince; but he was put under the ban of the Empire, and seized as a state prisoner. The memory of his grandfather the oft sung John Van Wert, alone saved him from a gibbet; but he was imprisoned in the strong tower of Horn-op-Zee. There he remained until he was eighty-two years of age, savage, violent, and unconquered to the last; for we are told that he never ceased fighting and thumping, as long as he could close a fist, or wield a cudgel.

In the mean time, a course of kind and gentle treatment and wholesome regimen, and above all, the tender and affectionate assiduity of his brother, the prince, produced the most salutary effects upon Count

Antoine. He gradually recovered his reason; but a degree of violence seemed always lurking at the bottom of his character, and he required to be treated with the greatest caution and mildness, for the least contradiction exasperated him.

In this state of mental convalescence. he began to find the supervision and restraints of brotherly affection insupportable; so he left the Netherlands furtively, and repaired to Paris, whither, in fact, it is said, he was called by motives of interest, to make arrangements concerning a valuable estate which he inherited from his relative the Princess d'Epinay.

On his arrival in Paris, he called upon the Marquis de Créqui and other of the high nobility with whom he was connected. He was received with great courtesy; but, as he brought no letters from his elder brother, the prince, and as various circumstances of his previous history had transpired, they did not receive him into their families, nor introduce him to their ladies. Still they fêted him in bachelor style, gave him gay and elegant suppers at their separate apartments, and took him to their boxes at the theatres. He was often noticed, too, at the doors of the most fashionable churches, taking his stand among the young men of fashion; and at such times, his tall elegant figure, his pale but handsome countenance, and his flashing eyes distinguished him from among the crowd; and the ladies declared that it was almost impossible to support his ardent gaze.

The Count did not afflict himself much at his limited circulation in the fastidious circles of the high aristocracy; he relished society of a wilder, and less ceremonious cast; and meeting with loose companions to his taste, soon ran into all the excesses of the capital in that most licentious period. It is said that, in the course of his wild carreer, he had an intrigue with a lady of quality, a favorite of the Regent; that he was surprized by that Prince in one of his interviews; that sharp words passed between them; and that the jealousy and vengeance thus awakened ended only with his life.

About this time the famous Mississippi scheme of Law was at its height; or rather it began to threaten that disastrous catastrophy which convulsed the whole financial world. Every effort was making to keep the bubble inflated. The vagrant population of France was swept off from the streets at night, and conveyed to Harve de Grace, to be shipped to the projected colonies; even laboring people and mechanics were thus crimped and spirited away. As Count Antoine, was in the habit of sallying forth at night in disguise, in pursuit of his pleasures, he came near being carried off by a gang of crimps; it seemed, in fact, as if they had been lying in wait for him, as he had experienced very rough treatment at their hands. Complaint was made of his case

by his relation the Marquis de Crequi, who took much interest in the
youth; but the Marquis received mysterious intimations not to inter-
fere in the matter, but to advise the Count to quit Paris immediately:
"If he lingers, he is lost!" This has been cited as a proof that vengeance
was dogging at the heels of the unfortunate youth, and only watching
for an opportunity to destroy him.

Such opportunity occurred but too soon. Among the loose companions
with whom the Count had become intimate, were two who lodged in the
same hotel with him. One was a youth only twenty years of age who
passed himself off as the chevalier d'Etampes, but whose real name was
Lestang, the prodigal son of a Flemish banker. The other, named Laur-
ent de Mille, a Piedmontese, was a cashiered captain, and at the time
an esquire in the service of the dissolute Princess de Carignan, who kept
gambling-tables in her palace. It is probable that gambling propensities had brought these young men together, and that their losses had
driven them to desperate measures; certain it is, that all Paris was suddenly astounded by a murder which they were said to have committed.
What made the crime more startling, was, that it seemed connected with
the great Mississippi scheme, at that time the fruitful source of all kinds
of panics and agitation. A Jew, a stock-broker, who dealt largely in
shares of the bank of Law, founded on the Mississippi scheme, was the
victim. The story of his death is variously related. The darkest account
states that the Jew was decoyed by these young men into an obscure tavern, under pretext of negotiating with him for bank shares to the amount
of one hundred thousand crowns, which he had with him in his pocket-
book. Lestang kept watch upon the stairs. The Count and De Mille entered with the Jew into a chamber. In a little while there were heard
cries and struggles from within. A waiter passing by the room, looked in,
and seeing the Jew weltering in his blood, shut the door again, double
locked it, and alarmed the house. Lestang rushed down stairs, made his
way to the hotel, secured his most portable effects, and fled the country.
The Count and De Mille endeavored to escape by the window, but were
both taken; and conducted to prison.

A circumstance which occurs in this part of the Count's story, seems to
point him out as a fated man. His mother, and his brother, the Prince Van
Horn, had received intelligence some time before at Baussigny, of the
dissolute life the Count was leading at Paris, and of his losses at play.
They despatched a gentleman of the prince's household to Paris, to pay
the debts of the Count, and persuade him to return to Flanders; or, if
he should refuse, to obtain an order from the Regent for him to quit the
capital. Unfortunately the gentleman did not arrive at Paris until the
day after the murder.

The news of the Count's arrest and imprisonment, on a charge of murder, caused a violent sensation among the high aristocracy. All those connected with him, who had treated him hitherto with indifference, found their dignity deeply involved in the question of his guilt or innocence. A general convocation was held at the Hotel of the Marquis de Créqui, of all the relatives and allies of the house of Horn. It was an assemblage of the most proud and aristocratic personages of Paris. Inquiries were made into the circumstances of the affair. It was ascertained, beyond a doubt, that the Jew was dead, and that he had been killed by several stabs of a poignard. In escaping by the window, it was said that the Count had fallen, and been immediately taken; but that De Mille had fled through the streets, pursued by the populace, and had been arrested at some distance from the scene of the murder. That the Count had declared himself innocent of the death of the Jew, and that he had risked his own life in endeavoring to protect him; but that De Mille on being brought back to the tavern, confessed to a plot to murder the broker, and rob him of his pocket-book, and inculpated the Count in the crime.

Another version of the story was, that the Count Van Horn had deposited with the broker bank shares to the amount of eighty-eight thousand livres; that he had sought him in this tavern, which was one of his resorts, and had demanded the shares; that the Jew had denied the deposit; that a quarrel had ensued, in the course of which the Jew struck the Count in the face; that the latter, transported with rage, had snatched up a knife from a table, and wounded the Jew in the shoulder; and that thereupon De Mille, who was present, and who had likewise been defrauded by the broker, fell on him, and despatched him with blows of a poniard, and seized upon his pocket-book: that he had offered to divide the contents of the latter with the Count, *pro rata*, of what the usurer had defrauded them; that the latter had refused the proposition with disdain, and that, at a noise of persons approaching, both had attempted to escape from the premises, but had been taken.

Regard the story in any way they might, appearances were terribly against the Count, and the noble assemblage was in great consternation. What was to be done to ward off so foul a disgrace and to save their illustrious escutcheons from this murderous stain of blood? Their first attempt was to prevent the affair from going to trial, and their relative from being dragged before a criminal tribunal, on so horrible and degrading a charge. They applied, therefore, to the Regent, to intervene his power; to treat the Count as having acted under an access of his mental malady; and to shut him up in a mad-house. The Regent was deaf to their solicitations. He replied, coldly, that if the Count was a madman, one could not get rid too quickly of madmen who were furious in their insanity. The crime was too public and atrocious, to be hushed up, or slurred over; justice must take its course.

Seeing there was no avoiding the humiliating scene of a public trial, the noble relatives of the Count endeavored to predispose the minds of the magistrates, before whom he was to be arraigned. They accordingly made urgent and eloquent representations of the high descent, and noble and powerful connexions of the Count; set forth the circumstances of his early history; his mental malady; the nervous irritability to which he was subject, and his extreme sensitiveness to insult or contradiction. By these means, they sought to prepare the judges to interpret every thing in favor of the Count, and, even if it should prove that he had inflicted the mortal blow on the usurer, to attribute it to access of insanity, provoked by insult.

To give full effect to these representations the noble conclave determined to bring upon the judges the dazzling rays of the whole assembled aristocracy. Accordingly, on the day that the trial took place, the relations of the Count to the number of fifty-seven persons, of both sexes, and of the highest rank, repaired in a body to the palace of Justice and took their stations in a long corridor which led to the court-room. Here, as the judges entered, they had to pass in review this array of lofty and noble personages, who saluted them mournfully and significantly, as they passed. Any one conversant with the stately pride and jealous dignity of the French noblesse of that day, may imagine the extreme state of sensitiveness that produced this self-abasement. It was confidently presumed, however, by the noble suppliants, that having once brought themselves to this measure, their influence over the tribunal would be irresistible. There was one lady present, however, Madame de Beauffremont, who was affected with the Scottish gift of second sight, and related such dismal and sinister apparitions as passing before her eyes, that many of her female companions were filled with doleful presentiments.

Unfortunately for the Count, there was another interest at work, more powerful even than the high aristocracy. The infamous but all potent Abbe Du Bois, the grand favorite and bosom counsellor of the Regent, was deeply interested in the scheme of Law, and the prosperity of his bank, and of course in the security of the stock-brokers. Indeed the regent himself is said to have dipped deep in the Mississippi scheme. Dubois and Law, therefore, exerted their influence to the utmost, to have the tragic affair pushed to the extremity of the law, and the murder of the broker punished in the most signal and appalling manner. Certain it is, the trial was neither long nor intricate. The Count and his fellow prisoner were equally inculpated in the crime, and both were condemned to a death the most horrible and ignominious—to be broken alive on the wheel!

As soon as the sentence of the court was made public, all the nobility, in any degree related to the house of Van Horn, went into mourning. Another grand aristocratical assemblage was held, and a petition to the Regent, on behalf of the Count, was drawn out and left with the Marquis de Créqui for signature. This petition set forth the previous insanity of the Count, and showed that it was a hereditary malady in his family. It stated various circumstances in mitigation of his offense, and implored that his sentence might be continued to perpetual imprisonment.

Upward of fifty names of the highest nobility, beginning with the Prince de Ligne, and including cardinals, archbishops, dukes, marquises, etc., together with ladies of equal rank, were signed to this petition. By one of the caprices of human pride and vanity it became an object of ambition to get enrolled among the illustrious suppliants, a kind of testimonial of noble blood, to prove relationship to a murderer! The Marquis de Créqui was absolutely besieged by applicants to sign, and had to refer their claims to this singular honor, to the Prince de Ligne, the grand-father of the Count. Many who were excluded, were highly incensed, and numerous feuds took place. Nay, the affronts thus given to the morbid pride of some aristocratical families, passed from generation to generation; for fifty years afterward the Duchess of Mazarin complained of a slight which her father had received from the Marquis de Créqui, which proved to be something connected with the signature of this petition!

This important document being completed, the illustrious body of petitioners, male and female, on Saturday evening, the eve of Palm Sunday, repaired to the Palais Royal, the residence of the Regent, and were ushered, with great ceremony, but profound silence, into his hall of council. They had appointed four of their number as deputies, to present the petition, viz. the Cardinal de Rohan, the Duke de Havré, the Prince de Ligne, and the Marquis de Créqui. After a little while, the deputies were summoned to the cabinet of the Regent. They entered, leaving the assembled petitioners in a state of the greatest anxiety. As time slowly wore away, and the evening advanced, the gloom of the company increased. Several of the ladies prayed devoutly; the good Princess of Armagnac told her beads.

The petition was received by the Regent with a most unpropitious aspect. "In asking the pardon of the criminal," said he, "you display more zeal for the house of Van Horn, than for the service of the King." The noble deputies enforced the petition by every argument in their power. They supplicated the Regent to consider that the infamous punishment in question would reach not merely the person of the condemned, not merely the House of Van Horn, but also the genealogies of princely and illustrious families, in whose armorial bearings might be found quarterings of this dishonored name.

"Gentlemen," replied the regent "it appears to me the disgrace consists in the crime, rather than in the punishment."

The Prince de Ligne spoke with warmth, "I have in my genealogical standard," said he, "four escutcheons of Van Horn, and of course have four ancestors of that house. I must have them erased and effaced, and there would be so many blank spaces like holes in my heraldic ensigns. There is not a sovereign family which would not suffer through the rigour of your Royal Highness; nay, all the world knows that in the thirty-two quarterings of Madame, your mother, there is an escutcheon of Van Horn."

"Very well," replied the Regent, "I will share the disgrace with you, gentlemen."

Seeing that a pardon could not be obtained, the Cardinal de Rohan and the Marquis de Créqui left the cabinet; but the Prince de Ligne and the Duke de Havré remained behind. The honor of their houses, more than the life of the unhappy Count, was the great object of their solicitude. They now endeavored to obtain a minor grace. They represented that in the Netherlands, and in Germany, there was an important difference in the public mind as to the mode of inflicting the punishment of death upon persons of quality. That decapitation had no influence on the fortunes of the family of the executed, but that the punishment of the wheel was such an infamy, that the uncles, aunts, brothers, and sisters, of the criminal, and his whole family, for three succeeding generations, were excluded from all noble chapters, princely abbeys, sovereign bishoprics, and even Teutonic commanderies of the Order of Malta. They showed how this would operate immediately upon the fortunes of a sister of the Count, who was on the point of being received as a canonness into one of the noble chapters.

While this scene was going on in the cabinet of the Regent, the illustrious assemblage of petitioners remained in the hall of council, in the most gloomy state of suspense. The reëntrance from the cabinet of the Cardinal de Rohan and the Marquis de Créqui, with pale, down-cast countenances, had struck a chill into every heart. Still they lingered until near midnight, to learn the result of the after application. At length the cabinet conference was at an end. The Regent came forth, and saluted the high personages of the assemblage in a courtly manner. One old lady of quality, Madame de Guyon, whom he had known in his infancy, he kissed on the cheek, calling her his "good aunt." He made a most ceremonious salutation to the stately Marchioness de Créqui, telling her he was charmed to see her at the Palais Royal; "a compliment very ill-timed, said the Marchioness, considering the circumstances which brought me there." He then conducted the ladies to the door of the second saloon, and there dismissed them, with the most ceremonious politeness.

The application of the Prince de Ligne and the Duke de Havré, for a change of the mode of punishment, had, after much difficulty, been suc-

cessful. The Regent had promised solemnly to send a letter of commuta-
tion to the attorney-general on Holy Monday, the 25th of March, at five
o'clock in the morning. According to the same promise, a scaffold would
be arranged in the cloister of the Conciergerie, or prison, where the Count
would be beheaded on the same morning, immediately after having received absolution. This mitigation of the form of punishment gave but
little consolation to the great body of petitioners, who had been anxious
for the pardon of the youth: it was looked upon as all-important, however, by the Prince de Ligne, who, as has been before observed, was exquisitely alive to the dignity of his family.

The Bishop of Bayeux and the Marquis de Créqui visited the unfortunate youth in prison. He had just received the communion in the chapel
of the Conciergerie, and was kneeling before the altar, listening to a mass
for the dead, which was performed at his request. He protested his innocence of any intention to murder the Jew, but did not deign to allude
to the accusation of robbery. He made the bishop and the Marquis
promise to see his brother the prince, and inform him of this his dying
asseveration.

Two other of his relations, the Prince Rebecq-Montmorency and the
Marshal Van Isenghein, visited him secretly, and offered him poison, as a
means of evading the disgrace of a public execution. On his refusing to
take it, they left him with high indignation. "Miserable man!" said they,
"You are fit only to perish by the hand of the executioner!"

The Marquis de Créqui sought the executioner of Paris, to bespeak an
easy and decent death for the unfortunate youth. "Do not make him suffer," said he; "uncover no part of him but the neck; and have his body
placed in a coffin, before you deliver it to his family." The executioner
promised all that was requested, but declined a rouleau of a hundred
louis-d'ors which the Marquis would have put into his hand. "I am paid
by the king for fulfilling my office," said he; and added, that he had already refused a like sum, offered by another relation of the Marquis.

The Marquis de Créqui returned home in a state of deep affliction.
There he found a letter from the Duke de St. Simon, the familiar friend of
the Regent, repeating the promise of that prince, that the punishment of
the wheel should be commuted to decapitation.

"Imagine," says the Marchioness de Créqui, who in her memoirs gives
a detailed account of this affair, "imagine what we experienced, and what
was our astonishment, our grief, and indignation, when, on Tuesday the
26th of March, an hour after mid-day, word was brought us that the
Count Van Horn had been exposed on the wheel, in the Place de Grève,
since half past six in the morning, on the same scaffold with the Piedmontese De Mille, and that he had been tortured previous to execution!"

One more scene of aristocratic pride closed this tragic story. The Marquis de Créqui, on receiving this astounding news, immediately arrayed himself in the uniform of a general officer, with his cordon of nobility on the coat. He ordered six valets to attend him in grand livery, and two of his carriages, each with six horses, to be brought forth. In this sumptuous state, he set off for the Place de Grève, where he had been preceded by the Princes de Ligne, de Rohan, de Crouy, and the Duke de Havré.

The Count Van Horn was already dead, and it was believed that the executioner had had the charity to give him the coup de grace, or 'death-blow,' at eight o'clock in the morning. At five o'clock in the evening, when the Judge Commissary left his post at the Hotel de Ville, these noblemen, with their own hands, aided to detach the mutilated remains of their relation; the Marquis de Créqui placed them in one of his carriages, and bore them off to his hotel, to receive the last sad obsequies.

The conduct of the Regent in this affair excited general indignation. His needless severity was attributed by some to vindictive jealousy; by others to the persevering machinations of Law and the Abbé Dubois. The house of Van Horn, and the high nobility of Flanders and Germany, considered themselves flagrantly outraged: many schemes of vengeance were talked of, and a hatred engendered against the Regent, that followed him through life, and was wreaked with bitterness upon his memory after his death.

The following letter is said to have been written to the Regent by the Prince Van Horn, to whom the former had adjudged the confiscated effects of the Count:

"I do not complain, Sir, of the death of my brother, but I complain that your Royal Highness has violated in his person the rights of the kingdom, the nobility, and the nation. I thank you for the confiscation of his effects; but I should think myself as much disgraced as he, should I accept any favor at your hands. *I hope that God and the King may render to you as strict justice as you have rendered to my unfortunate brother.*"

DON JUAN: A SPECTRAL RESEARCH

"I have heard of spirits walking with aërial bodies, and have been wondered at by others; but I must only wonder at myself, for, if they be not mad, I'me come to my own buriall."

SHIRLEY'S "WITTY FAIRIE ONE."

Every body has heard of the fate of DON JUAN, the famous libertine of Seville, who for his sins against the fair sex, and other minor peccadilloes, was hurried away to the infernal regions. His story has been illustrated in play, in pantomime, and farce, on every stage in christendom, until at length it has been rendered the theme of the opera of operas, and embalmed to endless duration is the glorious music of Mozart. I well recollect the effect of this story upon my feelings in my boyish days, though represented in grotesque pantomime; the awe with which I contemplated the monumental statue on horseback of the murdered commander, gleaming by pale moonlight in the convent cemetery: how my heart quaked as he bowed his marble head, and accepted the impious invitation of Don Juan: how each foot-fall of the statue smote upon my heart, as I heard it approach, step by step through the echoing corridor, and beheld it enter, and advance, a moving figure of stone, to the supper table! But then the convivial scene in the charnel house, where Don Juan returned the visit of the statue; was offered a banquet of skulls and bones, and on refusing to partake, was hurled into a yawning gulf, under a tremendous shower of fire! These were accumulated horrors enough to shake the nerves of the most pantomime-loving school-boy. Many have supposed the story of Don Juan a mere fable. I myself thought so once; but 'seeing is believing.' I have since beheld the very scene where it took place, and now to indulge any doubt on the subject, would be preposterous.

I was one night perambulating the streets of Seville, in company with a Spanish friend, a curious investigator of the popular traditions and other good-for-nothing lore of the city, and who was kind enough to imagine he had met, in me, with a congenial spirit. In the course of our rambles, we were passing by a heavy dark gate-way, opening into the court-yard of a convent, when he laid his hand upon my arm: "Stop!" said he; "this is the convent of San Francisco; there is a story connected with it, which I am sure must be known to you. You cannot but have heard of Don Juan and the marble statue."

"Undoubtedly," replied I; "it has been familiar to me from childhood."

"Well, then, it was in the cemetery of this very convent that the events took place."

"Why, you do not mean to say that the story is founded on fact?"

"Undoubtedly it is. The circumstances of the case are said to have occurred during the reign of Alfonso XI. Don Juan was of the noble family of Tenorio, one of the most illustrious houses of Andalusia. His father, Don Diego Tenorio, was a favorite of the king, and his family ranked among the *veintecuatros*, or magistrates, of the city. Presuming on his high descent and powerful connexions, Don Juan set no bounds to his excesses: no female, high or low, was sacred from his pursuit; and he soon became the scandal of Seville. One of his most daring outrages was, to penetrate by night into the palace of Don Gonzalo de Ulloa, commander of the order of Calatrava, and attempt to carry off his daughter. The household was alarmed; a scuffle in the dark took place; Don Juan escaped, but the unfortunate commander was found weltering in his blood, and expired without being able to name his murderer. Suspicions attached to Don Juan; he did not stop to meet the investigations of justice and the vengeance of the powerful family of Ulloa, but fled from Seville, and took refuge with his uncle, Don Pedro Tenorio, at that time ambassador at the court of Naples. Here he remained until the agitation occasioned by the murder of Don Gonzalo had time to subside; and the scandal which the affair might cause to both the families of Ulloa and Tenorio had induced them to hush it up. Don Juan, however, continued his libertine career at Naples, until at length his excesses forfeited the protection of his uncle, the ambassador, and obliged him again to flee. He had made his way back to Seville, trusting that his past misdeeds were forgotten, or rather trusting to his dare-devil spirit and the power of his family, to carry him through all difficulties.

"It was shortly after his return, and while in the height of his arrogance, that on visiting this very convent of Francisco, he beheld on a monument the equestrian statue of the murdered commander, who had been buried within the walls of this sacred edifice, where the family of Ulloa had a chapel. It was on this occasion that Don Juan, in a moment of impious levity, invited the statue to the banquet, the awful catastrophe of which has given such celebrity to his story."

"And pray how much of this story,' said I, 'is believed in Seville?"

"The whole of it by the populace; with whom it has been a favorite tradition since time immemorial, and who crowd to the theatres to see it represented in dramas written long since by Tyrso de Molina, and another of our popular writers. Many in our higher ranks also, accustomed from childhood to this story, would feel somewhat indignant at hearing it treated with contempt. An attempt has been made to explain the whole, by asserting that, to put an end to the extravagancies of Don Juan, and to pacify the family of Ulloa, without exposing the delinquent to the degrading penalties of justice, he was decoyed into this convent under false pretext, and either plunged into a perpetual dungeon, or privately hurried out of existence; while the story of the statue was circulated by the monks, to account for his sudden disappearance. The populace, however, are not to be cajoled out of a ghost story by any of these plausible explanations; and the marble statue still strides the stage, and Don Juan is still plunged into the infernal regions, as an awful warning to all rake-helly youngsters, in like case offending."

While my companion was relating these anecdotes, we traversed the exterior court-yard of the convent, and made our way into a great interior court; partly surrounded by cloisters and dormitories, partly by chapels, and having a large fountain in the centre. The pile had evidently once been extensive and magnificent; but it was for the greater part in ruins. By the light of the stars, and of twinkling lamps placed here and there in the chapels and corridors, I could see that many of the columns and arches were broken; the walls were rent and riven; while burnt beams and rafters showed the destructive effects of fire. The whole place had a desolate air; the night breeze rustled through grass and weeds flaunting out of the crevices of the walls, or from the shattered columns; the bat flitted about the vaulted passages, and the owl hooted from the ruined belfry. Never was any scene more completely fitted for a ghost story.

While I was indulging in picturings of the fancy, proper to such a place, the deep chaunt of the monks from the convent church came swelling upon the ear. "It is the vesper service," said my companion; "follow me."

Leading the way across the court of the cloisters, and through one or two ruined passages, he reached the portal of the church, and pushing open a wicket, cut in the folding doors, we found ourselves in the deep arched vestibule of the sacred edifice. To our left was the choir, forming one end of the church, and having a low vaulted ceiling, which gave it the look of a cavern. About this were ranged the monks, seated on stools, and chaunting from immense books placed on music-stands, and having the notes scored in such gigantic characters as to be legible from every part of the choir. A few lights on these music-stands dimly illumined the choir, gleamed on the shaven heads of the monks, and threw their shadows on the walls. They were gross, blue-bearded, bullet-headed men, with bass voices, of deep metallic tone, that reverberated out of the cavernous choir.

To our right extended the great body of the church. It was spacious and lofty; some of the side chapels had gilded grates, and were decorated with images and paintings, representing the sufferings of our Saviour. Aloft was a great painting by Murillo, but too much in the dark to be distinguished. The gloom of the whole church was but

faintly relieved by the reflected light from the choir, and the glim-
mering here and there of a votive lamp before the shrine of a saint.

As my eye roamed about the shadowy pile, it was struck with the
dimly seen figure of a man on horseback, near a distant altar. I
touched my companion, and pointed to it: "The spectre statue!"
said I.

"No," replied he; "it is the statue of the blessed St. Iago; the
statue of the commander was in the cemetery of the convent, and was
destroyed at the time of the conflagration. But," added he, "as I see
you take a proper interest in these kind of stories, come with me to
the other end of the church, where our whisperings will not disturb
these holy fathers at their devotions, and I will tell you another story,
that has been current for some generations in our city, by which you
will find that Don Juan is not the only libertine that has been the
object of supernatural castigation in Seville."

I accordingly followed him with noiseless tread to the farther part
of the church, where we took our seats on the steps of an altar, opposite to the suspicious-looking figure on horseback, and there, in a low
mysterious voice, he related to me the following narrative.

"There was once in Seville a gay young fellow, Don Manuel de
Manara by name, who having come to a great estate by the death of
his father, gave the reins to his passions, and plunged into all kinds
of dissipation. Like Don Juan, whom he seemed to have taken for
a model, he became famous for his enterprises among the fair sex,
and was the cause of doors being barred and windows grated with
more than usual strictness. All in vain. No balcony was too high for
him to scale; no bolt nor bar was proof against his efforts; and his
very name was a word of terror to all the jealous husbands and
cautious fathers of Seville. His exploits extended to country as well
as city; and in the village dependant on his castle, scarce a rural beauty
was safe from his arts and enterprises.

"As he was one day ranging the streets of Seville, with several of
his dissolute companions, he beheld a procession about to enter the
gate of a convent. In the centre was a young female, arrayed in the
dress of a bride; it was a novice, who, having accomplished her year
of probation, was about to take the black veil, and consecrate herself
to heaven. The companions of Don Manuel drew back, out of respect to the sacred pageant; but he pressed forward, with his usual
impetuosity, to gain a near view of the novice. He almost jostled
her, in passing through the portal of the church, when, on her turning
round, he beheld the countenance of a beautiful village girl, who had
been the object of his ardent pursuit, but who had been spirited

secretly out of his reach by her relatives. She recognized him at the same moment, and fainted; but was borne within the grate of the chapel. It was supposed the agitation of the ceremony and the heat of the throng had overcome her. After some time, the curtain which hung within the grate was drawn up: there stood the novice, pale and trembling, surrounded by the abbess and the nuns. The ceremony proceeded; the crown of flowers was taken from her head; she was shorn of her silken tresses, received the black veil, and went passively through the remainder of the ceremony.

"Don Manuel de Manara, on the contrary, was roused to fury at the sight of this sacrifice. His passion, which had almost faded away in the absence of the object, now glowed with tenfold ardor, being inflamed by the difficulties placed in his way, and piqued by the measures which had been taken to defeat him. Never had the object of his pursuit appeared so lovely and desirable as when within the grate of the convent; and he swore to have her, in defiance of heaven and earth. By dint of bribing a female servant of the convent, he contrived to convey letters to her, pleading his passion in the most eloquent and seductive terms. How successful they were, is only matter of conjecture; certain it is, he undertook one night to scale the garden wall of the convent, either to carry off the nun, or gain admission to her cell. Just as he was mounting the wall, he was suddenly plucked back, and a stranger muffled in a cloak, stood before him.

" 'Rash man, forbear!' cried he: 'is it not enough to have violated all human ties? Wouldst thou steal a bride from heaven!'

"The sword of Don Manuel had been drawn on the instant, and furious at this interruption, he passed it through the body of the stranger, who fell dead at his feet. Hearing approaching footsteps, he fled the fatal spot, and mounting his horse, which was at hand, retreated to his estate in the country, at no great distance from Seville. Here he remained throughout the next day, full of horror and remorse; dreading least he should be known as the murderer of the deceased, and fearing each moment the arrival of the officers of justice.

"The day passed, however, without molestation; and, as the evening advanced, unable any longer to endure this state of uncertainty and apprehension, he ventured back to Seville. Irresistibly his footsteps took the direction of the convent; but he paused and hovered at a distance from the scene of blood. Several persons were gathered round the place, one of whom was busy nailing something against the convent wall. After a while they dispersed, and one passed near to Don Manuel. The latter addressed him, with hesitating voice.

" 'Señor,' said he, 'may I ask the reason of yonder throng?'

" 'A cavalier,' replied the other, 'has been murdered.'

"'Murdered!' echoed Don Manuel; 'and can you tell me his name?'

"'Don Manuel de Manara,' replied the stranger, and passed on.

"Don Manuel was startled at this mention of his own name; especially when applied to the murdered man. He ventured, when it was entirely deserted, to approach the fatal spot. A small cross had been nailed against the wall, as is customary in Spain, to mark the place where a murder has been committed; and just below it he read, by the twinkling light of a lamp: 'Here was murdered Don Manuel de Manara. Pray to God for his soul!'

"Still more confounded and perplexed by this inscription, he wandered about the streets until the night was far advanced, and all was still and lonely. As he entered the principal square, the light of torches suddenly broke on him, and he beheld a grand funeral procession moving across it. There was a great train of priests, and many persons of dignified appearance, in ancient Spanish dresses, attending as mourners, none of whom he knew. Accosting a servant who followed in the train, he demanded the name of the defunct.

"'Don Manuel de Manara,' was the reply; and it went cold to his heart. He looked, and indeed beheld the armorial bearings of his family emblazoned on the funeral escutcheons. Yet not one of his family was to be seen among the mourners. The mystery was more and more incomprehensible.

"He followed the procession as it moved on to the cathedral. The bier was deposited before the high altar; the funeral service was commenced, and the grand organ began to peal through the vaulted aisles.

"Again the youth ventured to question this awful pageant. 'Father,' said he, with trembling voice, to one of the priests, 'who is this you are about to inter?'

"'Don Manuel de Manara!' replied the priest.

"'Father,' cried Don Manuel, impatiently, 'you are deceived. This is some imposture. Know that Don Manuel de Manara is alive and well, and now stands before you. I am Don Manuel de Manara!'

"'Avaunt, rash youth!' cried the priest; 'know that Don Manuel de Manara is dead!—is dead!—is dead— and we are all souls from purgatory, his deceased relatives and ancestors, and others that have been aided by masses from his family, who are permitted to come here and pray for the repose of his soul!'

"Don Manuel cast round a fearful glance upon the assemblage, in antiquated Spanish garbs, and recognized in their pale and ghastly countenances the portraits of many an ancestor that hung in the family picture-gallery. He now lost all self-command, rushed up to the bier, and beheld the counterpart of himself, but in the fixed and livid lineaments of death. Just at that moment the whole choir burst forth with a 'Requeiscat in pace,' that shook the vaults of the cathedral. Don Manuel sank senseless on the pavement. He was found there early the next morning by the sacristan, and conveyed to his home. When sufficiently recovered, he sent for a friar, and made a full confession of all that had happened.

"'My son,' said the friar, 'all this is a miracle and a mystery, intended for thy conversion and salvation. The corpse thou hast seen was a token that thou hadst died to sin and the world: take warning by it, and henceforth live to righteousness and heaven!'

"Don Manuel did take warning by it. Guided by the councils of the worthy friar, he disposed of all his temporal affairs; dedicated the greater part of his wealth to pious uses, especially to the performance of masses for souls in purgatory; and finally, entering a convent, became one of the most zealous and exemplary monks in Seville."

While my companion was relating this story, my eyes wandered from time to time, about the dusky church. Methought the burly countenances of the monks in the distant choir assumed a pallid, ghastly hue, and their deep metallic voices had a sepulchral sound. By the time the story was ended, they had ended their chaunt; and, extinguishing their lights, glided one by one, like shadows, though a small door in the side of the choir. A deeper gloom prevailed over the church; the figure opposite me on horseback grew more and more spectral; and I almost expected to see it bow its head.

"It is time to be off," said my companion, "unless we intend to sup with the statue."

"I have no relish for such fare nor such company," replied I; and, following my companion, we groped our way through the mouldering cloisters. As we passed by the ruined cemetery, keeping up a casual conversation, by way of dispelling the loneliness of the scene, I called to mind the words of the poet:

> ———— "The tombs
> And monumental caves of death look cold,
> And shoot a chilliness to my trembling heart!
> Give me thy hand, and let me hear thy voice;
> Nay, speak—and let me hear thy voice;
> Mine own affrights me with its echoes."

There wanted nothing but the marble statue of the commander, striding along the echoing cloisters, to complete the haunted scene.

Since that time, I never fail to attend the theatre whenever the story of Don Juan is represented, whether in pantomime or opera. In the sepulchral scene, I feel myself quite at home; and when the statue makes his appearance, I greet him as an old acquaintance. When the audience applaud, I look round upon them with a degree of compassion: "Poor souls!" I say to myself, "they think they are pleased; they think they enjoy this piece, and yet they consider the whole as a fiction! How much more would they enjoy it, if like me they knew it to be true—*and had seen the very place!*"

LEGEND
OF THE ENGULPHED CONVENT

At the dark and melancholy period when Don Roderick the Goth and his chivalry were overthrown on the banks of the Guadalete and all Spain was overrun by the Moors, great was the devastation of churches and convents, throughout that pious kingdom. The miraculous fate of one of those holy piles is thus recorded in an authentic legend of those days.

On the summit of a hill, not very distant from the capital city of Toledo, stood an ancient convent and chapel, dedicated to the invocation of Saint Benedict, and inhabited by a sisterhood of Benedictine nuns. This holy asylum was confined to females of noble lineage. The younger sisters of the highest families were here given in religious marriage to their saviour, in order that the portions of their elder sisters might be encreased, and they enabled to make suitable matches on earth, or that the family wealth might go undivided to elder brothers, and the dignity of their ancient honors be protected from decay. The convent was renowned, therefore, for enshrining within its walls a sisterhood of the purest blood, the most immaculate virtue, and most resplendent beauty of all Gothic Spain.

When the Moors overran the kingdom, there was nothing that more excited their hostility, than those virgin asylums. The very sight of a convent-spire was sufficient to set their Moslem blood in a foment, and they sacked it with as fierce a zeal as though the sacking of a nunnery were a sure passport to Elysium.

Tidings of such outrages, committed in various parts of the kingdom, reached this noble sanctuary, and filled it with dismay. The danger came nearer and nearer; the infidel hosts were spreading all over the country; Toledo itself was captured; there was no flying from the convent, and no security within its walls.

In the midst of this agitation, the alarm was given one day, that a great band of Saracens were spurring across the plain. In an instant the whole convent was a scene of confusion. Some of the nuns wrung their fair hands at the windows; others waved their veils, and uttered shrieks, from the tops of the towers vainly hoping to draw relief from a country overrun by the foe. The sight of these innocent doves thus fluttering about their dove-cote, but encreased the zealot fury of the whiskered Moors. They thundered at the portal and at every blow the ponderous gates trembled on their hinges.

The nuns now crowded round the abbess. They had been accustomed to look up to her as all powerful, and they now implored her protection. The mother abbess looked with a rueful eye upon the treasures of beauty and vestal virtue exposed to such imminent peril. Alas! how was she to protect them from the spoiler! She had, it is true, experienced many signal interpositions of providence in her individual favor. Her early days had been passed amid the temptations of a court, where her virtue had been purified by repeated trials, from none of which had she escaped but by miracle. But were miracles never to cease? Could she hope that the marvellous protection shown to herself, would be extended to a whole sisterhood? There was no resource. The Moors were at the threshold; a few moments more, and the convent would be at their mercy.

Summoning her nuns to follow her, she hurried into the chapel; and throwing herself on her knees before the image of the Blessed Mary. "Oh holy lady!" exclaimed she, "oh most pure and immaculate of virgins! thou seest our extremity. The ravager is at the gate and there is none on earth to help us! Look down with pity, and grant that the earth may gape and swallow us rather than that our cloister vows should suffer violation!"

The Moors redoubled their assault upon the portal; the gates gave way with a tremendous crash; a savage yell of exultation arose; when, of a sudden the earth yawned; down sank the convent, with its cloisters, its dormitories, and all its nuns. The chapel tower was the last that sank, the bell ringing forth a peal of triumph in the very teeth of the infidels.

Forty years had passed and gone, since the period of this miracle. The subjugation of Spain was complete. The Moors lorded it over city and country; and such of the christian population as remained, and were permitted to exercise their religion, did it in humble resignation to the Moslem sway.

At this time, a christian cavalier, of Cordova, hearing that a patriotic band of his countrymen had raised the standard of the cross in the mountains of the Asturias, resolved to join them, and unite in breaking the yoke of bondage. Secretly arming himself and caparisoning his steed, he set forth from Cordova, and pursued his course by unfrequented mule-paths, and along the dry channels made by winter torrents. His spirit burned with indignation, whenever, on commanding a view over a long sweeping plain, he beheld the Mosque swelling in the distance, and the Arab horsemen careering about, as if the rightful lords of the soil. Many a deep-drawn sigh, and heavy groan, also, did the good cavalier utter, on passing the ruins of churches and convents desolated by the conquerors.

It was on a sultry midsummer evening that this wandering cavalier, in skirting a hill thickly covered with forest, heard the faint tones of a vesper bell sounding melodiously in the air, and seeming to come from the summit of the hill. The cavalier crossed himself with wonder, at this unwonted and christian sound. He supposed it to proceed from one of those humble chapels and hermitages permited to exist through the indulgence of the Moslem conquerors. Turning his steed up a narrow path of the forest, he sought this sanctuary, in hopes of finding a hospitable shelter for the night. As he advanced, the trees threw a deep gloom around him and the bat flitted across his path. The bell ceased to toll, and all was silence.

Presently a choir of female voices came stealing sweetly through the forest, chaunting the evening service, to the solemn accompanyment of an organ. The heart of the good Cavalier melted at the sound, for it recalled the happier days of his country. Urging forward on his weary steed, he at length arrived at a broad grassy area, on the summit of the hill, and surrounded by the forest. Here the melodious voices rose in full chorus, like the swelling of the breeze, but whence they came he could not tell. Sometimes they were before, sometimes behind him; sometimes in the air, sometimes as if from within the bosom of the earth. At length they died away, and a holy stillness settled on the place.

The cavalier gazed around with bewildered eye. There was neither chapel nor convent, nor humble hermitage, to be seen; nothing but a moss-grown stone pinnacle, rising out of the centre of the area, and surmounted by a cross.—The green sward appeared to have been sacred from the tread of man or beast, and the surrounding trees bent toward the cross, as if in adoration.

The cavalier felt a sensation of holy awe. He alighted and tethered his steed on the skirts of the forest, where he might crop the tender herbage; then approaching the cross, he knelt and poured forth his evening prayers before this relique of the christian days of Spain. His orisons being concluded he laid himself down at the foot of the pinnacle, and reclining his head against one of its stones, fell into a deep sleep.

About midnight, he was awakened by the tolling of a bell, and found himself lying before the gate of an ancient convent. A train of nuns passed by, each bearing a taper. He rose and followed them into the chapel; in the centre was a bier, on which lay the corpse of an aged nun. The organ performed a solemn requiem: the nuns joining in chorus. When the funeral service was finished, a melodious voice chaunted, "requiescat in pace!"—"May she rest in peace!" The lights immediately vanished; the whole passed away as a dream, and the cavalier found himself at the foot of the cross, and beheld, by the faint rays of the rising moon, his steed quietly grazing near him.

When the day dawned, he descended the hill, and following the course of a small brook, came to a cave, at the entrance of which was seated an ancient man, in hermit's garb, with rosary and cross, and a beard that descended to his girdle. He was one of those holy anchorites permitted by the Moors to live unmolested in the dens, and caves, and humble hermitages, and even to practice the rites of their religion. The cavalier, dismounting, knelt and craved a benediction. He then related all that had befallen him in the night, and besought the hermit to explain the mystery.

"What thou hast heard and seen, my son," replied the other, "is but a type and shadow of the woes of Spain."

He then related the foregoing story of the miraculous deliverance of the convent.

"Forty years," added the holy man, "have elapsed since this event, yet the bells of that sacred edifice are still heard, from time to time, sounding from under ground, together with the pealing of the organ, and the chaunting of the choir. The Moors avoid this neighborhood, as haunted ground, and the whole place, as thou mayst perceive, has become covered with a thick and lonely forest."

The cavalier listened with wonder to the story. For three days and nights did he keep vigils with the holy man beside the cross; but nothing more was to be seen of nun or convent. It is supposed that, forty years having elapsed, the natural lives of all the nuns were finished, and the cavalier had beheld the obsequies of the last. Certain it is, that from that time, bell, and organ, and choral chaunt, have never more been heard.

The mouldering pinnacle, surmounted by the cross, remains an object of pious pilgrimage. Some say that it anciently stood in front of the convent, but others that it was the spire which remained above ground, when the main body of the building sank, like the top-mast of some tall ship that has foundered. These pious believers maintain, that the convent is miraculously preserved entire in the centre of the mountain, where, if proper excavations were made, it would be found, with all its treasures, and monuments, and shrines, and reliques, and the tombs of its virgin nuns.

Should any one doubt the truth of this marvellous interposition of the virgin to protect the vestal purity of her votaries, let him read the excellent work entitled "España Triumphante," written by Fray Antonio de Saneta Maria a bare-foot friar of the Carmelite order, and he will doubt no longer.

THE PHANTOM ISLAND

Break, Phantsie, from thy cave of cloud,
   And wave thy purple wings,
Now all thy figures are allowed,
   And various shapes of things.
Create of airy forms a stream;
   It must have blood and nought of phlegm;
And though it be a walking dream,
   Yet let it like an odor rise
    To all the senses here,
And fall like sleep upon their eyes,
    Or music on their ear.

BEN JONSON.

"There are more things in heaven and earth than are dreamed of in our philosophy," and among these may be placed that marvel and mystery of the seas, the Island of St. Brandan. Those who have read the history of the Canaries, the Fortunate Islands of the ancients, may remember the wonders told of this enigmatical island. Occasionally it would be visible from their shores, stretching away in the clear bright west, to all appearance substantial like themselves, and still more beautiful. Expeditions would launch forth from the Canaries to explore this land of promise. For a time its sun-gilt peaks and long, shadowy promontories would remain distinctly visible, but in proportion as the voyagers approached, peak and promontory would gradually fade away until nothing would remain but blue sky above, and deep blue water below. Hence this mysterious isle was stigmatized by ancient cosmographers with the name of Aprositus or the Inaccessible. The failure of numerous expeditions sent in quest of it, both in ancient and modern days, have at length caused its very existence to be called in question, and it has been rashly pronounced a mere optical illusion, like the Fata Morgana of the Straits of Messina, or has been classed with those unsubstantial regions known to mariners as Cape Fly Away and the coast of Cloud Land.

Let us not permit, however, the doubts of worldly-wise skeptics to rob us of all the glorious realms owned by happy credulity in days of yore. Be assured, O reader of easy faith!—thou for whom it is my delight to labor—be assured that such an island actually exists, and has, from time to time, been revealed to the gaze, and trodden by the feet, of favored mortals. Historians and philosophers may have their doubts, but is existence has been fully attested by that inspired race, the poets; who, being gifted with a kind of second sight, are enabled to discern those mysteries of nature hidden from the eyes of ordinary men. To this gifted race it has ever been a kind of wonder-land. Here once bloomed, and perhaps still blooms, the famous garden of the Hesperides, with its golden fruit. Here, too, the sorceress Armida had her enchanted garden, in which she held the christian paladin, Rinaldo, in delicious but inglorious thraldom, as set forth in the immortal lay of Tasso. It was on this island that Sycorax, the witch, held sway, when the good Prospero, and his infant daughter Miranda, were wafted to its shores. The isle was then

———— "full of noises,
Sounds, and sweet airs, that give delight, and hurt not."

Who does not know the tale, as told in the magic page of Shakespeare? The island, in fact at different times, has been under the sway of different powers, genii of earth, and air, and ocean, who have made it their shadowy abode. Hither have retired many classic but broken-down deities, shorn of almost all their attributes, but who once ruled the poetic world. Here Neptune and Amphithrite hold a diminished court; soverigns in exile. Their ocean chariot, almost a wreck, lies bottom upward in some sea-beaten cavern; their pursy Tritons and haggard Nereids bask listlessly like seals about the rocks. Sometimes those deities assume, it is said, a shadow of their ancient pomp, and glide in state about a summer sea; and then, as some tall Indiaman lies becalmed with idly flapping sail, her drowsy crew may hear the mellow note of the Triton's shell swelling upon the ear as the invisible pageant sweeps by.

On the shores of this wondrous isle, the kraken heaves its unwieldy bulk, and wallows many a rood; here the sea-serpent, that mighty but much contested reptile, lies coiled up during the intervals of its revelations to the eyes of true believers; here even the Flying Dutchman finds a port, and casts his anchor, and furls his shadowy sail, and takes a brief repose from his eternal cruisings.

In the deep bays and harbors of the island lies many a spellbound ship, long since given up as lost by the ruined merchant. Here too its crew, long, long bewailed in vain, lie sleeping from age to age, in mossy grottoes, or wander about in pleasing oblivion of all things. Here in caverns are garnered up the priceless treasures lost in the ocean. Here sparkles in vain the diamond and flames the carbuncle. Here are piled up rich bales of Oriental silks, boxes of pearls, and piles of golden ingots.

Such are some of the marvels related of this island, which may serve to throw light upon the following legend, of unquestionable truth, which I recommend to the implicit belief of the reader.

THE ADALANTADO OF THE SEVEN CITIES

A LEGEND OF ST. BRANDAN

In the early part of the fifteenth century, when Prince Henry of Portugal, of worthy memory, was pushing the career of discovery along the western coast of Africa, and the world was resounding with reports of golden regions on the main land, and new-found islands in the ocean, there arrived at Lisbon an old bewildered pilot of the seas, who had been driven by tempests, he knew not whither, and raved about an island far in the deep, upon which he had landed, and which he had found peopled with Christians, and adorned with noble cities.

The inhabitants, he said, having never before been visited by a ship, gathered round, and regarded him with surprise. They told him they were descendants of a band of Christians, who fled from Spain when that country was conquered by the Moslems. They were curious about the state of their father land, and grieved to hear that the Moslems still held possession of the kingdom of Granada. They would have taken the old navigator to church, to convince him of their orthodoxy; but, either through lack of devotion, or lack of faith in their words, he declined their invitation, and preferred to return on board of his ship. He was properly punished. A furious storm arose, drove him from his anchorage, hurried him out to sea, and he saw no more of the unknown island.

This strange story caused great marvel in Lisbon and elsewhere. Those versed in history, remembered to have read, in an ancient chronicle, that, at the time of the conquest of Spain, in the eighth century, when the blessed cross was cast down, and the crescent erected in its place, and when Christian churches were turned into Moslem mosques, seven bishops, at the head of seven bands of pious exiles, had fled from the peninsula, and embarked in quest of some ocean island, or distant land, where they might found seven Christian cities, and enjoy their faith unmolested.

The fate of these saints errant had hitherto remained a mystery, and their story had faded from memory; the report of the old tempest-tossed pilot, however, revived this long-forgotten theme; and it was determined by the pious and enthusiastic, that the island thus accidentally discovered, was the identical place of refuge, whither the wandering bishops had been guided by a protecting Providence, and where they had folded their flocks.

This most excitable of worlds has always some darling object of chimerical enterprise: the "Island of the Seven Cities" now awakened as much interest and longing among zealous Christians, as has the renowned city of Timbuctoo among adventurous travellers, or the North-east Passage among hardy navigators; and it was a frequent prayer of the devout, that these scattered and lost portions of the Christian family might be discovered, and reunited to the great body of christendom.

No one, however, entered into the matter with half the zeal of Don Fernando de Ulmo, a young cavalier, of high standing in the Portuguese court, and of most sanguine and romantic temperament. He had recently come to his estate, and had run the round of all kinds of pleasures and excitements, when this new theme of popular talk and wonder presented itself. The Island of the Seven Cities became now the constant subject of his thoughts by day, and his dreams by night; it even rivalled his passion for a beautiful girl, one of the greatest belles of Lisbon, to whom he was betrothed. At length, his imagination became so inflamed on the subject, that he determined to fit out an expedition, at his own expense, and set sail in quest of this sainted island. It could not be a cruise of any great extent; for, according to the calculations of the tempest-tossed pilot, it must be somewhere in the latitude of the Canaries; which at that time, when the new world was as yet undiscovered, formed the frontier of ocean enterprise. Don Fernando applied to the crown for countenance and protection. As he was a favorite at court, the usual patronage was readily extended to him; that is to say, he received a commission from the king, Don Ioam II., constituting him Adalantado, or military governor, of any country he might discover, with the single proviso, that he should bear all the expenses of the discovery, and pay a tenth of the profits to the crown.

Don Fernando now set to work in the true spirit of a projector. He sold acre after acre of solid land, and invested the proceeds in ships, guns, ammunition, and sea-stores. Even his old family mansion, in Lisbon, was mortgaged without scruple, for he looked forward to a palace in one of the Seven Cities, of which he was to be Adalantado. This was the age of nautical romance, when the thoughts of all speculative dreamers were turned to the ocean. The scheme of Don Fernando, therefore, drew adventurers of every kind. The merchant promised himself new marts of opulent traffic; the soldier hoped to sack and plunder some one or other of those Seven Cities; even the fat monk shook off the sleep and sloth of the cloister, to join in a crusade which promised such increase to the possessions of the church.

One person alone regarded the whole project with sovereign contempt and growing hostility. This was Don Ramiro Alvarez, the father of the beautiful Serafina, to whom Don Fernando was betrothed. He was one of those perverse, matter-of-fact old men, who are prone to oppose every thing speculative and romantic. He had no faith in the Island of the Seven Cities; regarded the projected cruise as a crack-brained freak; looked with angry eye and internal heart-burning on the conduct of his intended son-in-law, chaffering away solid lands for lands in the moon, and scoffingly dubbed him Adalantado of Cloud Land. In fact, he had never really relished the intended match, to which his consent had been slowly extorted, by the tears and entreaties of his daughter. It is true he could have no reasonable objections to the youth, for Don Fernando was the very flower of Portuguese chivalry. No one could excel him at the tilting match, or the riding at the ring; none was more bold and dexterous in the bull fight; none composed more gallant madigrals in praise of his lady's charms, or sang them with sweeter tones to the accompaniment of her guitar; nor could any one handle the castanets and dance the bolero with more captivating grace. All these admirable qualities and endowments, however, though they had been sufficient to win the heart of Serafina, were nothing in the eyes of her unreasonable father. Oh Cupid, god of Love! why will fathers always be so unreasonable!

The engagement to Serafina had threatened at first to throw an obstacle in the way of the expedition of Don Fernando, and for a time perplexed him in the extreme. He was passionately attached to the young lady; but he was also passionately bent on this romantic enterprise. How should he reconcile the two passionate inclinations? A simple and obvious arrangement at length presented itself: marry Serafina, enjoy a portion of the honeymoon at once, and defer the rest until his return from the discovery of the Seven Cities!

He hastened to make known this most excellent arrangement to Don Ramiro, when the long-smothered wrath of the old cavalier burst forth. He reproached him with being the dupe of wandering vagabonds and wild schemers, and with squandering all his real possessions, in pursuit of empty bubbles. Don Fernando was too sanguine a projector, and too young a man, to listen tamely to such language. He acted with what is technically called 'becoming spirit.' A high quarrel ensued; Don Ramiro pronounced him a mad man, and forbade all farther intercourse with his daughter, until he should give proof of returning sanity, by abandoning this mad-cap enterprise; while Don Fernando flung out of the house, more bent than ever on the expedition, from the idea of triumphing over the incredulity of the gray-beard, when he should return successful. Don Ramiro's heart misgave him. Who knows, thought he, but this crack-brained visionary may persuade my daughter to elope with him, and share his throne in this unknown paradise of fools? If I could only keep her safe until his ships are fairly out at sea!

He repaired to her apartment, represented to her the sanguine, unsteady character of her lover and the chimerical value of his schemes, and urged the propriety of suspending all intercourse with him until he should recover from his present hallucination. She bowed her head as if in filial acquiescence, whereupon he folded her to his bosom with parental fondness and kissed away a tear that was stealing over her cheek, but as he left the chamber quietly turned the key on the lock; for though he was a fond father, and had a high opinion of the submissive temper of his child, he had a still higher opinion of the conservative virtues of lock and key, and determined to trust to them until the caravels should sail. Whether the damsel had been in any wise shaken in her faith, as to the schemes of her lover by her father's eloquence, tradition does not say; but certain it is, the moment she heard the key turn in the lock, she became a firm believer in the Island of the Seven Cities.

The door was locked; but her will was unconfined. A window of the chamber opened into one of those stone balconies, secured by iron bars, which project like huge cages from Portuguese and Spanish houses. Within this balcony the beautiful Serafina had her birds and flowers, and here she was accustomed to sit on moonlight nights as in a bower, and touch her guitar and sing like a wakeful nightingale. From this balcony an intercourse was now maintained between the lovers, against which the lock and key of Don Ramiro were of no avail. All day would Fernando be occupied hurrying the equipments of his ships, but evening found him in sweet discourse beneath his lady's window.

At length the preparations were completed. Two gallant caravels lay at anchor in the Tagus ready to sail at sunrise. Late at night by the pale light of a waning moon the lover had his last interview. The beautiful Serafina was sad at heart and full of dark forebodings; her lover full of hope and confidence. "A few short months," said he, "and I shall return in triumph. Thy father will then blush at his incredulity, and hasten to welcome to his house the Adalantado of the Seven Cities."

The gentle lady shook her head. It was not on this point she felt distrust. She was a thorough believer in the Island of the Seven Cities, and so sure of the success of the enterprise that she might have been tempted to join it had not the balcony been high and the grating strong. Other considerations induced that dubious shaking of the head. She had heard of the inconstancy of the seas, and the inconstancy of those who roam them. Might not Fernando meet with other loves in foreign ports? Might not some peerless beauty in one or other of those Seven Cities efface the image of Serafina from his mind? Now let the truth be spoken, the beautiful Serafina had reason for her disquiet. If Don Fernando had any fault in the world, it was that of being rather inflammable and apt to take fire from every sparkling eye. He had been somewhat of a rover among the sex on shore, what might he be on sea?

She ventured to express her doubt, but he spurned at the very idea. "What! he false to Serafina! He bow at the shrine of another beauty?

Never! never!" Repeatedly did he bend his knee, and smite his breast, and call upon the silver moon to witness his sincerity and truth.

He retorted the doubt, "Might not Serafina herself forget her plighted faith? Might not some wealthier rival present himself while he was tossing on the sea; and, backed by her father's wishes, win the treasure of her hand!"

The beautiful Serafina raised her white arms between the iron bars of the balcony, and, like her lover, invoked the moon to testify her vows. Alas! how little did Fernando know her heart. The more her father should oppose, the more would she be fixed in faith. Though years should intervene, Fernando on his return would find her true. Even should the salt sea swallow him up (and her eyes shed salt tears at the very thought), never would she be the wife of another! Never, *never*, NEVER! She drew from her finger a ring gemmed with a ruby heart, and dropped it from the balcony, a parting pledge of constancy.

Thus the lovers parted with many a tender word and plighted vow. But will they keep those vows? Perish the doubt! Have they not called the constant moon to witness?

With the morning dawn the caravels dropped down the Tagus, and put to sea. They steered for the Canaries, in those days the regions of nautical discovery and romance, and the outposts of the known world, for as yet Columbus had not steered his daring barks across the ocean. Scarce had they reached those latitudes when they were separated by a violent tempest. For many days was the caravel of Don Fernando driven about at the mercy of the elements; all seamanship was baffled, destruction seemed inevitable and the crew were in despair. All at once the storm subsided; the ocean sank into a calm; the clouds which had veiled the face of heaven were suddenly withdrawn, and the tempest-tossed mariners beheld a fair and mountainous island, emerging as if by enchantment from the murky gloom. They rubbed their eyes and gazed for a time almost incredulously, yet there lay the island spread out in lovely landscapes, with the late stormy sea laving its shores with peaceful billows.

The pilot of the caravel consulted his maps and charts; no island like the one before him was laid down as existing in those parts; it is true he had lost his reckoning in the late storm, but, according to his calculations, he could not be far from the Canaries; and this was not one of that group of islands. The caravel now lay perfectly becalmed off the mouth of a river, on the banks of which, about a league from the sea, was descried a noble city, with lofty walls and towers, and a protecting castle.

After a time, a stately barge with sixteen oars was seen emerging from the river, and approaching the caravel. It was quaintly carved and gilt; the oarsmen were clad in antique garb, their oars painted of a bright crimson, and they came slowly and solemnly, keeping time as they rowed to the cadence of an old Spanish ditty. Under a silken canopy in the stern, sat a cavalier richly clad, and over his head was a banner bearing the sacred emblem of the cross.

When the barge reached the caravel, the cavalier stepped on board. He was tall and gaunt, with a long Spanish visage, moustaches that curled up to his eyes, and a forked beard. He wore gauntlets reaching to his elbows, a Toledo blade strutting out behind, with a basket hilt, in which he carried his handkerchief. His air was lofty and precise, and bespoke indisputably the hidalgo. Thrusting out a long spindle leg, he took off a huge sombrero, and swaying it until the feather swept the ground, accosted Don Fernando in the old Castilian language and with the old Castilian courtesy, welcoming him to the Island of the Seven Cities.

Don Fernando was overwhelmed with astonishment. Could this be true? Had he really been tempest-driven to the very land of which he was in quest?

It was even so. That very day the inhabitants were holding high festival in commemoration of the escape of their ancestors from the Moors. The arrival of the caravel at such a juncture was considered a good omen, the accomplishment of an ancient prophecy through which the island was to be restored to the great community of Christendom. The cavalier before him was grand-chamberlain, sent by the alcayde to invite him to the festivities of the capital.

Don Fernando could scarce believe that this was not all a dream. He made known his name, and the object of his voyage. The grand chamberlain declared that all was in perfect accordance with the ancient prophecy, and that the moment his credentials were presented, he would be acknowledged as the Adalantado of the Seven Cities. In the mean time the day was waning; the barge was ready to convey him to the land, and would as assuredly bring him back.

Don Fernando's pilot, a veteran of the seas, drew him aside and expostulated against his venturing, on the mere word of a stranger, to land in a strange barge on an unknown shore. "Who knows, Señor, what land this is, or what people inhabit it?"

Don Fernando was not to be dissuaded. Had he not believed in this island when all the world doubted? Had he not sought it in defiance of storm and tempest, and was he now to shrink from its shores when they lay before him in calm weather? In a word, was not faith the very corner-stone of his enterprise?

Having arrayed himself, therefore, in gala dress befitting the occasion, he took his seat in the barge. The grand chamberlain seated himself opposite. The rowers plied their oars, and renewed the mournful old ditty, and the gorgeous but unwieldly barge moved slowly through the water.

The night closed in before they entered the river, and swept along past rock and promontory, each guarded by its tower. At every post they were challenged by the sentinel.

"Who goes there?"

"The Adalantado of the Seven Cities."

"Welcome, Señor Adalantado. Pass on."

Entering the harbor they rowed close by an armed galley of ancient form. Soldiers with crossbows patrolled the deck.

"Who goes there?"

"The Adalantado of the Seven Cities."

"Welcome, Señor Adalantado. Pass on."

They landed at a broad flight of stone steps, leading up between two massive towers, and knocked at the water-gate. A sentinel, in ancient steel casque, looked from the barbecan.

"Who is there?"

"The Adalantado of the Seven Cities."

"Welcome, Señor Adalantado."

The gate swung open, grating upon rusty hinges. They entered between two rows of warriors in Gothic armor, with crossbows, maces, battle-axes and faces old-fashioned as their armor. There were processions through the streets, in commemoration of the landing of the seven Bishops and their followers, and bonfires, at which effiges of losel Moors expiated their invasion of Christendom by a kind of auto-da-fé. The groups round the fires, uncouth in their attire, looked like the fantastic figures that roam the streets in Carnival time. Even the dames who gazed down from Gothic balconies hung with antique tapestry, resembled effiges dressed up in Christmas mummeries. Every thing, in short, bore the stamp of former ages, as if the world had suddenly rolled back for several centuries. Nor was this to be wondered at. Had not the Island of the Seven Cities been cut off from the rest of the world for several hundred years; and were not these the modes and customs of Gothic Spain before it was conquered by the Moors?

Arrived at the palace of the Alcayde, the grand chamberlain knocked at the portal. The porter looked through a wicket, and demanded who was there.

"The Adalantado of the Seven Cities."

The portal was thrown wide open. The grand chamberlain led the way up a vast, heavily-moulded, marble staircase, and into a hall of ceremony, where was the Alcayde with several of the principal dignitaries of the city, who had a marvellous resemblance, in form and feature, to the quaint figures in old illuminated manuscripts.

The grand chamberlain stepped forward and announced the name and title of the stranger guest, and the extraordinary nature of his mission. The announcement appeared to create no extraordinary emotion or surprise, but to be received as the anticipated fulfilment of a prophecy.

The reception of Don Fernando, however, was profoundly gracious, though in the same style of stately courtesy which every where prevailed. He would have produced his credentials, but this was courteously declined. The evening was devoted to high festivity; the following day, when he should enter the port with his caravel, would be devoted to business, when the credentials would be received in due form, and he inducted into office as Adalantado of the Seven Cities.

Don Fernando was now conducted through one of those interminable suites of apartments, the pride of Spanish palaces, all furnished in a style of obsolete magnificence. In a vast saloon blazing with tapers was assembled all the aristocracy and fashion of the city; stately dames and cavaliers, the very counterpart of the figures in the tapestry which decorated the walls. Fernando gazed in silent marvel. It was a reflex of the proud aristocracy of Spain in the time of Roderick the Goth.

The festivities of the evening were all in the style of solemn and antiquated ceremonial. There was a dance, but it was as if the old tapestry were put in motion, and all the figures moving in stately measure about the floor. There was one exception, and one that told powerfully upon the susceptible Adalantado. The Alcayde's daughter— such a ripe, melting beauty! Her dress, it is true, like the dresses of her neighbors, might have been worn before the flood, but she had the black Andalusian eye, a glance of which, through its long dark lashes, is irresistible. Her voice, too, her manner, her undulating movements, all smacked of Andalusia, and showed how female charms may be transmitted from age to age, and clime to clime, without ever going out of fashion. Those who know the witchery of the sex, in that most amorous part of amorous old Spain, may judge of the fascination to which Don Fernando was exposed, as he joined in the dance with one of its most captivating descendants.

He sat beside her at the banquet! such an old world feast! such obsolete dainties! At the head of the table the peacock, that bird of state and ceremony, was served up in full plumage on a golden dish. As Don Fernando cast his eyes down the glittering board, what a vista presented itself of odd heads and head-dresses; of formal bearded dignitaries and stately dames, with castellated locks and towering plumes! Is it to be wondered at that he should turn with delight from these antiquated figures to the Alcayde's daughter, all smiles and dimples, and melting looks and melting accents? Beside, for I wish to give him every excuse in my power, he was in a particularly excitable mood from the novelty of the scene before him, from this realization of all his hopes and fancies, and from frequent draughts of the wine cup presented to him at every moment by officious pages during the banquet.

In a word—there is no concealing the matter—before the evening was over, Don Fernando was making love outright to the Alcayde's daughter. They had wandered together to a moon-lit balcony of the palace, and he was charming her ear with one of those love ditties with which, in a like balcony, he had serenaded the beautiful Serafina.

The damsel hung her head coply. "Ah! Señor, these are flattering words; but you cavaliers, who roam the seas, are unsteady as its waves. To-morrow you will be throned in state, Adalantado of the Seven Cities; and will think no more of the Alcayde's daughter."

Don Fernando in the intoxication of the moment called the moon to witness his sincerity. As he raised his hand in adjuration, the chaste moon cast a ray upon the ring that sparkled on his finger. It caught the damsel's eye. "Signor Adalantado," said she archly, "I have no great faith in the moon, but give me that ring upon your finger in pledge of the truth of what you profess."

The gallant Adalantado was taken by surprise; there was no parrying this sudden appeal: before he had time to reflect, the ring of the beautiful Serafina glittered on the finger of the Alcayde's daughter.

At this eventful moment the chamberlain approached with lofty demeanor, and announced that the barge was waiting to bear him back to the caravel. I forbear to relate the ceremonious partings with the Alcayde and his dignitaries, and the tender farewell of the Alcayde's daughter. He took his seat in the barge opposite the grand chamberlain. The rowers plied their crimson oars in the same slow and stately manner to the cadence of the same mournful old ditty. His brain was in a whirl with all that he had seen, and his heart now and then gave him a twinge as he thought of his temporary infidelity to the beautiful Serafina. The barge sallied out into the sea, but no caravel was to be seen; doubtless she had been carried to a distance by the current of the river. The oarsmen rowed on; their monotonous chant had a lulling effect. A drowsy influence crept over Don Fernando. Objects swam before his eyes. The oarsmen assumed odd shapes as in a dream. The grand chamberlain grew larger and larger, and taller and taller. He took off his huge sombrero, and held it over the head of Don Fernando, like an extinguisher over a candle. The latter cowered beneath it; he felt himself sinking in the socket.

"Good night; Señor Adalantado of the Seven Cities!" said the grand chamberlain.

"The sombrero slowly descended—Don Fernando was extinguished!

How long he remained extinct no mortal man can tell. When he returned to consciousness, he found himself in a strange cabin, surrounded by strangers. He rubbed his eyes, and looked round him wildly. Where was he?—On board of a Portuguese ship, bound to Lisbon. How came he there?—He had been taken senseless from a wreck drifting about the ocean.

Don Fernando was more and more confounded and perplexed. He recalled, one by one, every thing that had happened to him in the Island of the Seven Cities, until he had been extinguished by the sombrero of the grand chamberlain. But what had happened to him since? What had become of his caravel? Was it the wreck of her on which he had been found floating?

The people about him could give no information on the subject. He entreated them to take him to the Island of the Seven Cities, which could not be far off. Told them all that had befallen him there. That he had but to land to be received as Adalantado; when he would reward them magnificently for their services.

They regarded his words as the ravings of delirium, and in their honest solicitude for the restoration of his reason, administered such rough remedies that he was fain to drop the subject and observe a cautious taciturnity.

At length they arrived in the Tagus, and anchored before the famous city of Lisbon. Don Fernando sprang joyfully on shore, and hastened to his ancestral mansion. A strange porter opened the door, who knew nothing of him or of his family; no people of the name had inhabited the house for many a year.

He sought the mansion of Don Ramiro. He approached the balcony beneath which he had bidden farewell to Serafina. Did his eyes deceive him? No! There was Serafina herself among the flowers in the balcony. He raised his arms toward her with an exclamation of rapture. She cast upon him a look of indignation, and, hastily retiring, closed the casement with a slam that testified her displeasure.

Could she have heard of his flirtation with Alcayde's daughter? But that was mere transient gallantry. A moment's interview would dispel every doubt of his constancy.

He rang at the door; as it was opened by the porter he rushed up stairs; sought the well-known chamber, and threw himself at the feet of Serafina. She started back with affright, and took refuge in the arms of a youthful cavalier.

"What mean you, Señor," cried the latter, "by this intrusion?"

"What right have you to ask the question?" demanded Don Fernando fiercely.

"The right of an affianced suitor!"

Don Fernando started and turned pale. "Oh, Serafina! Serafina!" cried he, in a tone of agony; "is this thy plighted constancy?"

"Serafina? What mean you by Serafina, Señor? If this be the lady you intend, her name is Maria."

"May I not believe my senses? May I not believe my heart?" cried Don Fernando. "Is not this Serafina Alvarez, the original of yon portrait, which, less fickle than herself, still smiles on me from the wall?"

"Holy Virgin!" cried the young lady, casting her eyes upon the portrait. "He is talking of my great-grandmother!"

An explanation ensued, if that could be called an explanation, which plunged the unfortunate Fernando into tenfold perplexity. If he might believe his eyes, he saw before him his beloved Serafina; if he might believe his ears, it was merely her hereditary form and features, perpetuated in the person of her great grand-daughter.

His brain began to spin. He sought the office of the Minister of Marine, and made a report of his expedition, and of the Island of the Seven Cities, which he had so fortunately discovered. No body knew any thing of such an expedition, or such an island. He declared that he had undertaken the enterprise under a formal contract with the crown, and had received a regular commission, constituting him Adalantado. This must be matter of record, and he insisted loudly, that the books of the department should be consulted. The wordy strife at length attracted the attention of an old gray-headed clerk, who sat perched on a high stool, at a high desk, with iron rimmed spectacles on the top of a thin, pinched nose, copying records into an enormous folio. He had wintered and summered in the department for a great part of a century, until he had almost grown to be a piece of the desk at which he sat; his memory was a mere index of official facts and documents, and his brain was little better than red tape and parchment. After peering down for a time from his lofty perch, and ascertaining the matter in controversy, he put his pen behind his ear, and descended. He remembered to have heard something from his predecessor about an expedition of the kind in question, but then it had sailed during the reign of Dom Ioam II., and he had been dead at least a hundred years. To put the matter beyond dispute, however, the archives of the Torre do Tombo, that sepulchre of old Portuguese documents, were diligently searched, and a record was found of a contract between the crown and one Fernando de Ulmo, for the discovery of the Island of the Seven Cities, and of a commission secured to him as Adalantado of the country he might discover.

"There!" cried Don Fernando, triumphantly, "there you have proof, before your own eyes, of what I have said. I am the Fernando de Ulmo specified in that record. I have discovered the Island of the Seven Cities, and am entitled to be Adalantado, according to contract."

The story of Don Fernando had certainly, what is pronounced the best of historical foundation, documentary evidence; but when a man, in the bloom of youth, talked of events that had taken place above a century previously, as having happened to himself, it is no wonder that he was set down for a mad man.

The old clerk looked at him from above and below his spectacles, shrugged his shoulders, stroked his chin, rëascended his lofty stool, took the pen from behind his ears, and resumed his daily and eternal task, copying records into the fiftieth volume of a series of gigantic folios. The other clerks winked at each other shrewdly, and dispersed to their several places, and poor Don Fernando, thus left to himself, flung out of the office, almost driven wild by these repeated perplexities.

In the confusion of his mind, he instinctively repaired to the mansion of Alvarez, but it was barred against him. To break the delusion under which the youth apparently labored, and to convince him that the Serafina about whom he raved was really dead, he was conducted to her tomb. There she lay, a stately matron, cut out in alabaster; and there lay her husband beside her; a portly cavalier, in armor; and there knelt, on each side, the effigies of a numerous progeny, proving that she had been a fruitful vine. Even the very monument gave proof of the lapse of time; the hands of her husband, folded as if in prayer, had lost their fingers, and the face of the once lovely Serafina was without a nose.

Don Fernando felt a transient glow of indignation at beholding this moumental proof of the inconstancy of his mistress; but who could expect a mistress to remain constant during a whole century of absence? And what right had he to rail about constancy, after what had passed between himself and the Alcayde's daughter? The unfortunate cavalier performed one pious act of tender devotion; he had the alabaster nose of Serafina restored by a skilful statuary, and then tore himself from the tomb.

He could now no longer doubt the fact that, somehow or other, he had skipped over a whole century, during the night he had spent at the Island of the Seven Cities; and he was now as complete a stranger in his native city, as if he had never been there. A thousand times did he wish himself back to that wonderful island, with its antiquated banquet halls, where he had been so courteously received; and now that the once young and beautiful Serafina was nothing but a great grandmother in marble, with generations of descendants, a thousand times would he recall the melting black eyes of the Alcayde's daughter, who doubtless, like himself, was still flourishing in fresh juvenility, and breathe a secret wish that he were seated by her side.

He would at once have set on foot another expedition, at his own expense, to cruise in search of the sainted island, but his means were exhausted. He endeavored to rouse others to the enterprise, setting forth the certainty of profitable results, of which his own experience furnished such unquestionable proof. Alas! no one would give faith to his tale; but looked upon it as the feverish dream of a shipwrecked man. He persisted in his efforts; holding forth in all places and all companies, until he became an object of jest and jeer to the light-minded, who mistook his earnest enthusiasm for a proof of insanity; and the very children in the streets bantered him with the title of "The Adalantado of the Seven Cities."

Finding all efforts in vain, in his native city of Lisbon, he took shipping for the Canaries, as being nearer the latitude of his former cruise, and inhabited by people given to nautical adventure. Here he found ready listeners to his story; for the old pilots and mariners of those parts were notorious island-hunters and devout believers in all the wonders of the seas. Indeed, one and all treated his adventure as a common occurrence, and turning to each other, with a sagacious nod of the head, observed, "He has been at the Island of St. Brandan."

They then went on to inform him of that great marvel and enigma of the ocean; of its repeated appearance to the inhabitants of their islands; and of the many but ineffectual expeditions that had been made in search of it. They took him to a promontory of the island of Palma, from whence the shadowy St. Brandan had oftenest been descried, and they pointed out the very tract in the west where its mountains had been seen.

Don Fernando listened with rapt attention. He had no longer a doubt that this mysterious and fugacious island must be the same with that of the Seven Cities; and that there must be some supernatural influence connected with it, that had operated upon himself, and made the events of a night occupy the space of a century.

He endeavored, but in vain, to rouse the islanders to another attempt at discovery; they had given up the phantom island as indeed inaccessible. Fernando, however, was not to be discouraged. The idea wore itself deeper and deeper in his mind, until it became the engrossing subject of his thoughts and object of his being. Every morning he would repair to the promontory of Palma, and sit there throughout the live-long day, in hopes of seeing the fairy mountains of St. Brandan peering above the horizon; every evening he returned to his home, a disappointed man, but ready to resume his post on the follwing morning.

His assiduity was all in vain. He grew gray in his ineffectual attempt;

and was at length found dead at his post. His grave is still shown in the island of Palma, and a cross is erected on the spot where he used to sit and look out upon the sea, in hopes of the reappearance of the phantom island.

NOTE.—For various particulars concerning the *Island of St. Brandan* and the *Island of the Seven Cities,* those ancient problems of the ocean, the curious reader is referred to articles under those heads in the Appendix to the Life of Columbus.

RECOLLECTIONS OF THE ALHAMBRA

I have already given to the world some anecdotes of a summer's residence in the old Moorish palace of the Alhambra. It was a dreamy sojourn, during which I lived, as it were, in the midst of an Arabian tale, and shut my eyes as much as possible to every thing that should call me back to every day life. If there is any country in Europe where one can do so, it is among these magnificent but semi-barbaric ruins of poor, wild, legendary, romantic Spain. In the silent and deserted halls of the Alhambra, surrounded with the insignia of regal sway, and the vivid, though dilapidated traces of Oriental luxury, I was in the stronghold of Moorish story, where every thing spoke of the palmy days of Granada when under the dominion of the crescent.

Much of the literature of Spain turns upon the wars of the Moors and Christians, and consists of traditional ballads and tales or romances, about the "buenas andanzas," and "grandes hechos," the "lucky adventures," and "great exploits" of the warriors of yore. It is worthy of remark, that many of these lays which sing of prowess and magnanimity in war, and tenderness and fidelity in love, relate as well to Moorish as to Spanish cavaliers. The lapse of peaceful centuries has extinguished the rancor of ancient hostility; and the warriors of Granada, once the objects of bigot detestation, are now often held up by Spanish poets as mirrors of chivalric virtue.

None have been the theme of higher eulogy than the illustrious line of the Abencerrages, who in the proud days of Moslem domination were the soul of every thing noble and chivalric. The veterans of the family sat in the royal council, and were foremost in devising heroic enterprises to carry dismay into the Christian territories; and what the veterans devised the young men of the name were foremost to execute. In all adventures, enterprises, and hair-breadth hazards, the Abencerrages were sure to win the brightest laurels. In the tilt and tourney, in the riding at the ring, the daring bull fight, and all other recreations which bore an affinity to war, the Abencerrages carried off the palm. None equalled them for splendor of array, for noble bearing, and glorious horsemanship. Their open-handed munificence made them the idols of the people; their magnanimity and perfect faith gained the admiration of the high-minded. Never did they decry the merits of a rival, nor betray the confidings of a friend; and the word of an Abencerrage was a guarantee never to be doubted.

And then their devotion to the fair! Never did Moorish beauty consider the fame of her charms established, until she had an Abencerrage for a lover; and never did an Abencerrage prove recreant to his vows. Lovely Granada! City of delights! Who ever bore the favors of thy dames more proudly on their casques, or championed them more gallantly in the chivalrous tilts of the Vivarambla? Or who ever made thy moon-lit balconies, thy gardens of myrtles and roses, of oranges, citrons, and pomegranates, respond to more tender serenades?

Such were the fances I used to conjure up as I sat in the beautiful hall of the Abencerrages, celebrated in the tragic story of that devoted race, where thirty-six of its bravest cavaliers were treacherously sacrificed to appease the jealous fears of a tyrant. The fountain which once ran red with their blood, throws up a sparkling jet, and spreads a dewy freshness through the hall; but a deep stain on the marble pavement is still pointed out as a sanguinary record of the massacre. The truth of the record has been called in question, but I regarded it with the same determined faith with which I contemplated the stains of Rizzio's blood on the floor of the palace of Holyrood. I thank no one for enlightening my credulity on points of poetical belief. It is like robbing the statue of Memnon of its mysterious music. Dispel historical illusions, and there is an end to half the charms of travelling.

The hall of the Abencerrages is connected moreover with the recollection of one of the sweetest evenings and sweetest scenes I ever enjoyed in Spain. It was a beautiful summer evening, when the moon shone down into the Court of Lions, lighting up its sparkling fountain. I was seated with a few companions in the hall in question, listening to those traditional ballads and romances in which the Spaniards delight. They were sung to the accompaniment of the guitar, by one of the most gifted and fascinating beings that I ever met with even among the fascinating daughters of Spain. She was young and beautiful; and light and ethereal; full of fire, and spirit, and pure enthusiasm. She wore the fanciful Andalusian dress; touched the guitar with speaking eloquence: improvised with wonderful facility; and, as she became excited by her theme, or by the rapt attention of her auditors, would pour forth, in the richest and most melodious strains, a succession of couplets, full of striking description, or stirring narrative, and composed, as I was assured, at the moment. Most of these were suggested by the place, and related to the ancient glories of Granada, and the prowess of her chivalry. The Abencerrages were her favorite heroes; she felt a woman's admiration of their gallant courtesy, and high-souled honor; and it was touching and inspiring to hear the praises of that generous but devoted race, chanted in this fated hall of their calamity, by the lips of Spanish beauty.

Among the subjects of which she treated, was a tale of Moslem honor, and old-fashioned Spanish courtesy, which made a strong impression on me. She disclaimed all merit of invention, however, and said she had merely dilated into verse a popular tradition; and, indeed, I have since found the main facts inserted at the end of Conde's History of the Domination of the Arabs, and the story itself embodied in the form of an episode in the Diana of Montemayor. From these sources, I have drawn it forth, and endeavored to shape it according to my recollection of the version of the beautiful minstrel; but alas! what can supply the want of that voice, that look, that form, that action, which gave magical effect to her chant, and held every one rapt in breathless admiration! Should this mere travestie of her inspired numbers ever meet her eye, in her stately abode at Granada, may it meet with that indulgence which belongs to her benignant nature. Happy should I be, if it could awaken in her bosom one kind of recollection of the stranger, for whose gratification she did not think it beneath her to exert those fascinating powers, which were the delight of brilliant circles; and who will ever recall with enthusiasm the happy evening passed in listening to her strains, in the moon-lit halls of the Alhambra.

THE ABENCERRAGE

On the summit of a craggy hill, a spur of the mountains of Ronda, stands the castle of Allora, now a mere ruin, infested by bats and owlets, but in old times, a strong border-hold which kept watch upon the war-like kingdom of Granada, and held the Moors in check. It was a post always confided to some well-tried commander; and at the time of which we treat, was held by Roderigo de Narvaez, Alcayde, or military governor of Antiquera. It was a frontier post of his command; but he passed most of his time there, because its situation on the borders gave frequent opportunity for those adventurous exploits in which the Spanish chivalry delighted.

He was a veteran, famed among both Moors and Christians, not only for deeds of arms, but for that magnanimous courtesy, which should ever be entwined with the stern virtues of the soldier.

His garrison consisted of fifty chosen men, well appointed and well-mounted, with which he maintained such vigilant watch that nothing could escape his eye. While some remained on guard in the castle, he would sally forth with others, prowling about the highways, the paths and defiles of the mountains by day and night, and now and then making a daring foray into the very Vega of Granada.

On a fair and beautiful night in summer, when the moon was in the full, and the freshness of the evening breeze had tempered the heat of day, the Alcayde, with nine of his cavaliers, was going the rounds of the mountains in quest of adventures. They rode silently and cautiously, for it was a night to tempt others abroad, and they might be overheard by Moorish scout or traveller; they kept along ravines and hollow ways, moreover, lest they should be betrayed by the glittering of the moon upon their armor. Coming to a fork in the road, the Alcayde ordered five of his cavaliers to take one of the branches, while he, with the remaining four, would take the other. Should either party be in danger, the blast of a horn was to be the signal for succor. The party of five had not proceeded far, when, in passing through a defile, they heard the voice of a man singing. Concealing themselves among trees, they awaited his approach. The moon, which left the grove in shadow, shone full upon his person, as he slowly advanced, mounted on a dapple gray steed of powerful frame and generous spirit, and magnificently caparisoned. He was a Moorish cavalier of noble demeanor and graceful carriage, arrayed in a marlota, or tunic, and an albornoz of crimson damask fringed with gold. His Tunisian turban, of many folds, was of striped silk and cotton, bordered with a golden fringe; at his girdle hung a Damascus scimitar, with loops and tassels of silk and gold. On his left arm he bore an ample target, and his right hand grasped a long double-pointed lance. Apparently dreaming of no danger, he sat negligently on his steed, gazing on the moon, and singing, with a sweet and manly voice, a Moorish love ditty.

Just opposite the grove where the cavaliers were concealed, the horse turned aside to drink at a small fountain in a rock beside the road. His rider threw the reins on his neck to let him drink at his ease, and continued his song.

The cavaliers whispered with each other. Charmed with the gallant and gentle appearance of the Moor, they determined not to harm, but capture him; an easy task, as they supposed, in his negligent mood. Rushing forth, therefore, they thought to surround, and take him by surprise. Never were men more mistaken. To gather up his reins, wheel round his steed, brace his buckler, and couch his lance, was the work of an instant; and there he sat, fixed like a castle in his saddle.

The cavaliers checked their steeds, and reconnoitred him warily, loth to come to an encounter, which must prove fatal to him.

The Moor now held a parley. "If ye be true knights, and seek for honorable fame, come on singly, and I will meet each in succession; if ye be mere lurkers of the road, intent on spoil, come all at once, and do your worst."

The cavaliers communed together for a moment, when one parting from the others, advanced. "Although no law of chivalry," said he, "obliges us to risk the loss of a prize, when fairly in our power, yet we willingly grant as a courtesy what we might refuse as a right. Valiant Moor, defend thyself!"

So saying, he wheeled, took proper distance, couched his lance, and putting spurs to his horse, made at the stranger. The latter met him in mid career, transpierced him with his lance, and threw him from his saddle. A second and a third succeeded, but were unhorsed with equal facility, and thrown to the earth severely wounded. The remaining two, seeing their comrades thus roughly treated, forgot all compact of courtesy, and charged both at once upon the Moor. He parried the thrust of one, but was wounded by the other in the thigh, and, in the shock and confusion, dropped his lance. Thus disarmed, and closely pressed, he pretended to fly, and was hotly pursued. Having drawn the two cavaliers some distance from the spot, he wheeled short about, with one of those dexterous movements for which the Moorish horsemen were renowned; passed swiftly between them, swung himself down from his saddle, so as to catch up his lance, then, lightly replacing himself, turned to renew the combat.

Seeing him thus fresh for the encounter, as if just issued from his tent, one of the cavaliers put his lips to his horn, and blew a blast, that soon brought the Alcayde and his four companions to the spot.

Narvaez, seeing three of his cavaliers extended on the earth, and two others hotly engaged with the Moor, was struck with admiration, and coveted a contest with so accomplished a warrior. Interfering in the fight, he called upon his followers to desist, and with courteous words invited the Moor to a more equal combat. The challenge was readily accepted. For some time the contest was doubtful, and the Alcayde had need of all his skill and strength to ward off the blows of his antagonist. The Moor, however, exhausted by previous fighting, and by loss of blood. He no longer sat his horse firmly, nor managed him with his wonted skill. Collecting all his strength for a last assault, he rose in his stirrups, and made a violent thrust with his lance; the Alcayde received it upon his shield, and at the same time wounded the Moor in the right arm; then closing, in the shock, grasped him in his arms, dragged him from his saddle, and fell with him to the earth: when putting his knee upon his breast, and his dagger to his throat, "Cavalier," exclaimed he, "render thyself my prisoner, for thy life is in my hands!"

"Kill me, rather," replied the Moor, "for death would be less grievous than loss of liberty."

The Alcayde, however, with the clemency of the truly brave, assisted him to rise, ministered to his wounds with his own hands, and had him conveyed with great care to the castle of Allora. His wounds in a few days were nearly cured; but the deepest wound had been inflicted on his spirit. He was constantly buried in a profound melancholy.

The Alcayde, who had conceived a great regard for him, treated him more as a friend than a captive, and tried in every way to cheer him, but in vain; he was always sad and moody, and, when on the battlements of the castle, would keep his eyes turned to the south, with a fixed and wistful gaze.

"How is this?" exclaimed the Alcayde, reproachfully, "that you, who were so hardy and fearless in the field, should lose all spirit when a captive? If any secret grief preys on your heart, confide it to me, as to a friend, and I promise on the faith of a cavalier, that you shall have no cause to repent the disclosure."

The Moorish knight kissed the hand of the Alcayde. "Noble cavalier," said he, "that I am cast down in spirit, is not from my wounds, which are slight, nor from my captivity, for your kindness has robbed it of all gloom; nor from my defeat, for to be conquered by so accomplished and renowned a cavalier, is no disgrace. But to explain the cause of my grief, it is necessary to give you some particulars of my story; and this I am moved to do, by the sympathy you have manifested toward me, and the magnanimity that shines through all your actions."

"Know, then, that my name is Abendaraez, and that I am of the noble but unfortunate line of the Abencerrages. You have doubtless heard of the destruction that fell upon our race. Charged with treasonable designs, of which they were entirely innocent, many of them were beheaded, the rest banished; so that not an Abencerrage was permitted to remain in Granada, excepting my father and my uncle, whose innocence was proved, even to the satisfaction of their persecutors. It was decreed, however, that should they have children, the sons should be educated at a distance from Granada, and the daughters should be married out of the kingdom.

"Conformably to this decree, I was sent, while yet an infant, to be reared in the fortress of Cartama, the Alcayde of which was an ancient friend of my father. He had no children, and received me into his family as his own child, treating me with the kindness and affection of a father; and I grew up in the belief that he really was such. A few years afterward, his wife gave birth to a daughter, but his tenderness toward me continued undiminished. I thus grew up with Xarisa, for so the infant daughter of the Alcayde was called, as her own brother. I beheld her charms unfolding, as it were, leaf by leaf, like the morning rose, each moment disclosing fresh sweetness and beauty, and thought the growing passion which I felt for her was mere fraternal affection.

"At length one day I accidentally overheard a conversation between the Alcayde and his confidential domestic, of which I found myself the subject.

"In this I learnt the secret of my real parentage, which the Alcayde had withheld from me as long as possible, through reluctance to inform me of being of a proscribed and unlucky race. It was time now, he thought, to apprise me of the truth, that I might adopt a career in life.

"I retired without letting it be perceived that I had overheard the conversation. The intelligence it conveyed would have overwhelmd me at an earlier period; but now the intimation that Xarisa was not my sister, operated like magic. In an instant the brotherly affection with which my heart at times had throbbed almost to excess, was transformed into ardent love.

"I sought Xarisa in the garden, where I found her in a bower of jessamines, arranging her beautiful hair in the mirror of a crystal fountain. I ran to her with open arms, and was received with a sister's embraces; upbraiding me for leaving her so long alone.

"We seated ourselves by the fountain, and I hastened to reveal the secret conversation I had overheard.

"'Alas!' cried she, 'then our happiness is at an end!'

"'How!' cried I, 'wilt thou cease to love me because I am not thy brother?'

"'Alas, no!' replied she, gently withdrawing from my embrace, 'but when it is once made known we are not brother and sister, we shall no longer be permitted to be thus always together.'

"In fact, from that moment our intercourse took a new character. We met often at the fountain among the jessamines, but Xarisa no longer advanced with open arms to meet me. She became reserved and silent, and would blush, and cast down her eyes, when I seated myself beside her. My heart became a prey to the thousand doubts and fears that ever attend upon true love. Restless and uneasy, I looked back with regret to our unreserved intercourse, when we supposed ourselves brother and sister; yet I would not have had the relationship true, for the world.

"While matters were in this state between us, an order came from the King of Granada for the Alcayde to take command of the fortress of Coyn, on the Christian frontier. He prepared to remove, with all his family, but signified that I should remain at Cartama. I declared that I could not be parted from Xarisa. 'That is the very cause,' said he, 'why I leave thee behind. It is time, Abendaraez, thou shouldst know the secret of thy birth. Thou art no son of mine, neither is Xarisa thy sister.' 'I know it all,' exclaimed I, 'and I love her with ten fold the affection of a brother. You have brought us up together; you have made us necessary to each other's happiness; our hearts have entwined themselves with our growth; do not now tear them asunder. Fill up the measure of your kindness; be indeed a father to me, by giving me Xarisa for my wife.'

"The brow of the Alcayde darkened as I spoke. 'Have I then been deceived?' said he. 'Have those nurtured in my very bosom, been conspiring against me? Is this your return for my paternal tenderness?—to beguile the affections of my child, and teach her to deceive her father? It would have been cause enough to refuse thee the hand of my daughter, that thou wert of a proscribed race, who can never approach the walls of Granada; this, however, I might have passed over; but never will I give my daughter to a man who has endeavored to win her from me by deception.'

"All my attempts to vindicate myself and Xarisa were unavailing. I retired in anguish from his presence, and seeking Xarisa, told her of this blow, which was worse than death to me. 'Xarisa,' said I, 'we part for ever! I shall never see thee more! Thy father will guard thee rigidly. Thy beauty and his wealth will soon attract some happier rival, and I shall be forgotten!'"

"Xarisa reproached my wont of faith, and promised eternal constancy. I still doubted and desponded, until, moved by my anguish and despair, she agreed to a secret union. Our espousals made, we parted, with a promise on her part to send me word from Coyn, should her father absent himself from the fortress. The very day after our secret nuptials, I beheld the whole train of the Alcayde depart from Cartama, nor would he admit to me his presence, or permit me to bid farewell to Xarisa. I remained at Cartama, somewhat pacified in spirit by our secret bond of union; but every thing around fed my passion, and reminded me of Xarisa. I saw the windows at which I had so often beheld her. I wandered through the apartment she had inhabited; the chamber in which she had slept. I visited the bower of jessamines, and lingered beside the fountain in which she had delighted. Every thing recalled her to my imagination, and filled my heart with melancholy.

"At length, a confidential servant arrived with a letter from her, informing me, that her father was to depart that day for Granada, on a short absence, inviting me to hasten to Coyn, describing a secret portal at which I should apply, and the signal by which I would obtain admittance.

"If ever you have loved, most valiant Alcayde, you may judge of my transport. That very night I arrayed myself in gallant attire, to pay due honor to my bride; and arming myself against any casual attack, issued forth privately from Cartama. You know the rest, and by what sad fortune of war I find myself, instead of a happy bridegroom, in the nuptial bower of Coyn, vanquished, wounded, and a prisoner, within the walls of Allora. The term of absence of the father of Xarisa is nearly expired. Within three days he will return to Coyn, and our meeting will no longer be possible. Judge, then, whether I grieve without cause, and whether I may not well be excused for showing impatience under confinement."

Don Rodrigo was greatly moved by this recital; for, though more

used to rugged war, than scenes of amorous softness, he was of a kind
and generous nature.

"Abendaraez," said he, "I did not seek thy confidence to gratify an
idle curiosity. It grieves me much that the good fortune which delivered
thee into my hands, should have marred so fair an enterprise. Give me
thy faith, as a true knight, to return prisoner to my castle, within three
days, and I will grant thee permission to accomplish thy nuptials."

The Abencerrage, in a transport of gratitude, would have thrown
himself at his feet, but the Alcayde prevented him. Calling in his
cavaliers, he took the Abencerrage by the right hand, in their presence,
exclaiming solemnly, "You promise, on the faith of a cavalier, to return
to my castle of Allora within three days, and render yourself my
prisoner?" And the Abencerrage said, "I promise."

Then said the Alcayde, "Go! and may good fortune attend you. If
you require any safeguard, I and my cavaliers are ready to be your
companions."

The Abencerrage kissed the hand of the Alcayde, in grateful ac-
knowledgment. "Give me," said he, "my own armor, and my steed, and
I require no guard. It is not likely that I shall again meet with so valorous
a foe."

The shades of night had fallen, when the tramp of the dapple gray
steed resounded over the draw-bridge, and immediately afterwards
the light clatter of hoofs along the road, bespoke the fleetness with which
the youthful lover hastened to his bride. It was deep night, when the
Moor arrived at the castle of Coyn. He silently and cautiously walked his
panting steed under its dark walls, and having nearly passed round them,
came to the portal denoted by Xarisa. He paused and looked round to
see that he was not observed, and knocked three times with the butt of
his lance. In a little while the portal was timidly unclosed by the duenna
of Xarisa. "Alas! senor," said she, "what has detained you thus long?
Every night have I watched for you; and my lady is sick at heart with
doubt and anxiety."

The Abencerrage hung his lance, and shield, and scimitar against the
wall, and then followed the duenna, with silent steps, up a winding stair-
case, to the apartment of Xarisa. Vain would be the attempt to describe
the raptures of that meeting. Time flew too swiftly, and the Abencerrage
had nearly forgotten, until too late, his promise to return a prisoner to
the Alcayde of Allora. The recollection of it came to him with a pang, and
woke him from his dream of bliss. Xarisa saw his altered looks, and
heard with alarm his stifled sighs; but her countenance brightened, when
she heard the cause. "Let not thy spirit be cast down," said she, throwing
her white arms around him. "I have the keys of my father's treasures;

send ransom more than enough to satisfy the Christian, and remain with me."

"No," said Abendaraez, "I have given my word to return in person, and like a true knight, must fulfil my promise. After that, fortune must do with me as it pleases."

"Then," said Xarisa, "I will accompany thee. Never shalt thou return a prisoner, and I remain at liberty."

The Abencerrage was transported with joy at this new proof of devotion in his beautiful bride. All preparations were speedily made for their departure. Xarisa mounted behind the Moor, on his powerful steed; they left the castle walls before day-break, nor did they pause, until they arrived at the gate of the castle of Allora.

Alighting in the court, the Abencerrage supported the steps of his trembling bride, who remained closely veiled, into the presence of Rodrigo de Narvaez. "Behold, valiant Alcayde!" said he, "the way in which an Abencerrage keeps his word. I promised to return to thee a prisoner, but I deliver two captives into your power. Behold Xarisa, and judge whether I grieved without reason, over the loss of such a treasure. Receive us as your own, for I confide my life and her honor to thy hands."

The Alcayde was lost in admiration of the beauty of the lady, and the noble spirit of the Moor. "I know not," said he, "which of you surpasses the other; but I know that my castle is graced and honored by your presence. Consider it your own, while you deign to reside with me."

For several days, the lovers remained at Allora, happy in each other's love, and in the friendship of the Alcayde. The latter wrote a letter to the Moorish king of Granada, relating the whole event, extolling the valor and good faith of the Abencerrage, and craving for him the royal countenance.

The king was moved by the story, and was pleased with an opportunity of showing attention to the wishes of a gallant and chivalrous enemy; for though he had often suffered from the prowess of Don Rodrigo de Narvaez, he admired his heroic character. Calling the Alcayde of Coyn into his presence, he gave him the letter to read. The Alcayde turned pale, and trembled with rage, on the perusal. "Restrain thine anger," said the king; "there is nothing that the Alcayde of Allora could ask, that I would not grant, if in my power. Go thou to Allora; pardon thy children; take them to thy home. I receive this Abencerrage into my favor, and it will be my delight to heap benefits upon you all."

The kindling ire of the Alcayde was suddenly appeased. He hastened to Allora; and folded his children to his bosom, who would have fallen at his feet. Rodrigo de Narvaez gave liberty to his prisoner without ransom, demanding merely a promise of his friendship. He accompanied the youthful couple and their father to Coyn, where their nuptials were celebrated with great rejoicings. When the festivities were over, Don Rodrigo returned to his fortress of Allora.

After his departure, the Alcayde of Coyn addressed his children: "To your hands," said he, "I confide the disposition of my wealth. One of the first things I charge you, is not to forget the ransom you owe to the Alcayde of Allora. His magnanimity you can never repay, but you can prevent it from wronging him of his just dues. Give him, moreover, your entire friendship, for he merits it fully, though of a different faith."

The Abencerrage thanked him for his generous proposition, which so truly accorded with his own wishes. He took a large sum of gold, and enclosed it in a rich coffer; and, on his own part, sent six beautiful horses, superbly caparisoned; with six shields and lances, mounted and embossed with gold. The beautiful Xarisa, at the same time, wrote a letter to the Alcayde, filled with expressions of gratitude and friendship, and sent him a box of fragrant cypress wood, containing linen, of the finest quality, for his person. The Alcayde disposed of the present in a characteristic manner. The horses and armor he shared among the cavaliers who had accompanied him on the night of the skirmish. The box of cypress wood and its contents he retained, for the sake of the beautiful Xarisa; and sent her, by the hands of the messenger, the sum of gold paid as a ransom, entreating her to receive it as a wedding present. This courtesy and magnanimity raised the character of the Alcayde Rodrigo de Narvaez still higher in the estimation of the Moors, who extolled him as a perfect mirror of chivalric virtue; and from that time forward, there was a continual exchange of good offices between them.

Those who would read the foregoing story decked out with poetic grace in the pure Castilian, let them seek it in the Diana of Montemayor.

EDITORIAL APPENDIX

Textual Commentary,
Discussions, and Lists by
Roberta Rosenberg

LIST OF ABBREVIATIONS

The following symbols have been used in the editorial apparatus to designate the manuscript and previously published texts of *Wolfert's Roost*.

MSa   Author's manuscript, 267 pages (1805–1840)

MSb   Author's notebooks, 169 pages (1820–1838)

KnM   *Knickerbocker Magazine* (1839–1841)

LS   *The Literary Souvenir* (1826)

Mag   *The Magnolia* (1837)

NYA   *New York American* (1826)

NY   *The New-Yorker* (1840)

NI   *National Intelligencer* (1839)

C   *The Casket* (1827)

R   *The Romancist, and Novelist's Library* (1839–1840)

Ev   *The Evergreen* (1840)

KSB   *Knickerbocker Sketch-Book* (Burgess, Stringer & Company, 1845)

BH   *The Book of the Hudson* (Putnam's, 1849)

E   First English edition (Constable, 1855)

1A   First American edition (Putnam's, 1855)
    1Aa   First impression of first edition
    1Ab   Second impression of first edition
    1Ac   Possible later impressions of first edition
    1A56   Reimpression (1856)
    1A59   Reimpression (1859)
    1A61   Reimpression (1861)

2A   Second American edition (Putnam's, 1865)

T   Twayne edition

EXPLANATORY NOTES

The numbers before all notes indicate page and line respectively. Chapter numbers, chapter or section titles, epigraphs, author's chapter or section summaries, text quotations, and footnotes are included in the line count. Only running heads and rules added by the printer to separate the running head from the text are omitted from the count. The quotation from the text, to the left of the bracket, is the matter under discussion. For a key to identifying symbols used in referring to the manuscripts and previously published texts, see the List of Abbreviations, page 243.

3.10 Peter the Headstrong] Peter Stuyvesant (1592–1672), governor of New Netherlands (New York). He surrendered to the English in 1664.

4.20 Pocantico] Area in Westchester County, New York, which became known as Tarrytown.

5.10 Robert Juet] A shipmate of Henry Hudson; his description of their voyage appears in Samuel Purchas' *His Pilgrimes* (1625).

12.36 Diedrich Knickerbocker] Reputed author of Washington Irving's *A History of New York* (1809).

18.22–19.12 WHEN winter's . . . adore him.] "The Blue Bird" by Alexander Wilson (1766–1813). Scottish ornithologist and poet who emigrated to America in 1794. Wilson also wrote *American Ornithology or the Natural History of the Birds of the United States.*

20.14–21 Sweet bird . . . spring!] "Ode to the Cuckoo" by John Logan (1748–1788), English poet and divine.

22.4 Ariosto's] Lodovico Ariosto (1474–1533). Italian poet who wrote the romantic epic *Orlando Furioso* (1516).

22.5 Astolpho] An English knight who appears in *Orlando Furioso.*

29.6 edict of Nantz] April 15, 1598. It gave Huguenots equal political rights with Catholics but denied them religious freedom.

29.30 Children in the Wood] From Thomas Percy's *Reliques of Ancient English Poetry* (1765). An uncle who wishes to kill his wealthy niece and nephew hires two assassins who murder one another; the children die of overexposure in the woods and the uncle is jailed. See *Reliques*, bk. 3, chap. 2.

30.16–17 Robin Goodfellow] A character in Shakespeare's *A Midsummer Night's Dream* (1594).

33.19–20 Smith's Theory of Moral Sentiments] Adam Smith (1723–1790), political economist and author of *A Theory of Moral Sentiments* (1759) and *The Wealth of Nations* (1776).

33.30–33 "How charming . . . reigns."] From John Milton's *Comus: A Masque Presented at Ludlow Castle* (1634), lines 476–80.

36.29–30 "airy tongues . . . names"] From *A Midsummer Night's Dream*, V, i, 16–17.

36.43–37.1 Numa . . . nymph Egeria] Numa Pompillus, second king of Rome. Both Numa and Egeria are legendary figures who represent the rule of law and order. The two are thought to have created Roman ceremonial law.

53.5 Moore's Irish melodies] Thomas Moore (1779–1852) wrote *Irish Melodies* (1807) with music by Sir John Stevenson.

53.43–54.1 Tasso's Jerusalem Delivered] Historical, romantic poem set in the Middle Ages. Published in 1580–1581 by Torquato Tasso (1544–1595), an Italian poet. Characters from the work which are mentioned in "Mountjoy" are as follows: Godfrey De Bouillon (leader of Crusaders); Clorinda (female warrior); Argantes (pagan knight); Armida (enchantress); Rinaldo (Italian knight).

62.3–10 "Who did . . . 1613.] From Robert Juet's narrative in Samuel Purchas' *His Pilgrimes* (1625).

63.5 Oberon's] King of the fairies in *A Midsummer Night's Dream*.

63.7–13 _____ "Thou . . . music] From *A Midsummer Night's Dream*, II, i, 48–55.

63.27–33 Ah! . . . sand.] From Phineas Fletcher's *Piscatory Eclogues* (1663), eclogue I, stanza 18.

64.41–65.4 "For the . . . himself."*] From Silvester Jourdain's *A Plaine Description of the Barmudas, Now Called Sommer Islands* (1613).

65.32–39 "For the . . . first."] "Summer Islands" by Edmund Waller (1605–1687), an English poet.

68.37 Jack Tar] Nickname given to a lower-class Englishman.

68.39 Whittington] Richard Whittington (d. 1423), mayor of London who rose from the lower classes to an heroic figure in popular tales.

69.39–70.4 "a most. . . false report."*] This quotation and the allusion to a travel narrative entiled "Newes from the Barmudas: 1612" are unrecovered.

7.10–13 "Though this . . . green!"] From Shakespeare's *The Tempest*, II, i, 34, 37, 41, 45, 48, 51. Although Irving attributes this "eulogium" to Sebastian, it is actually spoken by Adrian (first 2 sentences) and Gonzalo (last two sentences).

70.19–34 "Had I . . . people."] From *The Tempest*, II, i, 144, 146, 148, 149–55, 160–65.

71.3–4 "Monster . . . viceroys."]   From *The Tempest*, III, ii, 101–3. The first two lines of the quotation are not found in the text of *The Tempest*.

82.1 *MALTA*]   An island south of Italy.

83.9 Count Cagliostro]   Alexander Cagliostro (1743–1795), Italian adventurer.

83.20 *MINORCA*]   Island off Spain's eastern coast, south of Mallorca.

83.22–23 Keep . . . open!]   unidentified quotation by (?) Fletcher.

90.30–31 Geoffrey a la Grand Dent]   Geoffrey Lusignan, twelfth-century French warrior.

96.21 "It is . . . of."]   From *The Tempest*, IV, i, 156–7. Irving misquotes the line.

123.25–29 "Je me . . . Matin."]   Unrecovered quotation.

124.18 Talma]   Francois Joseph Talma (1763–1826), French tragic actor and friend of Irving.

124.18 Duchesnois]   Catherine Josephine Duchesnois (1777–1835), French actress.

124.22 Munden's]   Joseph Shepherd Munden (1758–1832), English actor of comedies who is noted in the writings of Lamb, Hazlitt, and Hunt.

124.22 Liston's]   Henry Liston (1771–1836), Scottish comedian and composer.

124.37 Mrs. Glass]   Mrs. Hannah Glasse, an Englishwoman who wrote *The Art of Cookery Made Plain and Easy* (London, 1747).

132.13 De Latour D'Auvergne]   Henri de la Tour d'Auvergne Turenne (1611–1675), viscount and marshal of France.

133.6 "Sentimental Journey,"]   A novel by Laurence Sterne (1713–1768), published in 1768.

133.39 Mr. CANNING]   George Canning (1770–1827), Englishman, statesman and ambassador was in Paris in 1824–1826 and met Irving at that time.

134.19–20 Oh! . . . lost!]   Unrecovered quotation.

136.6 "Imperial . . . etc.]   From *Hamlet*, V, i, 199. The first word of the quotation should be "imperious."

147.38 Admiral Van Tromp]   Van Tromp (1597–1653), a Dutch admiral and naval hero, was satirized in *A History of New York*.

154.32–35 "For three . . . gallows-tree."]   Unrecovered Dutch freebooter's song.

157.34 Governor Duval]   William Pope Duval (1784–1854), lawyer, congressman, and governor of Florida.

202.2–5 "I have . . . ONE."]   *The Witty Fair One* (1628) by James Shirley (1596–1666). From act V, sc. iii.

203.3 Alfonso XI]   Alfonso's heroic actions against the Andalusian Moors are noted in *Crónica rimada de Alfonso Onceno* (1312–1350).

204.42 Murillo] Bartholomé Esteban Murillo (1617–1682), Spanish painter known for the works entitled "Immaculate Conception" and "Birth of the Virgin."

208.32–37 _____ "The tombs ... echoes."] Unrecovered quotation.

210.3 Don Roderick the Goth] A popular figure in Spanish history; see Robert Southey's *Roderick, The Last of the Goths* (1814).

213.40 "España Triumphante," written by Fray Antonio de Sancta Maria] Both the work and the author are unknown.

214.2–13 Break, ... JONSON.] From *The Vision of Delight*, presented at court in Christmas, 1617, by Ben Jonson (1572–1637).

214.14–15 "There are ... philosophy,"] From *Hamlet*, I, v, 165–66.

214.17 Canaries] Islands off the northwest coast of Africa.

214.31 Straits of Messina] Waterway between last island off the coast of Italy and the main "boot."

215.3–4 Armida ... Rinaldo] See note for 53.43–54.1.

215.6–7 Sycorax ... Miranda] Galiban's mother and Prospero's daughter respectively in *The Tempest*.

215.8–9 _____ "full ... not."] From *The Tempest*, III, ii, 129–30.

232.3–4 Conde's History ... of the Arabs] José Antonio Conde, Spanish historian and orientalist.

232.5 Diana of Montemayor] Jorge de Montemayor (1520–1561), wrote the pastoral romance *Diana* (ca. 1559).

TEXTUAL COMMENTARY

The theory of copy-text used in editing *Wolfert's Roost* is based on the work of W. W. Greg and Fredson Bowers.[1] Rather than adopting either manuscript or last edition of a text as sole authority, Greg and Bowers sought to establish a critical text which made use of all authorial editions. Both Greg and Bowers argued that when an editor publishes the manuscript of a text, he fails to incorporate the author's later revisions and corrections. Likewise, using the final version presents its own problems. The imposition of a publisher's house style upon the author's work creates a printed text at variance with the author's original intentions.

This editing theory is not completely relativistic, however. The text can be divided into two distinct parts: "substantives" or "the author's words themselves"[2] and "accidentals" or "the author's spelling, capitalization, punctuation, paragraphing, and word-division."[3] "Accidentals" which are found in the manuscript or earliest periodical text are not emended to reflect changes in later printed versions of the text; however, substantives which can be verified as the author's own, are incorporated into the Twayne text.

Since no single text is reprinted as a whole, it is necessary to select one as the copy-text. The copy-text, which is usually the manuscript or the earliest version of the text, is then collated with all printings in which the author is thought to have exercised control, up to and including the first posthumous edition.[4] While alterations in accidentals from edition to edition are usually ignored, the substantive revisions, which the editor has cause to believe to be authorial, are incorporated into the copy-text in order to create a newly edited critical edition.

In the case of *Wolfert's Roost*, no single, complete copy-text could be chosen for all of the nineteen different pieces. Although Irving read proof sheets for the *Knickerbocker Magazine*, his dealings with *The Magnolia, The Literary Souvenir,* and other periodicals are unknown.

1. See W. W. Greg, "The Rationale of Copy-Text," *Studies in Bibliography* 3 (1950), 19–36 and Fredson Bowers, "Current Theories of Copy-Text, with an Illustration from Dryden," *Modern Philology* 48 (1950), 12–20. The Bowers-Greg theory is applied in accordance with *Statement of Editorial Principles and Procedures*, rev. ed. (New York: Modern Language Association, 1972).

2. *Statement of Editorial Principles*, p. 3.

3. *Ibid.*, p. 3.

4. According to the principles and procedures as set forth by the Center for Editions of American Authors, Modern Language Association.

However, the regularization of accidentals in the 1855 Putnam edition of *Wolfert's Roost* disqualify it as a source for copy-text because the grab-bag nature of the sketches is lost in this edition's conformity to one house style. For this reason, the only solution is to use manuscript as copy-text whenever possible and first appearance periodical as a second choice when necessary.

The reason for selection of the manuscript instead of periodical can be explained in terms of Irving's stylistic inconsistencies. Since the pieces were written at different times, the spelling, punctuation, and other accidentals are quite different. Because the magazine editors took the liberty of partially regularizing spelling, capitalization, and punctuation, the periodical versions possess a uniformity which was never intended by Irving.

The importance of preserving the manuscript accidentals is discussed by Fredson Bowers in his article "Some Principles for Scholarly Editions of Nineteenth Century American Authors."[5] He contends that "if an author's habits of expression go beyond words and into the forms that these take, together with the punctuation that helps to shape the relationship of these words, then it is foolish to prefer a printing-house style to the author's style."[6]

Furthermore, Bowers notes that even when an author reads proofs for his work, his control over accidentals is somewhat limited. In the case of *The House of the Seven Gables* by Hawthorne, "almost every one [of the accidental variants] can be attributed to the printer. That Hawthorne passed them in proof is indisputable, but they differ from what he wrote in the manuscript and manifestly preferred is also indisputable."[7] Therefore, Bowers decided that "the editor must choose the manuscript as his major authority, correcting from the first edition only what are positive errors in the accidentals of the manuscript."[8] Of course, Bowers anticipated those critics who would argue that such a procedure would lead to an "amalgamated, or bastardized, text—in effect, the conflation of two or more editions."[9] He noted, however, that these objections have "no basis, once the distinction is grasped between a critical edition and a reprint of some single authority."[10]

Therefore, the final version of *Wolfert's Roost* utilizes the manuscript

5. Fredson Bowers, "Some Principles for Scholarly Editions of Nineteenth Century Authors," in *Bibliography and Textual Criticism*, ed. O. M. Brack and Warner Barnes (Chicago: University of Chicago Press, 1969), pp. 194–201.
6. *Ibid.*, p. 198.
7. *Ibid.*
8. *Ibid.*
9. Bowers, "Current Theories of Copy-text," p. 13.
10. *Ibid.*, p. 19.

as copy-text, whenever possible, and the first periodical publication, when necessary. All authorial revisions from later editions are incorporated into the text in order to create a "purified, eclectic or critical text, based upon the copy-text, and superior to any single relevant form: a text which the author would both sanction and approve."[11]

THE MANUSCRIPTS

Wolfert's Roost presents problems for the critical editor because of its numerous and varied manuscripts. The book is a collection of nineteen pieces which were written between 1805 and 1839. The desire to establish a text closest to that "which the author would both sanction and approve"[12] becomes difficult, since Irving's own literary goals and attitudes underwent change within this thirty-four-year period. In addition, only approximately one-half of the author's manuscripts are extant. Numerous notebooks, journals, and letters provide clues to spelling, punctuation, and capitalization; yet the editor does not have a complete manuscript on which to base the text.

To complicate matters further, the first edition of *Wolfert's Roost* (New York: Putnam, 1855) is not the next step in the publication history. Between the time of composition in the late teens through the early 1830's, some of the individual sketches were published and reprinted in nine different periodicals: *Knickerbocker Magazine*; *The Casket*; *The Romancist, and Novelist's Library*; *National Intelligencer*; *The Literary Souvenir*; *The Magnolia*; *The New-Yorker*; *The Evergreen*; and the *New York American*. Some of the stories were also reprinted in book form in *The Knickerbocker Sketch-Book* and *The Book of the Hudson*.

The only method for dealing with the varied manuscripts which comprise *Wolfert's Roost* is to treat each sketch separately. If manuscript for a particular piece is still extant,[13] then that manuscript is used, supplemented by first printed form. The pieces for which this is true are "Mountjoy Or Some Passages Out of the Life of a Castle Builder," "The Bermudas," and "The Knight of Malta." "The Sketches in Paris in 1825" presents an even more complicated problem, for the piece is actually a collection of short anecdotes. Fortunately, complete manuscripts are available for three whole anecdotes: "English and French Character," "The Tuilleries and Windsor Castle," and "Paris at the

11. *Statements of Editorial Principles*, p. 4.
12. *Ibid.*, p. 4.
13. For the location and description of extant manuscripts see section entitled "Ownership or Location of Extant Manuscripts," pp. 322–23.

Restoration." Copy-text for the three remaining sketches is *Knickerbocker Magazine*.

"The Seminoles," like "Sketches in Paris," is a collection within a collection. Two pieces, "The Seminoles" and "The Conspiracy of Neamathla" possess complete manuscripts while "The Origin of the White, the Red, and the Black Men" does not. For the copy-text of "A Contented Man" extant manuscript is used, supplemented by first periodical publication. Only two pages of manuscript for "Broek: or The Dutch Paradise" are extant; however, they serve as copy-text for the introduction of the tale. Partial manuscript, supplemented by first periodical publication, is also the copy-text for "Guests from Gibbet Island." The complete manuscript of "Legend of the Engulphed Convent" serves as the basis of copy-text.

The grab-bag quality of *Wolfert's Roost,* discussed in the Introduction, is even more apparent as one studies the condition and general characteristics of the various extant manuscripts. One manuscript differs so greatly from another that only a side-by-side comparison can reveal all the disparities in handwriting, spelling, punctuation, and general usage. For example, at first glance, "The Conspiracy of Neamathla," written in 1833–1834 and "A Contented Man," written in 1822–1823, seem to be the work of two different people. "A Contented Man" is in a carefully written, rather small handwriting. The larger, more slanted, and almost illegible hand of "The Conspiracy of Neamathla" shows Irving's handwriting some ten years later. "Contented Man" manuscript is written on 6 1/2 X 4 inches sheets of paper with an average of twenty-six lines per page. "The Conspiracy," however, is composed on 7 1/2 X 5 inches sheets with an average of nineteen lines per page. While "Contented Man" has few excisions and interpolations, "The Conspiracy" has whole passages which are deleted and contain an average five to six interlineations per page.

Differences in capitalization, usage, punctuation, and other accidentals in the two manuscripts are typical of the Irvingesque style. In "Contented Man" Irving uses Anglicized spelling such as the *our* ending in place of the American *or* in the word "neighbours" (MSa, 5; T, 138.18). "The Conspiracy" generally follows American spelling principles such as "neighborhood" (MSa, 13; T 190.25–6). However, it is impossible to detect any pattern in Irving's spelling because his usage alternates between British and American forms.

Although there are explanations for some of the manuscript disparities, other discrepancies remain incomprehensible; one can only ascribe them to Irving's mercurial nature. His practice of capitalization in "A Conspiracy" and "Contented Man" is especially puzzling. In "The Conspiracy" he does not capitalize direction and thus writes, "excepting

a district in the eastern part" (MSa, 1; T 186.32–3). However, the opening sentence in "Contented Man" contains a capitalized direction: "In
the garden of the Tuilleries there is a sunny corner under the wall of a
Terrace which fronts the South" (MSa, 1; T 137.2–3).

Irving alternately does and does not capitalize seasons, months, names,
and places. In "Contented Man" he omits the capitalization of the man's
nationality and continually calls him "a frenchman of the old school"
(MSa, 3; T 137.30). Yet in "The Conspiracy," the tribes are designated
as "Florida Indians" (MSa, 1; T 186.31).

These two manuscripts also reveal Irving's careless use of apostrophes
to show possession and contraction. "The Conspiracy" speaks of the
"Governor's throat" (MSa, 6; T 187.39), or "Neamathla's town" (MSa, 8;
T 188.22). "Contented Man" usually lacks apostrophes for possession:
"pinching the nursery maids cheek" (MSa, 3; T 137.30). However, this
grammatical error is not an exclusive characteristic of either the European or American manuscript; apostrophes are missing in most of the
Wolfert's Roost stories.[14]

Other forms of Irving's eccentric grammar can be found throughout
the manuscript. He uses and omits the comma: (1) before and after an
appositive; (2) in a list of items after a colon; (3) to separate restric-
tive modifiers; and (4) before the closing of quotation marks. He uses
and omits the semicolon: (1) when a comma would be sufficient; (2)
when creating sentence fragments out of dependent clauses by separat-
ing these clauses from the rest of the sentence; and (3) when listing
items in a series.

His system of quotation is equally puzzling. Irving vacillates between
the use of double and single quotation marks, although he usually pre-
fers double. He sometimes forgets to end a quotation. When quoting
from another source, he will use a single quotation at the beginning of
the paragraph with no other footnote or page/line citation.

He does and does not hyphenate compound words and, on occasion,
forgets to use a hyphen at the end of a line to denote a broken word;
often this hyphen, if written at all, appears at the beginning of the next
line instead of at the end of the previous line. In some of his manuscripts, dashes replace periods and ampersands are used instead of
"and." Occasionally an end point is omitted altogether.

The numerous revisions and corrections which the manuscripts underwent, partially account for grammatical inconsistencies. Since the stories

14. See "Treatment of Accidentals" for an explanation of how this problem
is handled in the Twayne edition. For a complete listing of Irving's grammatical
inconsistencies see the Textual Introduction to Irving's *Journals and Notebooks I:
1803–1806*, ed. Nathalia Wright (Madison: University of Wisconsin Press, 1970),
pp. xviii–xxvi.

were written at different times, when Irving was in distinctly different moods, the grammar and usage vary. The crossed-out numbers in the upper-right-hand corner of each manuscript page suggest manifold revisions. One page of "The Conspiracy" manuscript was renumbered three times as pages nine, seven, and sixteen. Likewise, page "10–11" was also eight and seventeen at different stages of composition. Irving's eccentric grammar is somewhat regularized and made to conform to standard usage in the magazine and book publications of *Wolfert's Roost*. For this reason, whenever possible, the manuscript serves as copy-text for accidentals. In this way, the typically Irvingesque texture of the book can be preserved.

THE TEXTS

When manuscript is not extant, it is necessary to select the published text closest to the author's hand as copy-text. The first edition of *Wolfert's Roost* is not chosen because it is preceded by the periodical version of each sketch. Those stories for which copy-text is *exclusively* periodical are as follows: "Wolfert's Roost,"[15] "The Birds of Spring,"[16] "The Creole Village,"[17] "The Widow's Ordeal,"[18] "A Time of Unexampled Prosperity,"[19] "The Early Experiences of Ralph Ringwood,"[20] "Don Juan—A Spectral Research,"[21] "The Enchanted [Phantom] Island,"[22] and "Recollections of the Alhambra."[23]

Those stories which have only partially extant manuscript are supplemented with periodical copy-text where the manuscript breaks off. They are: "Mountjoy,"[24] "The Sketches in Paris in 1825,"[25] "A Con-

15. "Wolfert's Roost," *Knickerbocker Magazine* 13 (April, 1839), 317–28.

16. "The Birds of Spring," *Knickerbocker Magazine* 13 (May, 1839), 434–37.

17. "The Creole Village," in *The Magnolia* (New York: Monson Bancroft, 1837), pp. 315–26.

18. "The Widow's Ordeal," in *The Magnolia* (New York: Monson Bancroft, 1837), pp. 257–74.

19. "A Time of Unexampled Prosperity," *Knickerbocker Magazine* 15 (April, 1840), 303–24.

20. "The Early Experiences of Ralph Ringwood," *Knickerbocker Magazine* 16 (August-September, 1840), 152–65, 258–66.

21. "Don Juan—A Spectral Research," *Knickerbocker Magazine* 17 (March, 1841), 247–53.

22. "The Enchanted Island," *Knickerbocker Magazine* 14 (July, 1839), 26–38.

23. "Recollections of the Alhambra," *Knickerbocker Magazine* 13 (June, 1839), 485–94.

24. "Mountjoy," *Knickerbocker Magazine* 14 (December, 1839), 524–33. The page numbers refer to *only* those sections which are utilized as copy-text. This is true for the pagination in footnotes 19–23 as well.

25. "Sketches in Paris in 1825," *Knickerbocker Magazine* 16 (November-December, 1840), 425–30, 523–27.

tented Man,"[26] "Broek: Or the Dutch Paradise,"[27] "Guests From Gibbet-Island,"[28] "The Seminoles,"[29] and "The Count Van Horn."[30]

There are various reasons why periodical is used as copy-text instead of the first edition of *Wolfert's Roost*. It is not only chronologically closer to the manuscript, but it is closer in accidentals and substantives as well. One illustration is found in the successive versions of "The Knight of Malta." The Anglicized spelling found in the manuscript is retained in the *Knickerbocker*. While both the manuscript (MSa, 2; T 82.20) and the periodical (KnM, 108) use the spelling "alchymy," the 1855 Putnam edition revises it to "alchemy." This is also true for the angelicized versions of "connexions" (MSa, 7; KnM, 111; T 85.33). In the 1855 edition, the Americanized spelling "connections" is adopted.

The *Knickerbocker* usually follows Irving's eccentric practice of hyphenation and word division, while the Putnam 1855 edition does not. In "The Knight of Malta," "craw-fish" appears in both manuscript (27.6; T 91.31) and magazine (KnM, 116.29), but is altered to "crawfish" (1A, 146.4) in *Wolfert's Roost*. Putnam also combines separated or hyphenated words into one compound word. For example, "ground work" (T 83.28) appears in both magazine and periodical versions of "The Knight of Malta" (MSa, 1.9–10; KnM, 110.24) but is altered to "groundwork" (132.25) in Putnam's 1855 edition. Generally, the American first edition of *Wolfert's Roost* tampers with the original word division or hyphenations of words more than any other edition. Similarly, punctuation in the manuscript is preserved in the magazine version and revised in the 1855 edition. Two examples from "The Knight of Malta" illustrate:

MSa	*Knickerbocker*	*1855 First Edition*
rëassured (31.20)	rëassured (117.38)	reassured (148.12)(T 93.7)
cap-à-pie (35.7)	cap-à-pie (118.28)	cap-á-pie (150.1)(T 93.21)

In both instances, the Putnam house style dictates the rules of punctuation and revises the copy-text accordingly.

26. "A Contented Man," in *The Literary Souvenir*, ed. A. A. Watts (London: Longman, 1827), pp. 1–9.

27. "Broek: Or the Dutch Paradise," *Knickerbocker Magazine* 17 (January, 1841), 228–33.

28. "Guests from Gibbet-Island," *Knickerbocker Magazine* 14 (October, 1839), 342–46.

29. "The Seminoles," *Knickerbocker Magazine* 16 (October, 1840), 341–42. Only "The Origin of the White, the Red and the Black Men" is based on *Knickerbocker* copy-text.

30. "The Count Van Horn," *Knickerbocker Magazine* 15 (March, 1840), 244, 245, 246, 247–49.

Another reason that periodical is used as copy-text can be explained through an analysis of Irving's own publishing procedure. When he decided to reprint "Mountjoy" in *Wolfert's Roost*, he asked Clark to send him "the two numbers of the *Knickerbocker* which contain the story of Mountjoy."[31] Irving's intention was to utilize the periodical as well as the manuscript for future Putnam publication; perhaps the periodical incorporated his last minute proof 'sheet revisions while the manuscript did not reflect these most current alterations.

An analysis of the manuscript—periodical—1855 first edition of "Mountjoy" bears out this theory of publication. Generally, the substantives and accidentals of the *Knickerbocker* version are reprinted in the 1855 edition. For example:

MSa	*Knickerbocker*	*1855 First Edition*
Hugonot (1.10)	Huguenot (402.8)	Huguenot (49.6–7)(T 29.5)
sweet-briar (4.16)	sweet-brier (402.47)	sweet-brier (50.28)(T 30.5)
too (31.7)	too, (408.51)	too, (62.13)(T 37.11)
feelings; (31.7)	feelings, (408.51)	feelings, (62.13)(T 37.11)
visitations, (32.7)	visitations (409.15)	visitations (62.29)(T 37.27)

Some substantive changes, which Irving made in *Knickerbocker* proof sheets, are also carried through the *Wolfert's Roost* edition of 1855. Although the manuscript reads, "No subject is frivolous, that has power to awaken" (35.5; T 38.19–20), both periodical and 1855 edition print "No subject is frivolous, that has the power to awaken" (KnM, 409.51; WR, 64.9). If the Putnam printer had returned to the manuscript for copy-text, Irving's last minute insertions in the *Knickerbocker* would have been neglected.

Wolfert's Roost is not the first book publication for many of the sketches. *The Knickerbocker Sketch-Book* (New York: Burgess, Stringer and Company, 1845) reprinted "The Early Experiences of Ralph Ringwood" (pp. 41–83), "Guests from Gibbet-Island, A Legend of Communipaw" (pp. 117–32) and "Mountjoy" (pp. 165–218). As previously mentioned in the "Individual Histories" to the sketches, the *Knickerbocker Sketch-Book* does not constitute a new version of the tales; in fact, it is poorly edited and contains numerous mistakes in accidentals and substantives.[32]

"Guests from Gibbet-Island" also appeared in "Geoffrey Crayon's" edition of *A Book of the Hudson: Collected from the Various Works of Diedrich Knickerbocker* (New York: Putnam, 1849). Both *Knickerbocker*

31. Letter from Irving to Lewis Gaylord Clark, April 27, 1849, in the possession of Herbert Kleinfield.
32. See the List of Rejected Substantives, pp. 315–18.

Sketch-Book and *Hudson* reprinted the periodical stories without
authorial revisions. They are not used as a basis for either accidental
or substantives in the 1855 edition.

The first publication of *Wolfert's Roost* occurs in *Chronicles of Wolfert's Roost and Other Papers*, published as part of the Author's Revised
Edition (Edinburgh: Constable, 1855).[33] It formed Volume 4 of Constable's *Miscellany of Foreign Literature* and contains 351 pages, no
pictures, and is set from different type than the Putnam first edition.
The January 13, 1855, publication of the English edition preceded the
February 6, 1855, publication of the American *Wolfert's Roost* because
of copyright laws. The Constable edition was probably set from a
periodical version of the pieces, which was copied by an amanuensis
and corrected by Irving. However, discrepancies in both substantives
and accidentals in the English and American editions reveal that Irving
probably revised in proof sheets the American edition once more before
publication. In "A Time of Unexampled Prosperity," the Putnam edition
speaks of "the slow accumulations of industry" (1A, 190.10; T 119.1);
the English edition retains "the safe pursuits of industry" (171.21), a
version which is found in the earlier *Knickerbocker Magazine* printing
of the story. Similarly, while the American edition of "Sketches in Paris
in 1825" prints "jingling spurs" (205.17; T 128.15), the Constable edition
contains "jingling spears" (185.29), the form which also appeared in the
Knickerbocker. Since the substantives as well as the accidentals[34] in
the Constable edition of *Wolfert's Roost* do not represent Irving's final
intentions, they are rejected.

The first American edition of *Wolfert's Roost and Other Papers, Now
First Collected* appeared approximately a month after the English
edition. There are two distinct printings of this first edition. In the first
printing, the address for Putnam's is "12 Park Place"; the second printing gives an address at "10 Park Place." When three different copies of
the "10 Park Place" version were collated, numerous batter smudges and
broken letters suggested possible later printings (1Ac) of the first
American edition.[35]

33. More information can be found in Jacob Blanck's *Bibliography of American
Literature* (New Haven: Yale University Press, 1969), Vol. V, pp. 54–55. Other
pirated editions of the Constable edition appeared in England in 1855. They
were published by Routledge and H. B. Bohn. Blanck notes that the Constable
edition announced on December 6, 1854 "By arrangement with the author . . .
simultaneously with the American edition."

34. For a list of all the English variants which appear in the Constable edition,
see List of Rejected Substantives, pp. 315–18.

35. The frequency in appearance of broken letters and batter-smudged words
in the "10 Park Place" printing supports the contention that this is the second
printing. After analyzing these two printings, Nelson F. Adkins came to the same

There are no variants in substantives within the first American edition. Once the type was set by John F. Trow of New York, Irving made no changes. In fact, the number of typographical errors in the Putnam first edition suggests that neither Irving nor Putnam corrected the proof sheets very carefully. In the first printing ("12 Park Place") the letters *e* and *o* are reversed in the word "moroever" (9.26); the "10 Park Place" printings also contains this error. Other misspellings and typographical mistakes common to all printings are: "philospher" (32.9), "herslf" (49.21), "imformation" (55.22–3), "eagarly" (69.32), "ahove" (74.37), "splended" (98.15), "Lous" (98.40, 109.25), "vilage" (142.8, 188.41), "imformed" (144.24), "enforcc" (145.16), "[a]nd" (145.32), "conncil" (189.43), "sculls" (202.22), "spain" (223.33), "tho" [instead of "the"] (240.1). Other errors include missing dot in "influence" (30.9), "down .." (67.9), "wonderat" (73.7), "worse" [missing] (176.43), latitude- [unnecessary hyphen] (217.15). These twenty-three unemended errors demonstrate the hurried, publication procedure which is typical of the entire history of *Wolfert's Roost*.

There is one change of no textual significance from 1Aa to 1Ab however. The "10 Park Place" printing contains a type resetting on page 154, although no words were added or deleted. The word "flushed," which was broken in the "12 Park Place" printing into "flush/-ed" (96.34) is moved to line 3. Therefore every word on the page is moved forward five spaces. This modification, however, affects only spacing, not meaning.

Putnam's 1856 and 1859 publications of *Wolfert's Roost* are only reimpressions of the first edition. No revisions or typographical emendations have been made in either printing. The only obvious change in the 1855, 1856, and 1859 reprints is the steady deterioration of the type. The 1A59 printing is replete with missing commas, broken letters, and smudges. A random examination of pages 30–34 of the 1A59 printing reveals four significant broken punctuation marks: "sun/-rise" (17.17), "fragrance:" (19.22), "sweet-briar" (19.26), and "music." (19.41).

The first posthumous edition of *Wolfert's Roost* (1861), published two years after the author's death, is also a reimpression of the first edition. The title page and story arrangement are identical, with the exception of the Putnam address, which is now 532 Broadway. Unlike the previous printings, however, three corrections of typographical errors and one revision were made. The printed name of "GEOFFREY

---

conclusion. See his article, *Notes and Queries*, January 21, 1933, pp. 42–43. Blanck in the *Bibliography of American Literature*, vol. 5, believes that there are at least six printings of 1A. However, this editor was unable to find verifiable proof for Blanck's assertion.

CRAYON." (21.26) in the 1855–1859 reprints is changed to a printed signature of "Geoffrey Crayon, Gent." in the 1861. Corrections were made in the spacing of "wonderat" (73.7) to "wonder at." "Ahove" is corrected to "above" (74.37) and an *a* is inserted before "nd" to produce "and" (145.32). Despite these few alterations the majority of typographical errors remain untouched.

Wolfert's Roost was reprinted again in 1863 and 1864. However, in 1865, six years after Irving's death, the volume was republished in a new edition under the title *Wolfert's Roost, and other papers* (New York: Putnam). The book contains 453 pages instead of the 383 pages of the first 1855 edition. There are no changes in substantives between the first American edition and the second edition, published ten years later. Although the 1865 edition is called an "author's revised edition," there is no evidence that Irving left directions for a new edition. The 1865 edition, which was reprinted in 1866, 1868, and 1869 by Putnam, was published in sets of *The Complete Works of Washington Irving* in "The Hudson Editon," and "Tappan Zee Edition."[36]

In 1870, J. B. Lippincott & Company reprinted both the 1865 "People's" and "Knickerbocker" editions of *Wolfert's Roost* in its own series of *Irving's Works*. Lippincott reprinted the volume in 1871, 1872, and 1873. In the 1880's the number of publishers of *Wolfert's Roost* grew in number. The book was reprinted by Belford, Clarke & Company, Belford Company, T. Y. Crowell & Company, J. B. Alden, J. B. Miller & Company, and J. W. Lovell Company. *Wolfert's Roost* was bound with other Irving books as well. Chicago: Belford, Clarke & Company reprinted it with *The Life and Voyages of Christopher Columbus* (188–); and Belford issued it with *Tales of a Traveller.*

Putnam continued to publish *The Complete Works of Washington Irving* in which *Wolfert's Roost* was included as Volume 15. In 1883, *Wolfert's Roost* was reprinted in the following series of complete works: "Geoffrey Crayon Edition," "The Hudson Edition," "The Spuyten Duyvil Edition," "The People's Edition," "Lighter Works," and "The Knickerbocker Edition." The last known printing of the book is by Current Literature Publishing Company (New York, 1912). Only one foreign language version of the book exists, a German edition translated by W. E. Drugulin (Leipzig: C. B. Lorck, 1855).

All manuscripts and authorized editions, up to and including the first posthumous edition, were collated according to the following pattern:

---

36. These "editions" differ only in the quality of binding and paper used to print them. They do not constitute separate editions in any technical sense because they were printed from the same plates.

1. Two sight collations[37] of *KnM* 12 (April, 1839), 317–28 vs. 1Aa (Wolfert's Roost)
2. Two sight collations of *NI* 16 (May, 1839), p. 2 vs. *KnM* 13 (May, 1839), 434–37 vs. 1Aa (The Birds of Spring)
3. Two sight collations of *Mag* (1837), 315–26 vs. 1Aa (The Creole Village)
4. Two sight collations of MSa vs. *KnM* 14 (November-December, 1839), 402–12, 522–38 vs. *KSB* (1845) vs. 1Aa (Mountjoy)
5. Two sight collations of MSa vs. *KnM* 15 (January, 1840), 17–25 vs. 1Aa (The Bermudas)
6. Two sight collations of *Mag* (1837), 259–74 vs. 1Aa (The Widow's Ordeal)
7. Two sight collations of MSa vs. *KnM* 15 (February, 1840), 108–19 vs. *Ev* 1 (March, 1840), 154–58 vs. 1Aa (The Knight of Malta)
8. Two sight collations of *KnM* 15 (April, 1840), 303–24 vs. 1Aa (A Time of Unexampled Prosperity)
9. Two sight collations of MSa vs. *KnM* 16 (November-December, 1840), 425–30, 519–30 vs. *NY* (December 26, 1840), 230–32 vs. 1Aa (Sketches in Paris in 1825)
10. Two sight collations of MSa vs. *LS* (1827), 1–9 vs. *C* (1827) vs. *NYA* (December 22, 1826), 2 vs. 1Aa (A Contented Man)
11. Two sight collations of MSa vs. *KnM* 17 (January, 1841), 55–58 vs. 1Aa (Broek: or the Dutch Paradise)
12. Two sight collations of MSa vs. *KnM* 14 (October, 1839), 342–50 vs. *BH* (1849), 14–30 vs. *KSB* (1845), 115–32 vs. 1Aa (Guests from Gibbet-Island)
13. Two sight collations of *KnM* 16 (August–September, 1840), 152–65, 258–66 vs. *KSB* (1845), 47–83 vs. 1Aa (The Early Experiences of Ralph Ringwood)
14. Two sight collations of MSa vs. *KnM* 16 (October, 1840), 339–40 vs. *NY* (October 17, 1840), 71 vs. *Ev* 1 (November, 1840), 583–84 vs. 1Aa (The Seminoles)
15. Two sight collations of MSa vs. *KnM* 15 (March, 1840), 241–49 vs. 1Aa (The Count Van Horn)
16. Two sight collations of *KnM* 17 (March, 1841), 247–53 vs. 1Aa (Don Juan: A Spectral Research)
17. Two sight collations of MSa vs. *KnM* 15 (March, 1840), 234–37 vs. 1Aa (Legend of the Engulphed Convent)

37. A sight collation is necessary when two editions are set from different type. Machine collation with a Hinman collating machine is used when the editions are identical.

18. Two sight collations of *KnM* 14 (July, 1839), 26–38 vs. *R* 2 (1839) 346–47 vs. 1Aa (The Phantom Island)
19. Two sight collations of *KnM* 13 (June, 1839), 485–94 vs. *R* 3 (1839) 223–24 vs. 1Aa (Recollections of the Alhambra)
20. One sight collation of three impressions of 1A
21. Three machine collations of 1Aa vs. 1Aa vs. 1Ab vs. 1Ab
22. One machine collation of 1Aa with 1A59
23. One sight collation of 1Aa vs. E vs. 1A61
24. One machine collation of 2A vs. 2A
25. Sight comparison of 1Aa with 2A[38]

TREATMENT OF SUBSTANTIVES

Throughout the composition and publication of the stories in *Wolfert's Roost*, Irving has made numerous substantive alterations. Excluding the four extensively revised stories, which will be discussed separately,

38. Copies for these twenty-five collations are recorded by library name and call number, or name of the present owner: (1) Univ. of N. Carolina P/K69 vs. Lewis Leary's copy; (2) Duke N/D614W vs. Lewis Leary's copy; (3) Univ. of N. Carolina 810.85/M198 vs. Lewis Leary's copy; (4) NYPL (67 pages) vs. Univ. of N. Carolina P/K69 vs. NYPL (Berg Collection) vs. Lewis Leary copy; (5) Folger (20 pages) and NYPL (14 pages) vs. Univ. of N. Carolina P/K69 vs. Lewis Leary's copy; (6) Univ. of N. Carolina 810.85/M198 vs. Lewis Leary's copy; (7) NYPL (40 pages) vs. Univ. of N. Carolina P/K69 vs. Duke XPer(Q)E938 vs. Lewis Leary's copy; (8) Univ. of N. Carolina P/K69 vs. Lewis Leary's copy; (9) Univ. of Virginia (34 pages) vs. Univ. of N. Carolina P/K69 vs. Duke XPer(Q)N567 vs. Lewis Leary's copy; (10) Univ. of Virginia (10 pages) vs. Univ. of N. Carolina PS535 vs. Duke N/N567n vs. Lewis Leary's copy; (11) Univ. of Virginia (2 pages) vs. Univ. of N. Carolina P/K69 vs. Lewis Leary's copy; (12) Univ. of Virginia (8 pages) vs. Univ. of N. Carolina P/K69 vs. NYPL F127.H8/186 vs. NYPL (Berg Collection) vs. Lewis Leary's copy; (13) Univ. of N. Carolina P/K69 vs. NYPL (Berg Collection) vs. Lewis Leary's copy; (14) Huntington HM3172 and HM2265 (27 pages) vs. Univ. of N. Carolina P/K69 vs. Duke XPer(Q)N567 vs. Duke XPer(Q)E938 vs. Lewis Leary's copy; (15) NYPL (14 pages) and Univ. of Virginia (1 page) and Knox College (1 page) and Redwood Library and Athenaeum (1 page) and Yale (1 page) vs. Univ. of N. Carolina P/K69 vs. Lewis Leary's copy; (16) Univ. of N. Carolina P/K69 vs. Lewis Leary's copy; (17) NYPL (17 pages) vs. Univ. of N. Carolina P/K69 vs. Lewis Leary's copy; (18) Univ. of N. Carolina P/K69 vs. Lewis Leary's copy; (19) Univ. of N. Carolina P/K69 vs. Lewis Leary's copy; (20) Univ. of N. Carolina T817/172w vs. Univ. of N. Carolina PS2071/A1/1855 vs. Lewis Leary's copy; (21) Richard Beale Davis 1 vs. UW/Y/IR8/W3 vs. Richard Beale Davis 2 vs. McClary copy; (22) UW/Y/IR8/W3 vs. Richard Beale Davis 3; (23) Lewis Leary copy vs. Univ. of Pennsylvania AC8/IR844.855wb vs. Virginia State Library PS2071/A1/1861; (24) Richard Beale Davis 4 vs. McClary (Julius Sachs bookplate); (25) Lewis Leary copy vs. Univ. of N. Carolina.

there are 25 additions, 103 substitutions, and 116 deletions from the copy-texts to the first American edition. The majority of these changes in copy-text, however, deal with style rather than meaning. Through his revisions, Irving sought to make his prose more concise, clear, and controlled.

Irving's additions to the copy-text are generally insignificant. He inserts an article before the noun or adds an "and" to two clauses previously joined with a semicolon. In one instance, the addition concerns the subject of a sentence which becomes the predicate nominative: "I delight" is altered to "it is my delight" (214.35).

Substitutions, which comprise about forty percent of the substantive changes, have both stylistic and thematic importance. In "A Time of Unexampled Prosperity," Irving substitutes "slow accumulations of industry" for "safe pursuits of industry" (KnM, 324.5; T 119.1). This revision suggests a less benevolent description of the financial system which is a vehicle of destruction. He also creates a more logical system for designating titles. In the manuscript of "The Knight of Malta" Irving calls both French and Spanish soldiers "chevaliers" and "cavaliers." In the *Knickerbocker* and Putnam editions, the French are referred to as "chevaliers" while the Spanish are "cavaliers" (85.15, 85.35, 85.39, 86.17, 91.40).

About forty-five to sixty percent of the revisions involve the deletion of material. When Irving revised "Guests from Gibbet-Island" for inclusion in *Wolfert's Roost*, he was particularly scrupulous in this area. Unnecessary adjectives or articles are eliminated: "where all the public affairs" becomes "where public affairs" (147.16); and "Of all true-hearted" is reduced to only "of true-hearted" (147.36). In this one story alone, there are ten deletions which affect verb tense and sentence structure: "lingered" (148.8), "but" (148.8), "we" (148.39), "were" (149.10), "declared" (149.14), "if" (149.16), "had" (151.29), and "whence" (153.12).

An important thematic change is the deletion of Geoffrey Crayon as the pseudonym for Washington Irving in the first American edition. Seventeen of the nineteen sketches in *Wolfert's Roost* were originally published with Crayon's name. The narratives are: "Wolfert's Roost," "The Birds of Spring," "Mountjoy," "A Contented Man," "Broek: Or the Dutch Paradise," "Sketches in Paris in 1825," "The Early Experiences of Ralph Ringwood," "The Knight of Malta," "Don Juan: A Spectral Research," and "Legend of the Engulphed Convent." Seven of the seventeen tales were ascribed to Geoffrey Crayon as "The Author of the Sketch-Book": "The Phantom Island," "The Widow's Ordeal," "The Creole Village," "A Time of Unexampled Prosperity," "The Bermudas," and "Recollections of the Alhambra." Only two stories, "The Count

Van Horn" and "The Seminoles," are printed without the Crayon authorship.

Of these seventeen pieces, only two retain the Geoffrey Crayon name in the first American edition. Why "Sketches in Paris in 1825" and "The Early Experiences of Ralph Ringwood" are left unaltered is unknown. One can only assume that during the fifteen year period from the stories' first periodical appearance to their Putnam publication in 1855, Irving had decided that he no longer desired a pseudonym.

The 244 additions, substitutions, and deletions are not the only substantive changes in the copy-text for *Wolfert's Roost*. Four pieces, "Wolfert's Roost," "The Phantom Island," "The Birds of Spring" and "Recollections of the Alhambra," are completely rewritten and revised. The alterations from copy-text to first American edition are so extensive that it is impossible to calculate the exact number or kinds of revisions. A few examples from "The Phantom Island" (T 219.27–40) will illustrate the alterations which were made from the 1839 *Knickerbocker* to the 1855 Putnam edition. While both versions have parallel plots, the sentence structure is quite dissimilar:

Putnam 1855 edition

The gentle lady shook her head. It was not on this point she felt distrust. She was a thorough believer in the Island of the Seven Cities, and so sure of the success of the enterprise that she might have been tempted to join it had not the balcony been high and the grating strong. Other considerations induced that dubious shaking of the head. She had heard of the inconstancy of the seas, and the inconstancy of those who roam them. Might not Fernando meet with other loves in foreign ports? Might not some peerless beauty in one or other of those Seven Cities efface the image of Serafina from his mind? Now let the truth be spoken, the beautiful Serafina had reason for her disquiet. If Don Fernando had any fault in the world, it was that of being rather inflammable and apt to take fire from every sparkling eye. He had been somewhat of a rover among the sex on shore, what might he be on the sea? (250.11–25)

Knickerbocker (July, 1839)

The beautiful Serafina shook her head mournfully. It was not on those points that she felt doubt or dismay. She believed most implicitly in the Island of the Seven Cities, and trusted devoutly in the success of the enterprise; but she had heard of the inconstancy of the seas, and the inconstancy of those who roamed them. Now, let the truth be spoken, Don Fernando, if he had any fault in the world, it was, that he was a little to subject to take fire from the sparkle of every bright eye; he had been somewhat of a rover among the sex on shore, what might he not be on sea? (31.13–22)

The 1855 Putnam version is about thirty-five percent longer because the early edition is less specific in its intimations about Don Fernando's infidelities. The periodical states that Serafina "had heard of the inconstancy of the seas, and the inconstancy of those who roam them" while the Putnam edition expands the discussion to an analysis of behavior at "foreign ports."

This revision from magazine to book form, however, reveals only one kind of alteration in the four extensively rewritten *Wolfert's Roost* stories. Generally, the 1855 version is more concise and controlled in tone. Many of the changes in these four stories involve the deletion of adjectives and phrases. The last meeting of Don Fernando and Serafina, in "The Phantom Island" (T 219.21–24) provides an illustration of Irving's modifications from magazine to 1855 edition.

Putnam 1855 edition	*Knickerbocker (July, 1839)*
at anchor in the Tagus ready to sail at sunrise. Late at night by the pale light of a waning moon the lover had his last interview. The beautiful Serafina was sad at heart and full of dark forebodings; her lover full of hope and confidence. (350.4–7)	anchored in the Tagus, ready to sail with the morning dawn; while late at night, by the pale light of a waning moon, Don Fernando sought the stately mansion of Alvarez, to take a last farewell of Serafina. The customary signal, of a few low touches of a guitar brought her to the balcony. She was sad at heart, and full of gloomy foreboding; but her lover strove to impart of her his own buoyant hope and youthful confidence. (31.2–9)

The description of the lovers' parting is extremely compressed in the 1855 edition. Irving shortens the line, "Don Fernando sought the stately mansion of Alvarez, to take a last farewell of Serafina" to "the lover had his last interview." The later version of "The Phantom Island" is generally less melodramatic as well as less verbose.

The various substantive revisions that Irving has made in the *Wolfert's Roost's* pieces have been incorporated into the Twayne edition. While a few of the changes seem to add little to or even detract from the smoothness of the prose, they are incorporated into the text as long as they are thought to be Irving's own.

TREATMENT OF ACCIDENTALS

Although a publisher or typesetter might be reluctant to change the substantives, or words, of a text, he would modify the accidentals in order to make the author's style conform to the particular house style. For this reason, the earliest text of the *Wolfert's Roost* stories would provide the fewest nonauthorial revisions in spelling, punctuation, hyphenation, and spacing.

Irving's own system of punctuation, spelling, and spacing is so inconsistent and eccentric that it almost amounts to the absence of a system altogether. An analysis of the "Mountjoy" manuscript reveals numerous accidental inconsistencies. Irving vacillates in his use of commas and semicolons, often selecting a semicolon where a comma will suffice: "Yet he indulged me in every vagary; for I was an only son, and of course a personage of importance in the household" (MSa, 2.11–12; T, 29.17–18).

Although Irving often complained that his editors ruined the flow of his prose by the insertion of excessive commas, or "overpointing," his own use of semicolons occasionally created a choppy sentence structure: "How I longed to be able to compress my form into utter littleness; to ride the bold dragon-fly; swing in the tall bearded grass; follow the ant into his subterraneous habitation, or drive into the cavernous depths of the honeysuckle" (MSa, 5.13–19; T, 30.18–21).

Irving's system of capitalization is often anarchic and personal. While "Englishman" usually appears in the manuscript in capitalized form, "frenchman" is often in lowercase letters. Whether this is intentional and indicative of Irving's preference for the English is doubtful; he can capitalize nationality in three instances and then fail to capitalize in the fourth. Another problem is the virtual impossibility of distinguishing between some lower- and uppercase letters in the author's manuscripts. Particular difficulties are presented by the letters *c, g, s, t, k, y,* and *m.* For this reason, one can never be certain whether some words are indeed improperly capitalized or uncapitalized.

By far, the most serious problem in Irving's system of punctuation is his misuse of the apostrophe for possessives or contractions. In the manucript of "A Contented Man" there are three apostrophe errors in eight pages of manuscript (3.7; T, 137.30) (6.7; T, 138.34) (6.13; T, 138.37). All three words are possessives, and without the apostrophe, they can be misinterpreted as plurals. Irving's failure to note possessive construction is not intentional, but rather indicative of his hurried method of composition. Although the "Contented Man" manuscript contains three such errors, there is one proper form, "St. James' " (7.6–7; T, 139.5), which demonstrates Irving's ability to use correct punctuation.

Irving's spelling, like his punctuation, follows no absolute grammatical principles. Although he mentions both Webster's dictionary and Bayle's English dictionary in his correspondence, he never ascribes to any one system of punctuation or spelling. He uses *our* and *ize* endings in words like "flavour" or "surprize" instead of the American *or* and *ise*. Yet, after using an Anglicized form three times on one page, it is not uncommon to find the American spelling. An example of this vacillation between American and British form is found in the ten extant manuscript pages of "A Contented Man." There are seven instances of the British *our* in "flavour" (1.12; T, 137.6), "favourable" (3.21; T, 137.38), "good humoured" (4.8; T, 138.5), "neighbours" (5.4; T, 138.18), "endeavoured" (6.25; T, 139.1), "good-humoured" (9.11; T, 139.37–38), and "good-humour" (10.23; T, 140.12). Anglicized spelling is also present in the words "reliques" (3.4; T, 137.34) and "surprize" (6.2; T, 138.32). Despite this preference for the British forms, there are five American spellings in the same manuscript: "neighbor" (6.4; T, 138.32), "favorable" (8.15; T, 139.25), "favorite" (8.16; T, 139.26) and "favorites" (8.20; T, 139.28), and "recognize" (6.4; T, 138.32). Irving's spelling of "favorable" and "favourable" emphasizes his inability or lack of desire to follow any one writing style.

Irving also divided and hyphenated words in an erratic fashion. In "A Contented Man" and "Sketches in Paris in 1825" it is possible to find as many as three spacing arrangements for any one word. He would separate "good humoured" (4.8; T, 138.5) into "good-humoured" (T, 133.5) or "goodhumoured" (9.8; T, 139.37–8).

Both the magazine editors and Putnam, however, regularized punctuation, spelling, and spacing. While G. P. Putnam and Clark did little tampering with the words of the text, they did manipulate accidentals to suit their own house styles. Both Clark and Putnam (1) revised the majority of English and eccentric spelling to conform to American usage; (2) joined hyphenated words; (3) inserted additional commas, periods, and semicolons; (4) capitalized all proper nouns; (5) added apostrophes to denote possession and contractions; and (6) regularized Irving's haphazard system of quotations. Clark made all the quotations single, while Putnam used double quotations throughout. In almost every case, these revisions are rejected in this edition in favor of the original Irving eclectic style.

There are, however, legitimate instances when an author's writing habits must be emended. In the Twayne edition of *Wolfert's Roost*, there are thirty-two punctuation, five spacing, twenty-four spelling, one hyphenation, six capitalization, and one italics alteration of copy-text.[39] When the spelling, punctuation, or spacing of a word is so at variance with common usage so as to confuse rather than communicate the

39. This does not include the single quotation of the *Knickerbocker* when it serves as copy-text. As noted previously, all *Knickerbocker* single quotation marks are changed to double quotation in order to conform to Irving's own usage.

author's original intention, the word or punctuation is emended. Most of the recorded emendations are corrections of quotation marks. Irving generally used double quotations throughout the stories. When a single quotation appears, and it is not a quotation within a quotation, the single is modified to a double. The other major punctuation change in copy-text is the revision of apostrophe errors. Without the apostrophe, the reader can easily mistake a possessive for a plural noun. Missing end points are also added when it is clear that it was Irving's intention.[40] Proper nouns are always capitalized in order to signal their difference to the reader.[41]

Generally very few copy-text accidentals are revised for the present edition of *Wolfert's Roost*. While there are 244 copy-text emendations of substantives, there are only 69 changes in original accidentals. Even in the cases of the four extensively revised pieces, manuscript or copy-text supplies spelling, punctuation, and hyphenation. Every effort is made to maintain the Irvingesque texture which the author himself intended.

40. For example, in the "Mountjoy" manuscript (New York Public Library, 67 pages), "... to the present moment" does not end in a period. Yet the next sentence begins "By degrees I called to mind . . . wreck." (54.29–60.1; T, 44.8–10). From Irving's capitalization, one may infer that the missing period is not intentional. Only in an obvious case such as this would punctuation be added to the copy-text.

41. In the "Mountjoy" manuscript (New York Public Library, 67 pages), Irving fails to capitalize "italian" (81.6; T, 54.26). This oversight, which is corrected in both *Knickerbocker* and the first American edition is emended in the Twayne edition. "Charlotte," which is also uncapitalized in the "Mountjoy" manuscript (42.12; T, 40.25), but capitalized in *Knickerbocker* and the first American edition, is emended in order to conform to Irving's practice.

DISCUSSIONS OF ADOPTED READINGS

In these discussions of decisions to emend or not to emend, the symbols used to designate manuscripts and published texts are those given in the List of Abbreviations, page 243.

The page and line figures are keyed in each case to a word or words in the text to which the discussion or comment refers. A bracket separates the key word or words from the comment that follows.

5.12 "Our] The only major change in accidentals which is not noted in every case is that of the quotation system. Irving's own practice was random. Often he used single and double quotation marks in the: (1) beginning and ending of a paragraph; (2) when writing dialogue; (3) when denoting a quotation within a quotation. Irving often neglected to conclude a quotation and thus his practice is quite confusing to the reader. Both the KnM and the 1A regularized the quotations as follows. KnM uses single quotation marks only (even for quotations within quotations) while 1A uses double and single quotations in the manner employed today. The Twayne edition will follow the manuscript quotations as closely as possible, yet when Irving's practice proves confusing to the reader, the punctuation will reflect the 1A system of quotation. No quotation marks will be added, however, unless specifically noted in the List of Emendations, pages 269–314.

6.3–20 In revenge . . . him] "Wolfert's Roost" as well as "The Birds of Spring," "The Phantom Island," and "Recollections of Alhambra" have been extensively revised by Irving for 1A. The 1A version of these stories reflects Irving's last wishes and thus it is the basis for substantive revisions. In these four stories listed above, accidentals as well as substantives have been altered, since the editor must assume that the revisions reflect Irving's arrangement of words and phrases. In the other fifteen stories, the 1A edition accidentals are not incorporated into the Twayne text because there is no proof that Irving made such changes.

29.5 Huguenot] Misspellings of proper nouns, cities, and countries are changed when the correct spelling can be found in another version of the story. All such emendations are noted in the List of Emendations. In the above example, Irving misspelled "Hugonot" in the manuscript version, but the error was corrected in both KnM and 1A.

57.29 moral] Although KnM, KSB, and 1A include the word "more" instead of "moral" it is obviously a printer's error, because the word "more" does not make sense in the context of the story. Miss Somerville has had no philosophical training and, therefore, she cannot add a little "more" to the absence of any training. In addition, MSa contains the correct word which is "moral."

63.5 Oberon's] Although Irving inserted apostrophes to note possession, he more often forgot them. The Twayne edition has revised the manuscript accidentals in this case, because the reader may often mistake a possessive for a plural. All such changes are noted in the List of Emendations. In the above example Irving neglected to insert the apostrophe in the manuscript; however, the apostrophe was inserted in both KnM and 1A.

89.29 wielded] The MSa, KnM, and Ev versions all include the word "wielded" while the 1A prints "yielded." In the context of the sentence, "yielded" makes no sense and is presumed to be an error.

91.12 supper] The MSa, KnM, and Ev versions all include the word "supper" while the 1A prints "upper." In the context of the sentence, "upper" makes no sense and is presumed to be an error.

100.30 depositary] The KnM version includes the word "depositary" while 1A and E print "depository." In the context of the sentence, "depositary" makes sense while the latter does not. It is therefore presumed that the emendation was made incorrectly by the compositor.

182.22 ball-play] When Irving originally copied this quotation from William Bartram's *Travels Through North and South Carolina, Georgia, East and West Florida* (1792), he mistook "bull" for the correct "ball." This error was reprinted in all editions of the story. The decision to emend was made because the error did not make sense in the context of the sentence.

194.11 de Créqui] In every other place "de" is used in place of "of." The substitution of the English "of" for the French "de" is incorrect in this context and the only exception in the story. "De" is used in every other context.

232.24 Alcayde] When Irving revised parts of this story for inclusion in 1A, the name of the "Alcayde" was uncapitalized. The Twayne edition retains the capitalized version found in KnM in order to maintain a uniformity in the use of proper nouns.

LIST OF EMENDATIONS

These notes identify all emendations of the copy-text The numbers before each note indicate the page and line. Chapter numbers, chapter or section titles, author's chapter or section summaries, texts, quotations, and footnotes are included in the line count. Only running heads are omitted from the count.

The reading to the left of the bracket is the portion of the text under consideration and represents an accepted reading that differs from the copy-text. The source of the reading is identified by symbol after the bracket.

The reading after the semicolon is the rejected reading of the copy-text and any other text in which that reading occurs; if other alternatives are also available, they are recorded following that reading.

The swung (wavy) dash $\sim$ represents the same word, words, or characters that appear before the bracket, and is used in recording punctuation variants; the caret $_\wedge$ indicates that a mark of punctuation is omitted. T signifies that a decision to emend or not to emend has been made on the authority of the editor of the Twayne edition. An asterisk * is placed before an entry when the reading is discussed in the Discussions of Adopted Readings, pages 267–68. The symbols used to designate manuscripts and previously published texts are those given in the List of Abbreviations, page 243.

3.1   *WOLFERT'S*] THE CRAYON PAPERS. /[bar]/ TO THE EDITOR OF THE KNICKERBOCKER. / WORTHY SIR: In a preceding communication, I have given you some brief notice of Wolfert's Roost, the mansion where I first had the good fortune to become acquainted with the venerable historian of the New-Netherlands. As this ancient edifice is likely to be the place whence I shall date many of my lucubrations, and as it is really a very remarkable little pile, intimately connected with all the great epochs of our local and national history, I have thought it but right to give some farther particulars concerning it. Fortunately, in rummaging in a ponderous Dutch chest of drawers, which serves as the archives of the Roost, and in which are preserved many inedited manuscripts of

Mr. KNICKERBOCKER, together with the precious records of New-Amsterdam, brought hither by Wolfert
Acker, at the downfall of the Dutch dynasty, as has
been already mentioned, I found in one corner,
among dried pumpkin-seeds, bunches of thyme and
pennyroyal, and crumbs of new-year cakes, a manuscript, carefully wrapped up in the fragment of an
old parchment deed, but much blotted, and the ink
grown foxy by time, which, on inspection, I discovered to be a faithful chronicle of the Roost. The
hand-writing, and certain internal evidences, leave
no doubt in my mind, that it is a genuine production
of the venerable historian of the New-Netherlands,
written, very probably, during his residence at the
Roost, in gratitude for the hospitality of its proprietor.
As such, I submit it for publication. As the entire
chronicle is too long for the pages of your Magazine,
and as it contains many minute particulars, which
might prove tedious to the general reader, I have
abbreviated and occasionally omitted some of its details; but may hereafter furnish them separately,
should they seem to be required by the curiosity of
an enlightened and document-hunting public. / Respectfully Yours, / GEOFFREY CRAYON.

A CHRONICLE OF KnM

3.2	CHRONICLE I.] 1A; Found Among The Papers Of The Late Diedrich Knickerbocker. KnM
3.9–11	It is said, . . . Lawrence.] 1A; It claims KnM
4.7–8	lines, in other words, he had the spirit of annexation;] 1A; lines; KnM
4.10	rugged] 1A; ragged KnM
4.14–15	hocus-pocus (or diplomacy)] 1A; hocus-pocus KnM
4.16–20	stream . . . ambuscades,] 1A; stream to stream, until

he found himself in legitimate possession of that
region of hills and valleys, bright fountains and limpid brooks, locked in by the mazy windings of the
Neperan and the Pocantico.*

This last-mentioned stream, or rather the valley
through which it flows, was the most difficult of all his
acquisitions. It lay half way to the strong hold of
the redoubtable sachem of Sing-Sing, and was claimed
by him as an integral part of his domains. Many were
the sharp conflicts between the rival chieftains, for

the sovereignty of this valley, and many the ambuscades, KnM

4.22   pursue] 1A; furnish KnM

4.39–43   *A corruption . . . nose.] 1A; *As EVERY one may not
recognise these boundaries by their original Indian
names, it may be well to observe, that the Neperan
is that beautiful stream, vulgarly called the Saw-Mill
River, which, after winding gracefully for many miles
through a lovely valley, shrouded by groves, and dotted by Dutch farm-houses, empties itself into the
Hudson, at the ancient dorp of Yonkers. The Pocantico is that hitherto nameless brook, that, rising among
woody hills, winds in many a wizard maze through
the sequestered haunts of Sleepy Hollow. We owe it
to the indefatigable researches of Mr. KNICKERBOCKER,
that those beautiful streams are rescued from modern
common-place, and reïnvested with their ancient Indian names. The correctness of the venerable historian may be ascertained, by reference to the records
of the original Indian grants to the Herr Frederick
Philipsen, preserved in the county clerk's   office, at
White Plains. KnM

5.5   Sea] 1A; Zee KnM

5.6–7   Hollow, . . . Wicquaes-Keck.] 1A; Hollow; all which
delectable region, if every one had his right, would
still acknowledge allegiance to the lord of the Roost—
Whoever he might be.* KnM

*5.8–12   The wizard . . . master] 1A; The wizard sachem was
succeeded by a line of chiefs, of whom nothing remarkable remains on record. The last who makes any
figure in history, is the one who ruled here at the
time of the discovery of the country by the white
man. This sachem is said to have been a renowned
trencherman, who maintained almost as potent a
sway by dint of good feeding, as his warlike predecessor had done by hard fighting. He diligently cultivated the growth of oysters along the aquatic
borders of his territories, and founded those great
oyster beds, which yet exist along the shores of the
Tappan Sea. Did any dispute occur between him and
a neighboring sachem, he invited him and all his
principal sages and fighting men to a solemn banquet,
and seldom failed of feeding them into terms. Enor-

mous heaps of oyster-shells, which encumber the
lofty banks of the river, remain as monuments of his
gastronomical victories, and have been occasionally
adduced, through mistake, by amateur geologists
from town, as additional proofs of the deluge. Modern investigators, who are making such indefatigable
researches into our early history, have even affirmed,
that this sachem was the very individual on whom
Master Hendrick Hudson, and his mate Robert Juet,
made that sage and astounding experiment, so gravely
recorded by the latter, in his narrative of the voyage:
'Our master KnM

5.30–31   The worthy government . . . this] 1A; Never has a territorial right, in these new countries, been more legiti-
mately and tradefully established; yet I grieve to
say, the worthy government of the New Netherlands
was not suffered to enjoy this KnM

5.31   unmolested. In] 1A; unmolested: for in KnM
5.38   and] 1A; and it KnM
5.39   hero. Without] 1A; hero; who, without KnM
5.40   he pounced] 1A; pounced KnM
5.42   *See Juet's Journal, Purchas Pilgrims.] 1A; *In recording the contest for the sovereignty of Sleepy
Hollow, I have called one sachem by the modern
name of his castle or strong-hold, viz: Sing-Sing. This,
I would observe, for the sake of historical exactness,
is a corruption of the old Indian name O-sin-sing, or
rather O-sin-song; that is to say, a place where any
thing may be had for a song—a great recommenda-
tion for a market town. The modern and melodious
alteration of the name to Sing-Sing, is said to have
been made in compliment to an eminent Methodist
singing-master, who first introduced into the neighborhood the art of singing through the nose. D. K.
        † See Juet's Journal, Purchas Pilgrim. KnM. [In
revising the story, Irving moved footnotes from one
place to another.]

6.2   into] 1A; into the bounds of KnM
*6.3–20   In revenge . . . him.] 1A; He then established certain
out-posts, far in the Indian country, to keep an eye
over these debateable lands: one of these border holds
was the Roost, being accessible from New Amsterdam
by water, and easily kept supplied. The Yankees,

however, had too great a hankering after this delectable region, to give it up entirely. Some remained,
and swore allegiance to the Manhattoes; but, while
they kept this open semblance of fealty, they went
to work secretly and vigorously to intermarry and
multiply, and by these nefarious means, artfully
propagated themselves into possession of a wide tract
of those open, arable parts of Westchester county,
lying along the Sound, where their descendants may
be found at the present day; while the mountainous
regions along the Hudson, with the valleys of the
Neperan and the Pocantico, are tenaciously held by
the lineal descendants of the Copperheads. KnM

6.21–31   At the time . . . gable] 1A; THE chronicle of the venerable Diedrich here goes on to relate how that,
shortly after the above-mentioned events, the whole
province of the New Netherlands was subjugated by
the British; how that Wolfert Acker, one of the
wrangling councillors of Peter Stuyvesant, retired
in dudgeon to this fastness in the wilderness, deter-
mining to enjoy 'lust in rust' for the remainder of his
days, whence the place first received its name of
Wolfert's Roost. As these and sundry other matters
have been laid before the public in a preceding
article, I shall pass them over, and resume the chronicle where it treats of matters not hitherto recorded:
KnM

6.32–7.6   Wolfert's . . . orchard] 1A; LIKE many men who retire
from a worrying world, says DIEDRICH KNICKERBOCKER,
to enjoy quiet in the country, Wolfert Acker soon
found himself up to the ears in trouble. He had a
termagant wife at home, and there was what is pro-
fanely called 'the deuce to pay,' abroad. The recent
irruption of the Yankees into the bounds of the
New Netherlands, had left behind it a doleful pesti-
lence, such as is apt to follow the steps of invading
armies. This was the deadly plague of witchcraft,
which had long been prevalent to the eastward. The
malady broke out at Vest Dorp, and threatened to
spread throughout the country. The Dutch burghers
along the Hudson, from Yonkers to Sleepy Hollow,
hastened to nail horse-shoes to their doors, which
have ever been found of sovereign virtue to repel this

awful visitation. This is the origin of the horse-shoes
which may still be seen nailed to the doors of barns
and farm-houses, in various parts of this sage and
sober-thoughted region.

The evil, however, bore hard upon the Roost;
partly, perhaps, from its having in old times been
subject to supernatural influences, during the sway
of the Wizard Sachem; but it has always, in fact,
been considered a fated mansion. The unlucky Wolfert had no rest day nor night. When the weather
was quiet all over the country, the wind would howl
and whistle round his roof; witches would ride and
whirl upon his weather-cocks, and scream down his
chimnies. His cows gave bloody milk, and his horses
broke bounds, and scampered into the woods. There
were not wanting evil tongues to whisper that Wolfert's termagant wife had some tampering with the
enemy; and that she even attended a witches' Sabbath
in Sleepy Hollow; nay, a neighbor, who lived hard
by, declared that he saw her harnessing a rampant
broom-stick, and about to ride to the meeting;
though others presume it was merely flourished in
the course of one of her curtain lectures, to give
energy and emphasis to a period. Certain it is, that
Wolfert Acker nailed a horse-shoe to the front door,
during one of her noctural excursions, to prevent
her return; but as she reëntered the house without
any difficulty, it is probable she was not so much
of a witch as she was represented.*

After the time of Wolfert Acker, a long interval
elapses, about which but little is known. It is hoped,
however, that the antiquarian researches so diligently
making in every part of this new country, may yet
throw some light upon what may be termed the
Dark Ages of the Roost.

* HISTORICAL NOTE.—The annexed extracts from the
early colonial records, relate to the irruption of witchcraft into Westchester county, as mentioned in the
chronicle:

'JULY 7, 1670.—Katharine Harryson, accused of
witchcraft on complaint of Thomas Hunt and Edward
Waters, in behalf of the town, who pray that she may
be driven from the town of Westchester. The woman

appears before the council. * * * She was a native of England, and had lived a year in Weathersfield, Connecticut, where she had been tried for witchcraft, found guilty by the jury, acquitted by the bench, and released out of prison, upon condition she would remove. Affair adjourned.

'AUGUST 24.—Affair taken up again, when, being heard at large, it was referred to the general court of assize. Woman ordered to give security for good behaviour,' etc.

In another place is the following entry:

'Order given for Katharine Harryson, charged with witchcraft, to leave Westchester, as the inhabitants are uneasy at her residing there, and she is ordered to go off. KnM.

7.7   CHRONICLE II] 1A; THE chronicle KnM

7.8–14   The next . . . line.] 1A; The next period at which we find this venerable and eventful pile rising to importance, and resuming its old belligerent character, is during the revolutionary war. It was at that time owned by Jacob Van Tassel, or Van Texel, as the name was originally spelled, after the place in Holland which gave birth to this heroic line. He was strong built, long-limbed, and as stout in soul as in body; a fit successor to the warrior sachem of yore, and like him, delighting in extravagant enterprises, and hardy deeds of arms. But, before I enter upon the exploits of this worthy cock of the Roost, it is fitting I should throw some light upon the state of the mansion, and of the surrounding country, at the time. KnM

7.15–8.21   The Roost . . . King George.] 1A; The situation of the Roost is in the very heart of what was the debateable ground between the American and British lines, during the war. The British held possession of the city of New-York, and the island of Manhattan on which it stands. The American drew up toward the Highlands, holding their head-quarters at Peekskill. The intervening country, from Croton River to Spiting Devil Creek, was the debateable land, subject to be harried by friend and foe, like the Scottish borders of yore. It is a rugged country, with a line of rocky hills extending through it, like a back bone,

sending ribs on either side; but among these rude
hills are beautiful winding valleys, like those watered
by the Pocantico and the Neperan. In the fastnesses
of these hills, and along these valleys, exist a race
of hard-headed, hard-handed, stout-hearted Dutchmen, descendants of the primitive Nederlanders. Most
of these were strong whigs, throughout the war, and
have ever remained obstinately attached to the soil,
and neither to be fought nor bought out of their
paternal acres. Others were tories, and adherents to
the old kingly rule; some of whom took refuge within
the British lines, joined the royal bands of refugees,
a name odious to the American ear, and occasionally
returned to harass their ancient neighbors.

In a little while, this debateable land was overrun
by predatory bands from either side; sacking hen-
roosts, plundering farm-houses, and driving off cattle.
Hence arose those two great orders of border chivalry,
the Skinners and the Cow-boys, famous in the heroic
annals of Westchester country. The former fought,
or rather marauded, under the American, the latter
under the British banner; but both, in the hurry
of their military ardor, were apt to err on the safe
side, and rob friend as well as foe. Neither of them
stopped to ask the politics of horse or cow, which
they drove into captivity; nor, when they wrung the
neck of a rooster, did they trouble their heads to
ascertain whether he were crowing for Congress or
King George. KnM

8.22–27   To check...highways.] 1A; While this marauding
system prevailed on shore, the Great Tappan Sea,
which washes this belligerent region, was domineered
over by British frigates, and other vessels of war,
anchored here and there, to keep an eye upon the
river, and maintain a communication between the
various military posts. Stout galleys, also, armed
with eighteen-pounders, and navigated with sails
and oars, cruised about like hawks, ready to pounce
upon their prey.

All these were eyed with bitter hostility by the
Dutch yeomanry along shore, who were indignant
at seeing their great Mediterranean ploughed by
hostile prows; and would occasionally throw up a

mud breast-work on a point or promontory, mount
an old iron field-piece, and fire away at the enemy,
though the greatest harm was apt to happen to themselves, from the bursting of their ordnance; nay,
there was scarce a Dutchman along the river, that
would hesitate to fire with his long duck gun, at any
British cruiser that came within reach, as he had
been accustomed to fire at water-fowl. KnM

8.28–35   Wolfert's . . . tale.] 1A; I have been thus particular in
my account of the times and neighborhood, that the
reader might the more readily comprehend the surrounding dangers, in this the Heroic Age of the Roost.

It was commanded at the time, as I have already
observed, by the stout Jacob Van Tassel. As I wish
to be extremely accurate in this part of my chronicle,
I beg that this Jacob Van Tassel of the Roost may
not be confounded with another Jacob Van Tassel,
commonly known in border story by the name of
'Clump-footed Jake,' a noted tory, and one of the
refugee band of Spiting Devil. On the contrary, he
of the Roost was a patriot of the first water, and,
if we may take his own word for granted, a thorn
in the side of the enemy. As the Roost, from its
lonely situation on the water's edge, might be liable
to attack, he took measures for defence. On a row of
hooks above his fire-place, reposed his great piece of
ordnance, ready charged and primed for action. This
was a duck, or rather goose-gun, of unparalleled
longitude, with which it was said he could kill a wild
goose, though half way across the Tappan Sea. Indeed, there are as many wonders told of this renowned
gun, as of the enchanted weapons of the heroes of
classic story.

In different parts of the stone walls of his mansion,
he had made loop-holes, through which he might fire
upon an assailant. His wife was stout-hearted as
himself, and could load as fast as he could fire; and
then he had an ancient and redoubtable sister, Nochie
Van Wurmer, a match, as he said, for the stoutest
man in the country. Thus garrisoned, the little Roost
was fit to stand a siege, and Jacob Van Tassel was the
man to defend it to the last charge of powder. KnM

8.36–9.6   The foraging . . . Morrisania.] 1A; He was, as I have

already hinted, of pugnacious propensities; and, not
content with being a patriot at home, and fighting for
the security of his own fire-side, he extended his
thoughts abroad, and entered into a confederacy
with certain of the bold, hard-riding lads of Tarrytown, Petticoat Lane, and Sleepy Hollow, who formed
a kind of Holy Brotherhood, scouring the country to
clear it of Skinner and Cow-boy, and all other border
vermin. The Roost was one of their rallying points.
Did a band of marauders from Manhattan island
come sweeping through the neighborhood, and driving
off cattle, the stout Jacob and his compeers were soon
clattering at their heels, and fortunate did the rogues
esteem themselves, if they could but get a part of
their booty across the lines, or escape themselves,
without a rough handling. Should the moss troopers
succeed in passing with their cavalgada, with thundering tramp and dusty whirlwind, across Kingsbridge,
the Holy Brotherhood of the Roost would rein up
at that perilous pass, and wheeling about, would
indemnify themselves by foraging the refugee region
of Morrissania. KnM

9.7–10.3   While the . . . powder.]   1A; When at home at the Roost,
the stout Jacob was not idle; but was prone to carry
on a petty warfare of his own, for his private recreation and refreshment. Did he ever chance to
espy, from his look-out place, a hostile ship or galley
anchored or becalmed near shore, he would take
down his long goose-gun from the hooks over the
fire-place, sally out alone, and lurk along shore,
dodging behind rocks and trees, and watching for
hours together, like a veteran mouser intent on a
rat-hole. So sure as a boat put off for shore, and
came within shot, bang! went the great goose gun;
a shower of slugs and buck-shot whistled about the
ears of the enemy, and before the boat could reach
the shore, Jacob had scuttled up some woody ravine,
and left no trace behind. KnM

10.4–18   In the . . . enemy.]   1A; About this time, the Roost ex-
experienced a vast accession of warlike importance,
in being made one of the stations of the water-guard.
This was a kind of aquatic corps of observation, composed of long, sharp, canoe-shaped boats, technically

called whale-boats, that lay lightly on the water, and could be rowed with great rapidity. They were manned by resolute fellows, skilled at pulling an oar, or handling a musket. These lurked about in nooks and bays, and behind those long promontories which run out into the Tappan Sea, keeping a look-out, to give notice of the approach or movements of hostile ships. They roved about in pairs; sometimes at night, with muffled oars, gliding like spectres about frigates and guard-ships riding at anchor, cutting off any boats that made for shore, and keeping the enemy in constant uneasiness. These musquito-cruisers generally kept aloof by day, so that their harboring places might not be discovered, but would pull quietly along, under shadow of the shore, at night, to take up their quarters at the Roost. Hither, at such time, would also repair the hard-riding lads of the hills, to hold secret councils of war with the 'ocean chivalry;' and in these nocturnal meetings were con- concerted many of those daring forays, by land and water, that resounded throughout the border. KnM

10.19–32　　The Roost, ... war!]　1A; THE chronicle here goes on to recount divers wonderful stories of the wars of the Roost, from which it would seem, that this little warrior nest carried the terror of its arms into every sea, from Spiting Devil Creek to Antony's Nose; that it even bearded the stout island of Manhattan, invading it at night, penetrating to its centre, and burning down the famous Delancy house, the conflagration of which makes such a blaze in revolutionary history. Nay more, in their extravagant daring, these cocks of the Roost meditated a nocturnal descent upon New-York itself, to swoop upon the British commanders, Howe and Clinton, by surprise, bear them off captive, and perhaps put a triumphant close to the war! KnM

10.33–39　　There is ... shot.]　1A; All these and many similar exploits are recorded by the worthy Diedrich, with his usual minuteness and enthusiasm, whenever the deeds in arms of his kindred Dutchmen are in question: but though most of these warlike stories rest upon the best of all authority, that of the warriors themselves, and though many of them are still current among the revolutionary patriarchs of this heroic neighborhood, yet I dare not expose them to the incredulity of a tamer and less chivalric age. Suffice it to say, the frequent gatherings at the Roost, and the hardy projects set on foot there, at length drew on it the fiery indignation of the enemy; and this was quickened by the conduct of the stout Jacob Van Tassel; with whose valorous achievements we resume the course of the chronicle.

THIS doughty Dutchman, continues the sage DIEDRICH KNICKERBOCKER, was not content with taking a share in all the magnanimous enterprises concocted at the Roost, but still continued his petty warfare along shore. A series of exploits at length raised his confidence in his prowess to such a height, that he began to think himself and his goose-gun a match for any thing. Unluckily, in the course of one of his prowlings, he descried a British transport aground, not far from shore, with her stern swung toward the land, within point blank shot. KnM

10.39–11.13   The temptation . . . weapons;]   1A; The temptation was too great to be resisted; bang! as usual, went the great goose-gun, shivering the cabin windows, and driving all hands forward. Bang! bang! the shots were repeated. The reports brought several sharp shooters of the neighborhood to the spot; before the transport could bring a gun to bear, or land a boat, to take revenge, she was soundly peppered, and the coast evacuated. This was the last of Jacob's triumphs. He fared like some heroic spider, that has unwittingly ensnared a hornet, to his immortal glory, perhaps, but to the utter ruin of his web.

It was not long after this, during the absence of Jacob Van Tassel on one of his forays, and when no one was in garrison but his stout-hearted spouse, his redoubtable sister, Nochie Van Wurmer, and a strapping negro wench, called Dinah, that an armed vessel came to anchor off the Roost, and a boat full of men pulled to shore. The garrison flew to arms, that is to say, to mops, broom-sticks, shovels, tongs, and all kinds of domestic weapons; KnM

11.24–25   spoilers to desist;]   1A; spoilers to let go their hold KnM
11.28–36   As to . . . ground.]   1A; THE fear of tiring my readers, who may not take such an interest as myself in these

heroic themes, induces me to close here my extracts
from this precious chronicle of the venerable Diedrich.
Suffice it briefly to say, that shortly after the catastrophe of the Roost, Jacob Van Tassel, in the course of
one of his forays, fell into the hands of the British;
was sent prisoner to New-York, and was detained in
captivity for the greater part of the war. In the mean
time, the Roost remained a melancholy ruin; its stone
walls and brick chimneys alone standing, blackened
by fire, and the resort of bats and owlets. It was not
until the return of peace, when this belligerent neighborhood once more resumed its quiet agricultural
pursuits, that the stout Jacob sought the scene of his
triumphs and disasters; rebuilt the Roost, and reared
again on high its glittering weather-cocks.

Does any one want farther particulars of the fortunes of this eventful little pile? Let him go to the
fountain-head, and drink deep of historic truth.
Reader! the stout Jacob Van Tassel still lives, a venerable, gray-headed patriarch of the revolution, now
in his ninety-fifth year! He sits by his fire-side, in the
ancient city of the Manhattoes, and passes the long
winter evening, surrounded by his children, and grand-
children, and great-grand-children, all listening to
his tales of the border wars, and the heroic days of
the Roost. His great goose-gun, too, is still in existence,
having been preserved for many years in a hollow
tree, and passed from hand to hand among the Dutch
burghers, as a precious relique of the revolution. It is
now actually in possession of a contemporary of the
stout Jacob, one almost his equal in years, who treasures it up at his house in the Bowerie of New-Amsterdam, hard by the ancient rural retreat of the chivalric
Peter Stuyvesant. I am not without hopes of one day
seeing this formidable piece of ordnance restored to
its proper station in the arsenal of the Roost.

Before closing this historic document, I cannot but
advert to certain notions and traditions concerning
the venerable pile in question. Old-time edifices are
apt to gather odd fancies and superstitions about
them, as they do moss and weather-stains; and this is
in a neighborhood a little given to old-fashioned notions, and who look upon the Roost as somewhat of a

fated mansion. A lonely, rambling, downhill lane
leads to it, overhung with trees, with a wild brook
dashing along, and crossing and re-crossing it. This
lane I found some of the good people of the neighborhood shy of treading at night; why, I could not for
a long time ascertain; until I learned that one or two
of the rovers of the Tappan Sea, shot by the stout
Jacob during the war, had been buried hereabout, in
unconsecrated ground. KnM

11.37–12.14   Even the . . . judgment.]   1A; Another local superstition
is of a less gloomy kind, and one which I confess I
am somewhat disposed to cherish. The Tappan Sea,
in front of the Roost, is about three miles wide,
bordered by a lofty line of waving and rocky hills.
Often, in the still twilight of a summer evening, when
the sea is like glass, with the opposite hills throwing
their purple shadows half across it, a low sound is
heard, as of the steady, vigorous pull of oars, far out
in the middle of the stream, though not a boat is to
be descried. This I should have been apt to ascribe
to some boat rowed along under the shadows of the
western shore, for sounds are conveyed to a great
distance by water, at such quiet hours, and I can
distinctly hear the baying of the watchdogs at night,
from the farms on the sides of the opposite mountains.
The ancient traditionists of the neighborhood, however, religiously ascribe these sounds to a judgment
upon one Rumbout Van Dam, of Spiting Devil, who
danced and drank late one Saturday night, at a Dutch
quilting frolic, at Kakiat, and set off alone for home
in his boat, on the verge of Sunday morning; swearing he would not land till he reached Spiting Devil,
if it took him a month of Sundays. He was never seen
afterward, but is often heard plying his oars across
the Tappan Sea, a Flying Dutchman on a small scale,
suited to the size of his cruizing-ground; being
doomed to ply between Kakiat and Spiting Devil till
the day of judgment, but never to reach the land.

There is one room in the mansion, which almost
overhangs the river, and is reputed to be haunted
by the ghost of a young lady who died of love and
green apples. I have been awakened at night by the
sound of oars and the tinkling of guitars beneath

the window; and seeing a boat loitering in the moon-light, have been tempted to believe it the Flying Dutchman of Spiting Devil, and to try whether a silver bullet might not put an end to his unhappy cruisings; but, happening to recollect that there was a living young lady in the haunted room, who might be terrified by the report of fire-arms, I have refrained from pulling trigger.

As to the enchanted fountain, said to have been gifted by the wizard sachem with supernatural pow-ers, it still wells up at the foot of the bank, on the margin of the river, and goes by the name of the Indian spring; but I have my doubts as to its rejuvenating powers, for though I have drank oft and copiously of it, I cannot boast that I find myself growing younger. GEOFFREY CRAYON. KnM

17.1	SPRING] 1A; By Geoffrey Crayon, Gent. KnM, NI
17.3	occupation] 1A; important occupation KnM, NI
17.5	few] 1A; free KnM, NI
18.31	grows] 1A, NI; glows KnM
20.33–21.19	into summer . . . boys;] 1A; into summer, his notes cease to vibrate on the ear. He gradually gives up his elegant tastes and habits, doffs his poetical and professional suit of black, assumes a russet or rather dusty garb, and enters into the gross enjoyments of common, vulgar birds. He becomes a bon vivant, a mere gourmand; thinking of nothing but good cheer, and gormandizing on the seeds of the long grasses on which he lately swung, and chaunted so musically. He begins to think there is nothing like 'the joys of the table,' if I may be allowed to apply that convivial phrase to his indulgences. He now grows discon-tented with plain, every-day fare, and sets out on a gastronomical tour, in search of foreign luxuries. He is to be found in myriads among the reeds of the Delaware, banqueting on their seeds; grows corpulent with good feeding, and soon acquires the unlucky renown of the ortolan. Wherever he goes, pop! pop! pop! the rusty firelocks of the country are cracking on every side; he sees his companions falling by thousands around him; he is the *reed-bird*, the much-sought-for tit-bit of the Pennsylvanian epicure.

Does he take warning and reform? Not he! He

wings his flight still farther south, in search of other
luxuries. We hear of him gorging himself in the rice
swamps; filling himself with rice almost to bursting;
he can hardly fly for corpulency. Last stage of his
career, we hear of him spitted by dozens, and served
up on the table of the gourmand, the most vaunted
of southern dainties, the *rice-bird* of the Carolinas.

Such is the story of the once musical and admired,
but finally sensual and persecuted, Boblink. It contains a moral, worthy the attention of all little birds
and little boys; KnM, NI

22.3	*First published in 1837*] 1A; By The Author Of The "Sketch Book." Mag
22.7	up in] 1A; up and perpetuated in Mag
22.8	handed down] 1A; continued Mag
22.22–23	Dutch villages,] 1A; some of the orthodox Dutch villages, still lingering Mag
22.27	which] 1A; that Mag
22.36–37	fortunate inhabitants have none of that] 1A; inhabitants are deficient in Mag
22.38	imports] 1A, E; imparts Mag
23.9	a] 1A; a kind of Mag
23.17–18	houses built by their forefathers] 1A; same houses in which their forefathers dwelt, Mag
23.19	The trees,] 1A; They suffer the trees, Mag
23.20	flourish] 1A; to flourish Mag
23.35	convention] 1A; conviction Mag
23.40–41	feature and deportment,] 1A; stamp of feature and peculiarity of deportment, Mag
23.42–43	that are to] 1A; the important man of a petty arrondisement, that are to Mag
24.5–6	grin; ... grown up] 1A; grin. This was evidently a privileged and favorite servant, and one that had grown up Mag
24.9	western] 1A; wide western Mag
24.11	to be met] 1A; one meets Mag
24.17	adding to their wealth, and making presidents] 1A; and of adding to their wealth, Mag
24.22–23	and a look of surly gravity.] 1A; that gave an air of surly gravity to his physiognomy. Mag
24.26	which] 1A; that Mag
24.29	like] 1A; that sounded like Mag

24.33   Small, thin, and weazen-faced,] 1A; He was small, thin, and weazen-faced, such Mag
24.42   an old French creole village,] 1A; one of these old French creole villages, Mag
25.1   fêtes] 1A, E; fetes Mag
25.13   most] 1A; homebred, most Mag
25.17   a] 1A; at a Mag
25.33   these worthies.] 1A; my fellow voyagers. Mag
25.35   of] 1A; of the Mag
26.3   was] 1A; commenced Mag
26.4   salutations,] 1A; greetings, and salutations, Mag
26.13–14   face,... stood out] 1A; horse face, which stood out in strong relief Mag
26.16–17   meeting ... electrify the] 1A; first meeting with each other, and exchanging compliments, were enough to electrify the whole Mag
26.21   Even] 1A; Soon Mag
27.14   the] 1A; then the Mag
27.22   I] 1A; that I Mag
27.28   dollar.*] 1A; dollar. Mag
27.38–42   *This ... worship] 1A; dollar. Mag
29.3   I] 1A; By Geoffrey Crayon, Gent. MSa, KnM, KSB
*29.5   Huguenot] KnM, KSB, 1A; Hugonot MSa
29.9   took] 1A; who took MSA, KnM, KSB
29.24   our] KnM, KSB, 1A; my MSa
31.7   home] KnM, KSB, 1A; house MSa
31.22   Ovid's] KnM, KSB, 1A; Ovids MSa
32.23   pallid] KnM, KSB, 1A; pal[l]id MSa
32.27   urbanity] 1A; urbanity of temper MSa, KnM, KSB
33.14   "humbug."] KSB, 1A; 'humbug' MSa, KnM
33.19   Smith's] KnM, KSB, 1A; Smiths MSa
33.20   of] 1A; of the MSa, KnM, KSB
33.30   "How charming,"] KSB, 1A; 'How charming,' MSa, KnM
33.31   "is divine philosophy;"] KSB, 1A; 'a divine philosophy:' MSa, KnM
33.32   "But] 1A; 'But MSa
33.32   nectar'd] KnM, KSB, 1A; nectared MSa
34.31   they were] 1A; that they were as KnM, KSB
35.30   as] KnM, KSB, 1A; as it MSa
36.10   would] KnM, KSB, 1A; could MSa
36.15   besides] 1A; beside MSa, KnM, KSB
36.32   became] 1A; became daily MSa, KnM, KSB

36.34–35	only be compared with that] 1A; be compared only to that MSa, KnM, KSB
36.42	if] 1A; though MSa, KnM, KSB
37.20	"I] 1A; 'Oh Sophy—I MSa, KnM, KSB
37.30	she's] 1A; shes MSa, KnM, KSB
38.12	happened?"] 1A; happened? MSa; happened?' KnM, KSB
38.17	but] KnM, KSB, 1A; but but MSa
38.19	has the] KnM, KSB, 1A; has MSa
38.28	by] KnM, KSB, 1A; by the MSa
39.29	buildings] KnM, KSB, 1A; building MSa
40.8	held] KnM, KSB, 1A; be MSa
40.27	Charlotte] KnM, KSB, 1A; charlotte MSa
40.29	of] KnM, KSB, 1A; for MSa
40.30	fervid] KnM, KSB, 1A; fervent MSa
41.8	such] KnM, KSB, 1A; such MSa
42.2	tragic-comical] 1A; tragi-comical MSa, KnM, KSB
42.5	For] KSB, 1A; To Be Continued MSa, KnM
42.5	occurrence] KSB, 1A; occurrence, mentioned in the last number MSa, KnM
42.25	borne] KnM, KSB, 1A; born MSa
43.28	foam] KnM, KSB, 1A; a foam MSa
44.8	moment.] KnM, KSB, 1A; ~∧ MSa
44.17	good] KnM, KSB, 1A; very good MSa
45.17	hideous] 1A; a KnM, KSB
46.29	finished] 1A; furnished KnM, KSB
47.37	frightened] 1A; frighted KnM, KSB
49.24	Besides] 1A; Beside KnM, KSB
52.30	besides] 1A; beside KnM, KSB
54.24	passage."] 1A; passage, KnM
55.32	Mountjoy] 1A; Somerville KnM, KSB
56.10	I was no longer] KnM, KSB, 1A; I no longer was MSa
56.35	whole,] KnM, KSB, 1A; On the whole, On the whole, MSa
56.38	Italian] KnM, KSB, 1A; italian MSa
57.17	Besides] 1A; Beside MSa, KnM, KSB
58.3	and who] KnM, KSB, 1A; and MSa
58.7	as] 1A; as it MSa, KnM, KSB
58.20	nor] 1A; or MSa, KnM, KSB
58.21	opinion] 1A; opinions MSa, KnM, KSB
60.35	there is] KnM, KSB, 1A; there's MSa
61.3–4	to excite] KnM, 1A; in exciting MSa

61.4	curiosity.] KSB, 1A; —End—; MSa; To Be Continued KnM
62.7	misprision] KnM, 1A; misprison MSa
*63.5	*Oberon's] KnM, 1A; Oberons MSa
63.9	dolphin's] KnM, 1A; dolphins MSa
63.13	sea-maid's] KnM, 1A; sea-maids MSa
63.15	has] KnM, 1A; was MSa
63.22	and] KnM, 1A; & MSa
64.36	or heard] KnM, 1A; seen MSa
65.2	weather, which] KnM, 1A; weather. Which MSa
65.10	borne] KnM, 1A; born MSa
65.27	ship's] KnM, 1A; ships MSa
66.37	nine] KnM, 1A; 19 MSa
66.39	that they] 1A; they MSa, KnM
67.3	small] KnM, 1A; smaller MSa
67.22	Whitechurch] KnM, 1A; Whitchurch MSa
67.24	fired] 1A; were fired MSa, KnM
67.27	Matthew] 1A; Mathew MSa, KnM
68.10	picture] 1A; pictures MSa, KnM
68.12	George's] 1A, KnM; Georges MSa
68.23	Besides] 1A; Beside MSa, KnM
68.33	to] 1A; to a MSa, KnM
70.2	about] KnM, 1A; about it MSa
70.19	"Had] 1A; 'Had MSa, KnM
70.19	I a] 1A; I MSa, I the KnM
70.28	all.] 1A; all.' MSa, KnM
71.8	Shakespeare] KnM, 1A; Shake-/spear MSa
72.1	ORDEAL] 1A; By The Author Of the "Sketch Book" Mag
73.3	no one measure adopted by him] 1A; not any one measure that he adopted Mag
73.4	his] 1A; all his Mag
73.5	such] 1A; so many Mag
73.5–6	the jaws . . . were nigh] 1A; his high chamberlain had jaws Mag
73.9	at length] 1A; when Mag
73.15	sent forth emissaries to summon his court] 1A; sending emissaries to all parts, he summoned to his court Mag
73.35	there was still no] 1A; he still remained without any Mag
73.43	sorrowfully and dubiously] 1A; with sorrowful eyes Mag

74.3–4	thou wilt ... so long."] 1A; I shall be no more, and in the arms of another husband thou wilt forget him who has loved thee so tenderly. Mag
74.8	brook the thought] 1A; endure the thoughts Mag
74.14	effect, but the] 1A; effect. The Mag
74.16	bequeathing;] 1A; in which he bequeathed Mag
74.22	when] 1A; however, when Mag
74.25	declared] 1A; was declared Mag
74.28–29	counsellors,—swaggering] 1A; counsellors. These were two swaggering Mag
74.31–32	"Prithee, man, ... "the] 1A; They took their nephew aside. 'Prithee, man," said they, "be of good cheer. The Mag
74.36	Pooh, pooh—impossible] 1A; Impossible! Mag
74.39	Keep] 1A; Keep a Mag
76.6	are indistinct.] 1A; indistinct. Mag
76.8	The] 1A; The whole Mag
76.20	of] 1A; of a Mag
78.4	prancing steeds, and splendid retinues;] 1A; splendid retinues, and prancing steeds; Mag
78.42	were] 1A; were soon
79.8	with] 1A; that went about with Mag
80.16	and] 1A; and in that Mag
80.29	had been round the world] 1A; had long been absent, Mag
80.31	wounded] 1A; wounded in the battle, Mag
80.34	illness; ... with] 1A; illness. A tender passion grew up between them, and she finally rewarded his gallantry by giving him Mag
80.38	combat à l'outrance] E; combat to outrance Mag, 1A
81.2	sons] 1A; sons all Mag
81.3	and] 1A; and all Mag
82.1	MALTA] 1A; To The Editor Of The Knickerbocker MSa, KnM, Ev
82.2	In the course of a tour in Sicily,] 1A; SIR: In the course of a tour which I made in Sicily, MSa, KnM, Ev
82.18	instruments, and black-letter] KnM, Ev, 1A; instruments; black-letter MSa
82.19	had] KnM, Ev, 1A; dipped MSa
83.5	of] 1A; others of MSa, KnM, Ev
83.6	on] 1A; in MSa, KnM, Ev
83.13	merits] KnM, Ev, 1A; merit MSa

83.16   the ghost-hunting reader] 1A; your ghost-hunting readers MSa, KnM, Ev

83.16   subjoin it.] 1A; offer it, Mr. Editor, for insertion in your Magazine. MSa, KnM, Ev

83.19   Malta] 1A; Your obt, servant., GEOFFREY CRAYON MSa, KnM, Ev

83.27   in] KnM, Ev, 1A; at MSa

84.33   St. John] KnM, Ev, 1A; S'John MSa

85.10   at the] 1A; the MSa, KnM, Ev

85.15   chevaliers] 1A; cavaliers MSa, KnM, Ev

85.35   cavaliers] 1A; chevaliers MSa, KnM, Ev

85.39   abuses.] KnM, Ev, 1A; ~∧ MSa

86.17   cavaliers] 1A; chevaliers MSa, KnM, Ev

87.12   called the "Strada Stretta,"] KnM, 1A; and which is called the 'Strada Stretta,' MSa, Ev

87.39   his] KnM, 1A; guard MSa

88.18   deserved] 1A; had deserved MSa, KnM, Ev

88.32   my] 1A; and my MSa, KnM, Ev

88.37   Friday!] KnM, Ev, 1A; Friday!" MSa

88.40   following Friday] 1A; of the following Friday MSa, KnM, Ev

89.8   some] 1A; at some MSa, KnM, Ev

89.9   Friday] KnM, Ev, 1A; friday MSa

89.22   afterwards] 1A; afterward MSa, KnM, Ev

*89.29   wielded] MSa, KnM, Ev; yielded 1A

89.30   or] 1A; or in MSa, KnM, Ev

89.30   combat] KnM, Ev, 1A; combat." MSa

91.17   " 'I] 1A; I MSa; 'I KnM, Ev

91.20   the great] KnM, Ev, 1A; great MSa

91.40   cavaliers] 1A; chevaliers MSa, KnM, Ev

94.26   fiction.] Ev, 1A; fiction. G.C. MSa, KnM. [Initials of Geoffrey Crayon (G.C.) have been removed in later editions.]

95.1   PROSPERITY] 1A; By The Author Of The Sketch-Book KnM

95.36   maddening] 1A; madding KnM

103.37   finance] 1A; finances KnM

108.34   payments] 1A; payment KnM

113.7   fortunes] 1A; fortune KnM

113.21   once] 1A; that was KnM

115.15   the troops] 1A; troops KnM

119.1   slow accumulations] 1A; safe pursuits E, KnM

119.30   acquitted] 1A; have acquitted KnM

290   WOLFERT'S ROOST

119.31	was] 1A; is KnM
120.2	CRAYON, GENT] 1A; Crayon. KnM
120.3	THE] 1A; A KnM
120.4–7	A great hotel . . . pile,] 1A; Is a street set on end, the grand stair-case forming the highway, and every floor a separate habitation. Let me describe the one in which I am lodged, which may serve as a specimen of its class. It is a huge quadrangular pile of stone KnM
120.11	is a] 1A; is like a distinct KnM
120.13	conveniences] 1A; conveniences for the accommodation of a family. KnM
120.35	grand] 1A; spacious KnM
121.18	*sonnez*] 1A; *souvez* KnM
121.19	*ou à gauche;"*] 1A; *or a gàuche;* KnM
122.17	at] 1A; in KnM
125.37	ENGLISH AND] KnM, NY, 1A; ENGLISH & MSa
126.14	other's] KnM, NY, 1A; others MSa
126.20	and] KnM, NY, 1A; & MSa
126.21	and meditation] KnM, NY, 1A; & meditation MSa
126.23	and amusement] KnM, NY, 1A; & amusement MSa
126.30	Englishman] KnM, NY, 1A; englishman MSa
127.3	to equal] KnM, NY, 1A; to be equal to MSa
127.4	Frenchman's] KnM, NY, 1A; Frenchmans MSa
127.6	and] KnM, NY, 1A; & MSa
127.7–8	and . . . and . . . and . . . and] KnM, NY, 1A; & . . . & . . . & . . . & MSa
127.15	and spring-guns and] KnM, NY, 1A; & spring-guns & MSa
127.17	and privacy] KnM, NY, 1A; & privacy MSa
127.23	and great] KnM, NY, 1A; & great MSa
127.27	and be] KnM, NY, 1A; & be MSa
127.34	be victorious] 1A; is victorious MSa, KnM, NY
127.34	expense,] KnM, NY, 1A; ~∧ MSa
128.13	tramp] 1A; the tramp MSa, KnM, NY
128.14	Dismounted] KnM, NY, 1A; Dismounted Dismounted MSa
128.30	seem] KnM, NY, 1A; seemed MSa
128.33	dormer] 1A; dormant MSa, KnM, NY
129.14	young] 1A; the MSa, KnM, NY
124.14	grown] 1A; that has grown MSa; that have grown NY, KnM, E
129.15	equipped] 1A; all MSa, KnM, NY

129.22	talked of law,] KnM, NY, 1A; talked of law of MSa
130.1	neighbors'] KnM, NY, 1A; neighbors MSa
130.40	*The] 1A; *NOTE. MSa, KnM
130.41	made] 1A; that have been made MSa, KnM, NY, E
131.39	towered] 1A; turned KnM, NY
132.6	the] 1A; many a KnM, NY
132.22	at the battle of Neuburg] 1A; in 1809 or '10 KnM, NY
135.23	morning's] KnM, NY, 1A; mornings MSa
135.36	afterwards] 1A; afterward MSa, KnM, NY
135.36	evening's] KnM, NY, 1A; evenings MSa
136.6	Caesar] KnM, NY, 1A; Casar MSa
137.1	A CONTENTED] LS, NYA, 1A; Washington Irving/ A CONTENTED MSa
137.2	In] 1A; By Geoffrey Crayon, Gent. MSa, LS; By Washington Irving NYA
137.30	nursery maid's] LS, NYA, 1A; nursery maids MSa
137.30	Frenchman] LS, NYA, 1A; frenchman MSa
137.31	sex.] LS, NYA, 1A; sex MSa
138.6	through] LS, NYA, 1A; strolling MSa
138.34	evening's] LS, NYA, 1A; evenings MSa
138.37	friend's] LS, NYA, 1A; friends MSa
139.3	restaurateur] LS, NYA, 1A; restaurants MSa
139.5	St. James'] LS, NYA, 1A; S'James' MSa
139.15	that] LS, NYA, 1A; true MSa
139.27	Paris] LS, NYA, 1A; paris MSa
139.28	friend] LS, NYA, 1A; friends MSa
139.40	St. Cloud] LS, NYA, 1A; S'Cloud MSa
139.42	promenades] LS, NYA, 1A; S'Cloud MSa
140.6	Paris] LS, NYA, 1A; paris MSa
140.6	a] LS, NYA, 1A; with MSa
140.9	there's] LS, NYA, 1A; theres MSa
140.20	to] 1A; again to LS, NYA
141.6	praises] 1A; pruises LS, NYA
142.1	BROEK] 1A; The Crayon Papers MSa, KnM
142.4	It] 1A; By Geoffrey Crayon KnM, MSa
142.6	whence] 1A; from whence MSa, KnM
142.6	put] KnM, 1A; set MSa
142.27	ten;] KnM, 1A; ten MSa
145.11	by] 1A; with KnM
146.19	nor ass, . . . nor anything.] 1A; or ass, or cat, or dog, or any thing KnM
147.1	GUESTS] KSB, BH, 1A; A LEGEND OF COM-MUNIPAW./[bar]/TO THE EDITOR OF THE KNICKER-

BOCKER MAGAZINE./ SIR: I observed in your last month's
periodical, a communication from a Mr. VANDERDONK,
giving some information concerning Communipaw.
I herewith send you, Mr. Editor, a legend connected
with that place; and am much surprised it should
have escaped the researches of your very authentic
correspondent, as it relates to an edifice scarcely less
fated than the House of the Four Chimnies. I give
you the legend in its crude and simple state, as I
heard it related; it is capable, however, of being
dilated, inflated, and dressed up into very imposing
shape and dimensions. Should any of your ingenious
contributors in this line feel inclined to take it in
hand, they will find ample materials, collateral and
illustrative, among the papers of the late Reinier
Skaats, many years since crier of the court, and keeper
of the City Hall, in the city of the Manhattoes; or in
the library of that important and utterly renowned
functionary, Mr. Jacob Hays, long time high constable,
who, in the course of his extensive researches, has
amassed an amount of valuable facts, to be rivalled
only by that great historical collection, 'The Newgate
Calendar.'/ Your humble servant,/ BARENT VAN
SCHAICK. KnM

147.2–3	FOUND AMONG THE KNICKERBOCKER PAPERS AT WOLFERT'S ROOST] 1A; Communipaw. KnM, KSB, BH
147.16	where] 1A; where all the KnM, KSB, BH
147.16	affairs] 1A; of Communipaw KnM, KSB, BH
147.36	of] 1A; of all KnM, KSB, BH
148.8	lingered] BH, 1A; had lingered KnM, KSB
148.8	but] 1A; but that KnM, KSB, BH
148.10–11	the infinite . . . rider] 1A; his infinite astonishment and discomfiture KnM, KSB, BH
148.16	another] KSB, BH, 1A; an other KnM
148.31	opposite] 1A; to KnM, KSB, BH
148.39	we] 1A; that we KnM, KSB, BH
149.10	were] 1A; were all KnM, KSB, BH
149.12	tempest] 1A; tempests KnM, KSB, BH
149.14	declared] 1A; declared that KnM, KSB, BH
149.16	if] 1A; if they KnM, KSB, BH
151.29	had] 1A; had got KnM, KSB, BH
151.31	quiet and] KSB, BH, 1A; quiet, KnM
152.6	feasts] KnM, KSB, BH, 1A; revels MSa

152.21	he] KnM, KSB, BH, 1A; they MSa
152.31	into] KnM, KSB, BH, 1A; in to MSa
153.10	glance] KnM, KSB, BH, 1A; gleam MSa
153.12	whence] 1A; from whence MSa, KnM, KSB, BH
153.38	who's] KnM, KSB, BH, 1A; whos MSa
153.40	I would] KnM, KSB, BH, 1A; I'd MSa
153.42	here's] KnM, KSB, BH, 1A; heres MSa
154.2	I'll] KnM, KSB, BH, 1A; Ill MSa
154.5	they] 1A; there MSa, KnM, KSB, BH
155.36	Vanderscamp's] KnM, KSB, BH, 1A; Vanderscamps MSa
155.42	a tempest] KnM, KSB, BH, 1A; the tempest MSa
156.1	pirates'] KnM, KSB, BH, 1A; pirates MSa
157.1	THE EARLY] 1A; THE CRAYON PAPERS THE EARLY KnM, KSB
157.16	arrangements] 1A; arrangement KnM, KSB
157.33–34	late Governor Duval of Florida.] 1A; worthy original is now living, and flourishing in honorable station. KnM, KSB
158.13	the common] 1A; this common KnM, KSB
158.30	at] 1A; at the very KnM, KSB
159.4	waking] 1A; awaking KnM, KSB
160.26	too far] KSB, 1A; to far KnM
161.38	at] 1A; and as KnM, KSB
162.12	don't] KSB, 1A; do n't KnM
164.37	suffered] 1A; had suffered KnM, KSB
166.26	woodsman] 1A; woodman KnM, KSB
166.31	part] 1A; parts KnM, KSB
167.25	I don't] 1A I do n't KnM, KSB
168.5	towards] 1A; toward KnM, KSB
169.33	and leggins] 1A; with leggins KnM, KSB
171.27	don't] 1A; do n't KnM, KSB
171.29	don't] 1A; do n't KnM, KSB
171.30	won't] 1A; wont KnM, KSB
171.37	afterwards] 1A; afterward KnM, KSB
171.41	had] 1A; HAD KnM, KSB
172.16	of but] 1A; but of KnM, KSB
172.16	I had] 1A; I had had KnM, KSB
172.17	wider] 1A; wide KnM, KSB
173.30	don't] IA; do n't KnM, KSB
174.37	isn't] 1A; is n't KnM, KSB
177.22	there would] 1A; would KnM, KSB
179.13	thence] 1A; from thence KnM, KSB

182.1   THE SEMINOLES] 1A; THE CRAYON PAPERS./
                 THE SEMINOLES MSa, KnM
182.13   whom] 1A; which MSa, KnM
°182.22   ball-play] T; bull-play MSa, KnM, 1A
182.26–27   We are ... English,] 1A; About the year 1763, when
                 Florida was ceded by the Spaniards to the English,
                 we are told that MSa, KnM
183.32   tents] KnM, 1A; camp MSa
183.42   "Travels in North America."] 1A; 'Travels in N.
                 America' MSa, KnM
184.26   passing] KnM, 1A; and passing MSa
186.28–29   NEAMATHLA / AN AUTHENTIC SKETCH] 1A; NEAMATHLA
                 MSa, KnM, NY
187.13   country."] KnM, NY, 1A; country" MSa
187.19   hunters'] KnM, NY, Ev, 1A; hunters MSa
187.43   knew] 1A; saw MSa, KnM, NY, Ev
188.14   log-cabin] KnM, NY, Ev, 1A; log-house MSa
188.31   which] KnM, NY, Ev, 1A; that MSa
189.8   proceed.] KnM, NY, Ev, 1A; proceed." MSa
189.11   once more] KnM, NY, Ev, 1A; again MSa
189.35   to] 1A; on MSa, KnM, NY, Ev
190.2   moment's] KnM, NY, Ev, 1A; moments MSa
190.36   soldiers stationed] KnM, Ev, NY, 1A; stationed MSa
190.38   that] KnM, NY, Ev, 1A; over MSa
190.38   they might] KnM, NY, Ev, 1A; might MSa
190.42   "Well,"] NY, 1A; 'Well,' MSa, KnM, Ev
191.16   afterwards] 1A; afterward MSa, KnM, NY, Ev
191.19–20   Note.—The ... Ringwood).] 1A; Government. MSa,
                 KnM, NY, Ev
192.6   circles] KnM, 1A; circle MSa
192.30   of affinity.] KnM, 1A; affinity MSa
193.8   a manner] KnM, 1A; manner MSa
193.29   aroused] 1A; roused MSa, KnM
193.35   and] KnM, 1A; & MSa
194.9   valuable] 1A; noble MSa, KnM
194.17   apartments] KnM, 1A; appartments MSa
195.26   De Mille] KnM, 1A; Mille MSa
195.32   De Mille] KnM, 1A; Mille MSa
195.34–42   A circumstance ... murder.] KnM, 1A; prison. MSa
196.9   said that] KnM, 1A; said the MSa
196.10   De Mille] KnM, 1A; Mille MSa
196.14   De Mille] KnM, 1A; Mille MSa
198.12   murderer!] KnM, 1A; murderer. MSa

198.18	afterward] KnM, 1A; afterwards MSa
198.39	also] KnM, 1A; also also MSa
202.1	DON] 1A; The Crayon Papers. KnM
202.1	RESEARCH.] 1A; By Geoffrey Crayon, Gent. KnM
204.8	traversed] 1A; entered the gateway, traversed KnM
204.27	portal] 1A; distant KnM
208.27	nor] 1A; or KnM
210.2	CONVENT] 1A; By Geoffrey Crayon, Gent. MSa, KnM
210.7	an authentic legend] 1A; one of the authentic legends MSa, KnM
210.23	Moslem] KnM, 1A; Mozlem MSa
210.23	foment] KnM, 1A; firment MSa
211.39	horsemen] KnM, 1A; horseman MSa
211.39	lords] KnM, 1A; lord MSa
212.10–11	a hospitable] KnM, 1A; hospitable MSa
212.27	appeared] 1A; around appeared MSa, KnM
212.33	prayers] KnM, 1A; orisons MSa
212.38	He] 1A; The Cavalier MSa, KnM
212.39	was] 1A; of which was MSa, KnM
213.3	he] 1A; the cavalier MSa, KnM
213.5	in] 1A; clad in MSa, KnM
213.5	hermit's] KnM, 1A; hermits MSa
213.7	in the dens] 1A; in dens MSa, KnM
213.8–9	cavalier, dismounting] 1A; cavalier checked his horse, and dismounting, MSa, KnM
213.22	story.] 1A; story of this engulphed convent, as related by the Holy man. MSa, KnM
213.23	he keep vigils with the holy man beside] 1A; they keep vigils beside MSa, KnM
213.25	and the] 1A; and that the MSa, KnM
213.26	beheld] KnM, 1A; witnessed MSa
213.26	last.] 1A; last of the sisterhood. MSa, KnM
213.28	heard.] KnM, 1A; ~∧ MSa
213.29	remains] 1A; still remains MSa, KnM
213.31	that] 1A; assert that MSa, KnM
213.31–33	spire which … foundered.] 1A; spire of the sacred edifice, and that, when the main body of the building sank, this remained above ground, like the top-mast of some tall ship that has been foundered at sea. MSa, KnM
213.40	Fray] 1A; Padre Fray MSa, KnM
214.1	PHANTOM ISLAND] 1A; ENCHANTED ISLAND

By The Author Of The Sketch-Book KnM, By Washington Irving. R

214.16–17   Those who have read the history of] 1A; Every school-
boy can enumerate and call by name KnM, R

214.17   ancients,] 1A; ancients; KnM, R

214.17–32   may remember . . . Land.] 1A; which, according to
some ingenious and speculative minds, are mere
wrecks and remnants of the vast island of Atalantis,
mentioned by Plato, as having been swallowed up
by the ocean. Whoever has read the history of those
isles, will remember the wonders told of another island, still more beautiful, seen occasionally from their
shores, stretching away in the clear bright west, with
long shadowy promontories, and high, sun-gilt peaks.
Numerous expeditions, both in ancient and modern
days, have launched forth from the Canaries in quest
of that island; but, on their approach, mountain and
promontory have gradually faded away, until nothing
has remained but the blue sky above, and the deep
blue water below. Hence it was termed by the
geographers of old, Aprositus, or the Inaccessible;
while modern navigators have called its very existence
in question, pronouncing it a mere optical illusion,
like the Fata Morgana of the Straits of Messina; or
classing it with those unsubstantial regions known to
mariners as Cape Flyaway, and the Coast of Cloud
Land. KnM, R

214.33–35   Let us . . . yore.] 1A; Let not, however, the doubts of
the worldly-wise sceptics of modern days rob us of
all the glorious realms owned by happy credulity in
days of yore. KnM, R

214.35   it is my delight] 1A; I delight KnM, R

214.36   actually exists,] 1A; does actually exist, KnM, R

214.38–41   Historians . . . men.] 1A; Nay, though doubted by historians and philosophers, its existence is fully attested
by the poets, who, being an inspired race, and gifted
with a kind of second sight, can see into the mysteries
of nature, hidden from the eyes of ordinary mortals.
KnM, R

215.1   kind of wonder-land] 1A; region of fancy and romance, teeming with all kinds of wonders. KnM, R

215.3–5   Here, too, . . . Tasso.] 1A; Here, too, was the enchanted
garden of Armida, in which that sorceress held the

christian paladin, Rinaldo, in delicious but inglorious thraldom; as is set forth in the immortal lay of Tasso. KnM, R

215.5–6   on this island that] 1A; on this island, also, that KnM, R

215.7–10   shores . . . Shakespeare?] 1A; shores. KnM, R

215.11–15   The island . . . world.] 1A; In fact, the island appears to have been, at different times, under the sway of different powers, genii of earth, and air, and ocean; who made it their shadowy abode; or rather, it is the retiring place of old worn-out deities and dynasties, that once ruled the poetic world, but are now nearly shorn of all their attributes. KnM, R

215.15   court; sovereigns] 1A; court, like sovereigns KnM, R

215.16–18   Their ocean-chariot . . . rocks.] 1A; Their ocean-chariot lies bottom upward, in a cave of the island, almost a perfect wreck, while their pursy Tritons and haggard Nereids bask listlessly like seals, about the rocks. KnM, R

215.18–22   Sometimes . . . by.] 1A; Sometimes they assume a shadow of their ancient pomp, and glide in state about the glassy sea; while the crew of some tall Indiaman, that lies becalmed with flapping sails, hear with astonishment the mellow note of the Triton's shell swelling upon the ear, as the invisible pageant sweeps by. Sometimes the quondam monarch of the ocean is permitted to make himself visible to mortal eyes, visiting the ships that cross the line, to exact a tribute from new-comers; the only remnant of his ancient rule, and that, alas! performed with tattered state, and tarnished splendor. KnM, R

215.23   isle, the kraken heaves its unwieldy] 1A; island, the mighty kraken heaves his KnM, R

215.24–25   here . . . its] 1A; here, too, the sea-serpent lies coiled up, during the intervals of his much contested KnM, R

215.26   here even] 1A; and here, it is said, even KnM, R

215.28   brief] 1A; short KnM, R

215.28   cruisings] 1A; wanderings KnM, R

215.29–35   In the . . . ingots.] 1A; Here all the treasures lost in the deep, are safely garnered. The caverns of the shores are piled with golden ingots, boxes of pearls, rich bales of oriental silks; and their deep recesses sparkle with diamonds, or flame with carbuncles. Here, in

deep bays and harbors, lies many a spell-bound ship,
long given up as lost by the ruined merchant. Here,
too, its crew, long bewailed as swallowed up in ocean,
lie sleeping in mossy grottoes, from age to age, or
wander about enchanted shores and groves, in pleasing oblivion of all things. KnM, R

215.36   island, which] 1A; island, and which KnM, R
215.37   light] 1A; some light KnM, R
215.38   implicit belief] 1A; entire belief KnM, R
216.8   and raved] 1A; and who raved KnM, R
216.9   upon which] 1A; on which KnM, R
216.11–12 said, . . . surprise.] 1A; said, gathered round, and re-
           garded him with surprise, having never before been
           visited by a ship. KnM, R
216.31   saints] 1A; pious saints KnM, R
218.1   Cloud Land] 1A; Lubberland KnM, R
218.23   forth] 1A; forth in a storm about his ears. KnM, R
218.25   and with] 1A; and of KnM, R
218.34–37 Don Ramiro's . . . sea!] 1A; successful. KnM, R
218.38–41 He repaired . . . hallucination.] 1A; Don Ramiro re-
           paired to his daughter's chamber, the moment the
           youth had departed. He represented to her the san-
           guine, unsteady character of her lover, and the
           chimerical nature of his schemes; showed her the
           propriety of suspending all intercourse with him, until
           he should recover from his present hallucination;
           KnM, R
218.41–219.1 She bowed . . . lock;] 1A; folded her to his bosom
           with parental fondness, kissed the tear that stole down
           her cheek, and, as he left the chamber, gently locked
           the door; KnM, R
219.1–2   for though] 1A; for although KnM, R
219.4–5   key, . . . sail.] 1A; key KnM, R
219.6   lover by her father's eloquence.] 1A; lover, and the
           existence of Islands of the Seven Cities, by the sage
           representations of her father, KnM, R
219.7–9   but certain . . . Seven Cities.] 1A; but it is certain,
           that she became a firm believer, the moment she heard
           him turn the key in the lock. KnM, R
219.10–19 The door . . . window.] 1A; Notwithstanding the in-
           terdict of Don Ramiro, therefore, and his shrewd pre-
           precautions, the intercourse of the lovers continued,
           although clandestinely. Don Fernando toiled all day,

hurrying forward his nautical enterprise, while at
night he would repair, beneath the grated balcony of
his mistress, to carry on, at equal pace, the no less
interesting enterprise of the heart. KnM, R

219.20 preparations were] 1A; preparations for the expeditions were KnM, R

219.21–24 at anchor ... confidence] 1A; anchored in the Tagus,
ready to sail with the morning dawn; while late at
night, by the pale light of the waning moon, Don
Fernando sought the stately mansion of Alvarez, to
take a last farewell of Serafina. The customary signal,
of a few low touches of a guitar, brought her to the
balcony. She was sad at heart, and full of gloomy
forebodings; but her lover strove to impart to her
his own buoyant hope and youthful confidence.
KnM, R

219.26 hasten to welcome to his house the] 1A; will once
welcome me to his house, when I cross its threshold
a wealthy suitor, and KnM, R

219.27–40 The gentle ... sea?] 1A; The beautiful Serafina shook
her head mournfully. It was not on those points that
she felt doubt or dismay. She believed most implicitly
in the Island of the Seven Cities, and trusted
devoutly in the success of the enterprise; but she
had heard of the inconstancy of the seas, and the
inconstancy of those who roam them. Now, let the
truth be spoken, Don Fernando, if he had any
fault in the world, it was, that he was a little too
inflammable; that is to say, a little too subject to
take fire from the sparkle of every bright eye: he
had been somewhat of a rover among the sex on
shore, what might he not be on sea? KnM, R

219.41–220.6 She ventured ... hand!"] 1A; Might he not meet with
other loves in foreign ports? Might he not behold
some peerless beauty in one or other of those seven
cities, who might efface the image of Serafina from
his thoughts?
At length, she ventured to hint her doubts; but
Don Fernando spurned at the very idea. Never could
his heart be false to Serafina! Never could another be
captivating in his eyes!—never—never! Repeatedly did
he bend his knee, and smite his breast, and call upon
the silver moon to witness the sincerity of his vows.

But might not Serafina, herself, be forgetful of her plighted faith? Might not some wealthier rival present, while he was tossing on the sea, and, backed by the authority of her father, win the treasure of her hand? KnM, R

220.7–16   The beautiful . . . vow.] 1A; Alas, how little did he know Serafina's heart! The more her father should oppose, the more would she be fixed in her faith. Though years should pass before his return, he would find her true to her vows. Even should the salt seas swallow him up, (and her eyes streamed with salt tears at the very thought,) never would she be the wife of another—never—never! She raised her beautiful white arms between the iron bars of the balcony, and invoked the moon as a testimonial of her faith.

Thus, according to immemorial usage, the lovers parted, with many a vow of eternal constancy. KnM, R

220.21–33   nautical . . . billows.] 1A; nautical romance. Scarcely had they reached those latitudes, when a violent tempest arose. Don Fernando soon lost sight of the accompanying caravel, and was driven out of all reckoning by the fury of the storm. For several weary days and nights he was tossed to and fro, at the mercy of the elements, expecting each moment to be swallowed up. At length, one day, toward evening, the storm subsided; the clouds cleared up, as though a veil had suddenly been withdrawn from the face of heaven, and the setting sun shone gloriously upon a fair and mountainous island, that seemed close at hand. The tempest-tossed mariners rubbed their eyes, and gazed almost incredulously upon this land, that had emerged so suddenly from the murky gloom; yet there it lay, spread out in lovely landscapes; enlivened by villages, and towers, and spires, while the late stormy sea rolled in peaceful billows to its shores. KnM, R

220.34–221.15   The pilot . . . Cities.] 1A; About a league from the sea, on the banks of a river, stood a noble city, with lofty walls and towers, and a protecting castle. Don Fernando anchored off the mouth of the river, which appeared to form a spacious harbor. In a little while, a barge was seen issuing from the river. It was evi-

dently a barge of ceremony, for it was richly though
quaintly carved and gilt, and decorated with a
silken awning, and fluttering streamers, while a banner, bearing the sacred emblem of the cross, floated
to the breeze. The barge advanced slowly, impelled
by sixteen oars, painted of a bright crimson. The
oarsmen were uncouth, or rather antique, in their
garb, and kept stroke to the regular cadence of an
old Spanish ditty. Beneath the awning sat a cavalier,
in a rich though old-fashioned doublet, with an
enormous sombrero and feather.

When the barge reached the caravel, the cavalier
stepped on board. He was tall and gaunt, with a long,
Spanish visage, and lack-lustre eyes, and an air of
lofty and somewhat pompous gravity. His mustaches
were curled up to his ears, his beard was forked and
precise; he wore gauntlets that reached to his
elbows, and a Toledo blade, that strutted out behind,
while in front, its huge basket hilt might have served
for a porringer.

Thrusting out a long spindle leg, and taking off his
sombrero with a grave and stately sweep, he saluted
Don Fernando by name, and welcomed him, in old
Castilian language, and in the style of old Castilian
courtesy. KnM, R

221.16–25   Don Fernando . . . capital.]   1A;   Don Fernando was
startled at hearing himself accosted by name, by an
utter stranger, in a strange land. As soon as he could
recover from his surprise, he inquired what land it
was, at which he had arrived.

'The Island of the Seven Cities!'

Could this be true? Had he indeed been thus
tempest-driven upon the very land of which he was
in quest? It was even so. The other caravel, from
which he had been separated in the storm, had made
a neighboring port of the island, and announced the
tidings of this expedition, which came to restore the
country to the great community of christendom. The
whole island, he was told, was given up to rejoicings
on the happy event; and they only awaited his arrival
to acknowledge allegiance to the crown of Portugal,
and hail him as Adalantado of the Seven Cities. A
grand fête was to be solemnized that very night, in

the palace of the Alcayde, or governor of the city; who, on beholding the most opportune arrival of the caravel, had despatched his grand chamberlain, in his barge of state, to conduct the future Adalantado to the ceremony. KnM, R

221.26–41   Don   Fernando ... enterprise?]   1A;   Don   Fernando could scarcely believe but that this was all a dream. He fixed a scrutinizing gaze upon the grand chamberlain, who, having delivered his message, stood in buckram dignity, drawn up to his full stature, curling his whiskers, stroking his beard, and looking down upon him with inexpressible loftiness, through his lack-lustre eyes. There was no doubting the word of so grave and ceremonious a hidalgo. KnM, R

221.42–222.8   Having arrayed ... Cities."]   1A;   Don Fernando now arrayed himself in gala attire. He would have launched his boat, and gone on shore with his own men, but he was informed the barge of state was expressly provided for his accommodation, and, after the fête, would bring him back to his ship; in which, on the following day, he might enter the harbor in befitting style. He accordingly stepped into the barge, and took his seat beneath the awning. The grand chamberlain seated himself on the cushion opposite. The rowers bent to their oars, and renewed their mournful old ditty, and the gorgeous, but unwieldly barge moved slowly and solemnly through the water.

The night closed in, before they entered the river. They swept along, past rock and promontory, each guarded by its tower. The sentinels at every post challenged them as they passed by.

'Who goes there?'

'The Adalantado of the Seven Cities.'

'He is welcome. Pass on.'

On entering the harbor, they rowed close along an armed galley, of the most ancient form. Soldiers with cross bows were stationed on the deck.

'Who goes there?' was again demanded.

'The Adalantado of the Seven Cities.'

'He is welcome. Pass on.'

They landed at a broad flight of stone steps, leading up, between two massive towers, to the water-gate of the city, at which they knocked for admission. A sentinel, in an ancient steel casque, looked over the wall. 'Who is there?'

'The Adalantado of the Seven Cities.'

The gate swung slowly open, grating upon its rusty hinges. They entered between two rows of iron-clad warriors, in battered armor, with cross bows, battle-axes, and ancient maces, and with faces as old-fash-ioned and rusty as their armor. They saluted Don Fernando in military style, but with perfect silence, as he passed between their ranks. The city was il-luminated, but in such manner as to give a more shad-owy and solemn effect to its old-time architecture. There were bonfires in the principal streets, with groups about them in such old-fashioned garbs, that they looked like the fantastic figures that roam the streets in carnival time. Even the stately dames who gazed from the balconies, which they had hung with antique tapestry, looked more like effigies dressed up for a quaint mummery, than like ladies in their fashionable attire. Every thing, in short, bore the stamp of former ages, as if the world had suddenly rolled back a few centuries. Nor was this to be won-dered at. Had not the Island of the Seven Cities been for several hundred years cut off from all com-munication with the rest of the world, and was it not natural that the inhabitants should retain many of the modes and customs, brought here by their ancestors?

One thing certainly they had conserved; the old-fashioned Spanish gravity and stateliness. Though this was a time of public rejoicing, and though Don Fernando was the object of their gratulations, every thing was conducted with the most solemn ceremony, and wherever he appeared, instead of acclamations, he was received with profound silence, and the most formal reverences and swayings of their sombreros.

Arrived at the palace of the Alcayde, the usual ceremonial was repeated. The chamberlain knocked for admission.

'Who is there?' demanded the porter.

'The Adalantado of the Seven Cities.'

'He is welcome. Pass on.' KnM, R

222.40–223.6   The portal . . . prophecy.]   1A; The grand portal was

thrown open. The chamberlain led the way up a vast
but heavily moulded marble stair-case, and so through
one of those interminable suites of apartments, that
are the pride of Spanish palaces. All were furnished
in a style of obsolete magnificence. As they passed
through the chambers, the title of Don Fernando was
forwarded on by servants stationed at every door;
and every where produced the most profound reverences and courtesies. At length they reached a magnificent saloon, blazing with tapers, in which the
Alcayde, and the principal dignitaries of the city,
were waiting to receive their illustrious guest. The
grand chamberlain presented Don Fernando in due
form, and falling back among the other officers of the
household, stood as usual curling his whiskers, and
stroking his forked beard.

Don Fernando was received by the Alcayde and
the other dignitaries with the same stately and formal
courtesy that he had every where remarked. In fact,
there was so much form and ceremonial, that it
seemed difficult to get at any thing social or substantial. Nothing but bows, and compliments, and old-
fashioned courtesies. The Alcayde and his courtiers
resembled, in face and form, those quaint worthies to
be seen in the pictures of old illuminated manuscripts;
while the cavaliers and dames who thronged the
saloon, might have been taken for the antique figures
of gobelin tapestry suddenly vivified and put in motion.
KnM, R

223.7–20   The reception ... Goth]   1A; The banquet, which had
                been kept back until the arrival of Don Fernando, was
                now announced; and such a feast! such unknown
                dishes and obsolete dainties; with the peacock, that
                bird of state and ceremony, served up in full plumage,
                in a golden dish, at the head of the table. And then,
                as Don Fernando cast his eyes over the glittering
                board, what a vista of odd heads and head-dresses, of
                formal bearded dignitaries, and stately dames, with
                castellated locks and towering plumes! KnM, R

223.21–224.24   The festivities ... daughter.]   1A; As fate would have
                it, on the other side of Don Fernando, was seated the
                daughter of the Alcayde. She was arrayed, it is true,
                in a dress that might have been worn before the flood;

but then she had a melting black Andalusian eye, that
was perfectly irresistible. Her voice, too, her manner,
her movements, all smacked of Andalusia, and showed
how female fascination may be transmitted from age to
age, and clime to clime, without ever losing its power,
or going out of fashion. Those who know the witchery
of the sex, in that most amorous region of old Spain,
may judge what must have been the fascination to
which Don Fernando was exposed, when seated
beside one of the most captivating of its descendants.
He was, as has already been hinted, of an inflammable
temperament; with a heart ready to get in a light
blaze at every instant. And then he had been so
wearied by pompous, tedious old cavaliers, with their
formal bows and speeches; is it to be wondered at
that he turned with delight to the Alcayde's daughter,
all smiles, and dimples, and melting looks and melting
accents? Beside, for I wish to give him every excuse
in my power, he was in a particularly excitable mood,
from the novelty of the scene before him, and his
head was almost turned with this sudden and complete realization of all his hopes and fancies: and
then, in the flurry of the moment, he had taken frequent draughts at the wine cup, presented him at
every instant by officious pages, and all the world
knows the effect of such draughts in giving potency
to female charms. In a word, there is no concealing
the matter, the banquet was not half over, before Don
Fernando was making love, outright, to the Alcayde's
daughter. It was his old habitude, contracted long before his matrimonial engagement. The young lady
hung her head coyly; her eye rested upon a ruby
heart, sparkling in a ring on the hand of Don Fernando, a parting gage of love from Serafina. A blush
crimsoned her very temples. She darted a glance of
doubt at the ring, and then at Don Fernando. He
read her doubt, and in the giddy intoxication of the
moment, drew off the pledge of his affianced bride,
and slipped it on the finger of the Alcayde's daughter.
KnM, R

224.25–225.9   At this . . . ocean.]   1A; At this moment the banquet
broke up. The chamberlain with his lofty demeanor,
and his lack-lustre eyes, stood before him, and an-

nounced that the barge was waiting to conduct him
back to the caravel. Don Fernando took a formal leave
of the Alcayde and his dignitaries, and a tender farewell of the Alcayde's daughter, with a promise to
throw himself at her feet on the following day. He
was rowed back to his vessel in the same slow and
stately manner, to the cadence of the same mournful
old ditty. He retired to his cabin, his brain whirling
with all that he had seen, and his heart now and then
giving him a twinge, as he recollected his temporary
infidelity to the beautiful Serafina. He flung himself
on his bed, and soon fell into a feverish sleep. His
dreams were wild and incoherent. How long he slept
he knew not, but when he awoke he found himself,
in a strange cabin, with persons around him of whom
he had no knowledge. He rubbed his eyes to ascertain
whether he were really awake. In reply to his inquiries, he was informed that he was on board of a
Portuguese ship, bound to Lisbon; having been taken
senseless from a wreck drifting about the ocean.
KnM, R

225.10–24   Don Fernando ... taciturnity.]   1A; Don Fernando was
confounded and perplexed. He retraced every thing
distinctly that had happened to him in the Island of
the Seven Cities, and until he had retired to rest on
board of the caravel. Had his vessel been driven from
her anchors, and wrecked during his sleep? The people about him could give him no information on the
subject. He talked to them of the Island of the
Seven Cities, and of all that had befallen him there.
They regarded his words as the ravings of delirium,
and in their honest solicitude, administered such rough
remedies, that he was fain to drop the subject, and
observe a cautious taciturnity. KnM, R

225.27–29   A strange porter ... year.]   1A; To his surprise, it was
inhabited by strangers; and when he asked about his
family, no one could give him any information concerning them. KnM, R

225.30–42   He sought ... cavalier.]   1A; He now sought the mansion of Don Ramiro, for the temporary flame kindled
by the bright eyes of the Alcayde's daughter had long
since burnt itself out, and his genuine passion for
Serafina had revived with all its fervor. He approached

the balcony, beneath which he had so often serenaded
her. Did his eyes deceive him? No! There was Serafina
herself at the balcony. An exclamation of rapture burst
from him, as he raised his arms toward her. She cast
upon him a look of indignation, and hastily retiring,
closed the casement. Could she have heard of his
flirtation with the Alcayde's daughter? He would soon
dispel every doubt of his constancy. The door was
open. He rushed up stairs, and entering the room,
threw himself at her feet. She shrank back with
affright, and took refuge in the arms of a youthful
cavalier. KnM, R

225.43   Señor]   1A; Sir KnM, R
226.1–2   "What right ... fiercely.]   1A; 'What right have you,'
            replied Don Fernando, 'to ask the question?' KnM, R
226.6   Serafina, Señor!]   1A; Serafina? KnM, R
226.6   If this be the lady]   1A; If it be this young lady
            KnM, R
226.8–12   "May I ... great-grandmother!"]   1A; 'Is not this Sera-
            fina Alvarez, and is not that her portrait?' cried Don
            Fernando, pointing to a picture of his mistress.
                'Holy Virgin!' cried the young lady; 'he is talking
            of my great grandmother!' KnM, R
227.25   time; the hands of her husband,]   1A; time, for the
            hands of her husband, which were KnM, R
227.26   was without a nose.]   1A; was noseless. KnM, R
227.31   himself]   1A; him KnM, R
228.14   all]   1A; all his KnM, R
229.4   phantom island]   1A; enchanted island KnM, R
229.5–8   NOTE.–For ... Columbus.]   1A; island. KnM, R
230.1   ALHAMBRA]   1A; By The Author Of The Sketch-
            Book. KnM; By Washington Irving R
230.2–38   I have ... doubted.]   1A; DURING a summer's residence
            in the old Moorish palace of the Alhambra, of which
            I have already given numerous anecdotes to the
            public, I used to pass much of my time in the beautiful
            hall of the Abencerrages, beside the fountain cele-
            brated in the tragic story of that devoted race. Here it
            was, that thirty-six cavaliers of that heroic line were
            treacherously sacrificed, to appease the jealousy or
            allay the fears of a tyrant. The fountain which now
            throws up its sparkling jet, and sheds a dewy fresh-
            ness around, ran red with the noblest blood of Gra-

nada, and a deep stain on the marble pavement is
still pointed out, by the cicerones of the pile, as a
sanguinary record of the massacre. I have regarded it
with the same determined faith with which I have
regarded the traditional stains of Rizzio's blood on
the floor of the chamber of the unfortunate Mary, at
Holyrood. I thank no one for endeavoring to enlighten
my credulity, on such points of popular belief. It is
like breaking up the shrine of the pilgrim; it is
robbing a poor traveller of half the reward of his toils;
for, strip travelling of its historical illusions, and
what a mere fag you make of it!

For my part, I gave myself up, during my sojourn
in the Alhambra, to all the romantic and fabulous
traditions connected with the pile. I lived in the
midst of an Arabian tale, and shut my eyes, as much
as possible, to every thing that called me back to every-
day life; and if there is any country in Europe where
one can do so, it is in poor, wild, legendary, proud-
spirited, romantic Spain; where the old magnificent
barbaric spirit still contends against the utilitarianism
of modern civilization.

In the silent and deserted halls of the Alhambra;
surrounded with the insignia of regal sway, and the
still vivid, though dilapidated traces of oriental volup-
tuousness, I was in the strong-hold of Moorish story,
and every thing spoke and breathed of the glorious
days of Granada, when under the dominion of the
crescent. When I sat in the hall of the Abencerrages,
I suffered my mind to conjure up all that I had read
of that illustrious line. In the proudest days of Moslem domination, the Abencerrages were the soul
of every thing noble and chivalrous. The veterans of
the family, who sat in the royal council, were
the foremost to devise those heroic enterprises, which
carried dismay into the territories of the Christians;
and what the sages of the family devised, the young
men of the name were the foremost to execute. In
all services of hazard; in all adventurous forays, and
hair-breadth hazards; the Abencerrages were sure to
win the brightest laurels. In those noble recreations,
too, which bear so close an affinity to war; in the tilt
and tourney, the riding at the ring, and the daring

bull-fight; still the Abencerrages carried off the palm. None could equal them for the splendor of their array, the gallantry of their devices; for their noble bearing, and glorious horsemanship. Their open-handed munificence made them the idols of the populace, while their lofty magnanimity, and perfect faith, gained them golden opinions from the generous and high-minded. Never were they known to decry the merits of a rival, or to betray the confidings of a friend; and the 'word of an Abencerrage' was a guarantee that never admitted of a doubt. KnM, R

231.6   Serenades?] 1A; Serenades? I speak with enthusiasm on this theme; for it is connected with the recollection of one of the sweetest evenings and sweetest scenes that ever I enjoyed in Spain. One of the greatest pleasures of the Spaniards is, to sit in the beautiful summer evenings, and listen to traditional ballads, and tales about the wars of the Moors and Christians, and the 'buenas andazas' and 'grandes hechos,' the 'good fortunes' and 'great exploits' of the hardy warriors of yore. It is worthy of remark, also, that many of these songs, or romances, as they are called, celebrate the prowess and magnanimity in war, and the tenderness and fidelity in love, of the Moorish cavaliers, once their most formidable and hated foes. But centuries have elapsed, to extinguish the bigotry of the zealot; and the once detested warriors of Granada are now held up by Spanish poets, as the mirrors of chivalric virtue. KnM, R

231.7–41   Such ... beauty.] 1A; Such was the amusement of the evening in question. A number of us were seated in the Hall of the Abencerrages, listening to one of the most gifted and fascinating beings that I had ever met with in my wanderings. She was young and beautiful; and light and ethereal; full of fire, and spirit, and pure enthusiasm. She wore the fanciful Andalusian dress; touched the guitar with speaking eloquence; improvised with wonderful facility; and, as she became excited by her theme, or by the rapt attention of her auditors, would pour forth, in the richest and most melodious strains, a succession of couplets, full of striking description, or stirring narration, and composed, as I was assured, at the moment. Most of

these were suggested by the place, and related to
the ancient glories of Granada, and the prowess of her
chivalry. The Abercerrages were her favorite heroes;
she felt a woman's admiration of their gallant courtesy,
and high-souled honor; and it was touching and
inspiring to hear the praises of that generous but
devoted race, chanted in this fated hall of their
calamity, by the lips of Spanish beauty. KnM, R

232.13   stranger,] 1A; lonely stranger and sojourner, KnM, R
232.17   in the moon-lit halls of the Alhambra.] 1A; which were
the delight of brilliant circles; and who will ever
recall with enthusiasm the happy evening passed in
listening to her strains, in the moon-lit halls of
the Alhambra. Geoffrey Crayon, KnM, R

232.18   ABENCERRAGE] 1A; A SPANISH TALE. KnM, R
232.19–31 On the ... soldier.] 1A; ON the summit of a craggy
hill, a spur of the mountains of Ronda, stands the
castle of Allora, now a mere ruin, infested by bats and
owlets, but in old times one of the strong border holds
of the Christians, to keep watch upon the frontiers
of the warlike kingdom of Granada, and to hold the
Moors in check. It was a post always confided to
some well-tried commander; and, at the time of which
we treat, was held by Rodrigo de Narvaez, a veteran,
famed, both among Moors and Christians, not only for
his hardy feats of arms, but also for that magnanimous
courtesy, which should ever be entwined with the
sterner virtues of the soldier.

   The castle of Allora was a mere part of his command; he was Alcayde, or military governor of
Antiquera, but he passed most of his time at this
frontier post, because its situation on the borders gave
more frequent opportunity for those adventurous exploits which were the delight of the Spanish chivalry.
KnM, R

*232.24   Alcayde] KnM: alcayde 1A; R
232.32–37 His garrison ... Granada.] 1A; His garrison consisted
of fifty chosen cavaliers, all well mounted, and well
appointed: with these he kept vigilant watch upon
the Moslems; patrolling the roads, and paths, and
defiles, of the mountains, so that nothing could escape
his eye; and now and then signalizing himself by

some dashing foray into the very Vega of Granada. KnM, R

232.38–233.7   On a . . . succor.] 1A; On a fair and beautiful night in summer, when the freshness of the evening breeze had tempered the heat of day, the worthy Alcayde sallied forth, with nine of his cavaliers, to patrol the neighborhood, and seek adventures. They rode quietly and cautiously, lest they should be overheard by Moorish scout or traveller; and kept along ravines and hollow ways, lest they should be betrayed by the glittering of the full moon upon their armor. Coming to where the road divided, the Alcayde directed five of his cavaliers to take one of the branches, while he, with the remaining four, would take the other. Should either party be in danger, the blast of a horn was to be the signal to bring their comrades to their aid. KnM, R

233.7–21   The party . . . ditty.] 1A; The party of five had not proceeded far, when, in passing through a defile, overhung with trees, they heard the voice of a man, singing. They immediately concealed themselves in a grove, on the brow of a declivity, up which the stranger would have to ascend. The moonlight, which left the grove in deep shadow, lit up the whole person of the wayfarer, as he advanced, and enabled them to distinguish his dress and appearance, with perfect accuracy. He was a Moorish cavalier, and his noble demeanor, graceful carriage, and splendid attire, showed him to be of lofty rank. He was superbly mounted, on a dapple-gray steed, of powerful frame, and generous spirit, and magnificently caparisoned. His dress was a marlota, or tunic, and an Albernoz of of crimson damask, fringed with gold. His Tunisian turban, of many folds, was of silk and cotton striped, and bordered with golden fringe. At his girdle hung a scimetar of Damascus steel, with loops and tassels of silk and gold. On his left arm he bore an ample target, and his right hand grasped a long double-pointed lance. Thus equipped, he sat negligently on his steed, as one who dreamed of no danger, gazing on the moon, and singing, with a sweet and manly voice, a Moorish love ditty. KnM, R

233.22–25   Just opposite . . . his song.] 1A; Just opposite the place where the Spanish cavaliers were concealed, was a small fountain in the rock, beside the road, to which the horse turned to drink; the rider threw the reins on his neck, and continued his song. KnM, R

233.26–30   The cavaliers . . . surprise.]   1A; The Spanish cavaliers conferred together; they were all so pleased with the gallant and gentle appearance of the Moor, that they resolved not to harm, but to capture him, which, in his negligent mood, promised to be an easy task; rushing, therefore, from their concealment, they thought to surround and seize him. KnM, R

233.32   saddle.]   1A; saddle beside the fountain. KnM, R

233.33   cavaliers]   1A; Christian cavaliers KnM, R

233.34   prove fatal to him.]   1A; his destruction. KnM, R

233.35–43   The Moor . . . thyself!"]   1A; The Moor now held a parley: 'If you be true knights,' said he, 'and seek for honorable fame, come on, singly, and I am ready to meet each in succession; but if you be mere lurkers of the road, intent on spoil, come all at once, and do your worst!'
The cavaliers communed for a moment apart, when one, advancing singly, exclaimed: 'Although no law of chivalry obliges us to risk the loss of a prize, when clearly in our power, yet we willingly grant, as a courtesy, what we might refuse as a right. Valiant Moor! defend thyself!' KnM, R

243.3   from]   1A; headlong from KnM, R

234.11   wheeled]   1A; suddenly wheeled KnM, R

234.12   horsemen]   1A; horseman KnM, R

234.19   Narvaez,]   1A; The valiant Narvaez KnM, R

234.22–24   with courteous . . . contest was]   1A; addressing the Moor, with courteous words, invited him to a more equal combat. The latter readily accepted the challenge. For some time, their contest was fierce and KnM, R

234.26   exhausted]   1A; was exhausted KnM, R

234.31   grasped]   1A; he grasped KnM, R

234.38   him]   1A; the Moor KnM, R

234.39–40   in a few days]   1A; were slight, and in a few days KnM, R

235.5–6   when a captive?]   1A; in prison? KnM, R

235.7   promise]   1A; promise you, KnM, R

235.13   the cause]   1A; to you the cause KnM, R

235.15   sympathy]   1A; great sympathy KnM, R
235.18   Abencerrages.]   1A; Abencerrages of Granada. KnM, R
235.28   the Alcayde]   1A; the worthy Alcayde KnM, R
235.34–37   brother . . . affection.]   1A; brother, and thought the
                growing passion which I felt for her, was mere fraternal
                affection. I beheld her charms unfolding, as it were,
                leaf by leaf, like the morning rose, each moment dis-
                closing fresh beauty and sweetness. KnM, R
235.38–236.2   At length . . . life.]   1A; 'At this period, I overheard a
                conversation between the Alcayde and his confidential
                domestic, and found myself to be the subject. 'It is
                time,' said he, 'to apprise him of his parentage, that
                he may adopt a career in life. I have deferred the
                communication as long as possible, through reluctance
                to inform him that he is of a proscribed and an un-
                lucky race.' KnM, R
236.3–20   "I retired . . . together.']   1A; 'This intelligence would
                have overwhelmed me at an earlier period, but the
                intimation that Xarisa was not my sister, operated
                like magic, and in an instant transformed my brotherly
                affection into ardent love.
                    'I sought Xarisa, to impart to her the secret I had
                learned. I found her in the garden, in a bower of
                jessamines, arranging her beautiful hair by the mir-
                ror of a crystal fountain. The radiance of her beauty
                dazzled me. I ran to her with open arms, and she
                received me with a sister's embraces. When we had
                seated ourselves beside the fountain, she began to
                upbraid me for leaving her so long alone.
                    'In reply, I informed her of the conversation I had
                overheard. The recital shocked and distressed her.
                'Alas! cried she, then is our happiness at an end!'
                    "How!' exclaimed I; 'wilt thou cease to love me,
                because I am not thy brother?'
                    'Not so,' replied she; 'but do you not know that
                when it is once known we are not brother and sister,
                we can no longer be permitted to be thus always
                together?' KnM, R
236.26–27   Restless . . . intercourse]   1A; I was restless and uneasy,
                and looked back with regret to the unreserved inter-
                course that had existed between us, KnM, R
236.31   on the Christian]   1A; which lies directly on the
                Christian KnM, R

236.32   I declared]   1A; I exclaimed against the separation,
                and declared KnM, R
236.34   thou]   1A; that thou KnM, R
236.35   birth. Thou art]   1A; birth; that thou art KnM, R
237.2   It would have been cause]   1A; It was cause KnM, R
237.13   my wont of faith, and promised]   1A; me with my want
                of faith, and promised me KnM, R
237.20   by our]   1A; by this KnM, R
237.21   around]   1A; around me KnM, R
237.26   with]   1A; with tender KnM, R
237.27–28   arrived with . . . that]   1A; brought me word, that
                KnM, R
237.32–33   my transport.]   1A; the transport of my bosom. KnM, R
237.33   in]   1A; in my most KnM, R
237.36   I find]   1A; I found KnM, R
237.42   Don Rodrigo]   1A; Don Rodrigo de Narvaez KnM, R
238.8–9   Abencerrage, . . . his feet, but]   1A; Abencerrage would
                have thrown himself at his feet, to pour out protesta-
                tions of eternal gratitude, but KnM, R
238.22   afterwards]   1A; afterward KnM, R
238.28   and knocked]   1A; and then knocked KnM, R
238.38–39   and awoke]   1A; and suddenly awoke KnM, R
239.6   shalt thou]   1A; shall you KnM, R
239.12   Allora.]   1A; Allora, which was flung wide to receive
                them. KnM, R
239.19   thy]   1A; your KnM, R
239.23   Consider it]   1A; Enter into it, and consider it KnM, R
239.25   the Alcayde]   1A; the brave Alcayde KnM, R
239.25   letter to]   1A; letter, full of courtesy, to KnM, R
239.32   his heroic character.]   1A; the heroic character he had
                gained throughout the land. KnM, R
239.41   Rodrigo]   1A; The gallant Rodrigo KnM, R
240.2   Rodrigo]   1A; Rodrigo de Narvaez KnM, R
240.16   The Alcayde]   1A; The valiant Alcayde KnM, R
240.27–28   Those . . . Montemayor.]   1A, E; them. KnM, R

LIST OF REJECTED SUBSTANTIVES

This list provides an historical record of substantive variants in the authorized texts that appeared during Irving's lifetime, but that were not adopted for the Twayne text. The reading to the left of the bracket is the portion of the text under discussion and represents an accepted reading that differs from the rejected substantive to the right of the bracket. Some of these editorial decisions are explained among the Discussions of Adopted Readings. Discussion is marked by an asterisk * . The symbols used to designate manuscripts and previously published texts are those given in the List of Abbreviations, page 243.

19.35	long] 1A; some NI
20.5	of the] 1A; in the NI
31.37	that] 1A; which E
32.12	in the] 1A; in a E
37.28	of] 1A; of a E
40.34	you] 1A; that you KSB, KnM
41.28	was] 1A; wast KSB
45.22	hare-] 1A; hair- KSB
42.25	in restoring] 1A; of restoring KSB
45.39	tinkling] 1A; tinkle E
47.31	ramping] 1A; romping KSB, E
49.5	was being] 1A; was KSB
51.40	who] 1A; which E
55.8	ordnance] 1A; ordinance KSB
55.26	Martius Scævola] 1A; Musius Scævola E
*57.29	moral] MSa; more KnM, KSB, 1A
58.8	instructions] 1A; instruction KnM, KSB
64.16	Sea-Venture] MSa; Sea-Vulture KnM, 1A
80.6	of darkness in the open day] 1A; in open day E
84.20	favored] 1A; famed KnM
84.21	kindliness] 1A; kindness KnM
84.25	boast of their amours] 1A; boast E
85.5	slights] 1A; fights KnM
85.20	up on] 1A; upon E
85.26	Lima] 1A; Liona KnM
88.35	to a] 1A; of a E
*89.29	wielded] MSa; yielded 1A
*91.12	supper] MSa; upper 1A

94.12	risen] 1A; arisen KnM, Ev
*100.30	depositary] KnM; depository 1A, E
126.4	gathering place of nations] 1A; gathering-place of the French and English NY
127.23	easily] 1A; easy NY
127.25	aroused] 1A; roused NY
128.15	spurs] 1A; speres KnM, NY, E
128.25	Mingled] 1A; Mangled NY
128.27	cut up] 1A; cut NY
129.35	palace] 1A; place NY
130.21	roots . . . fissures] 1A; root . . . fissure NY
131.2	prowess] 1A; powers NY
131.30	afterward] 1A; afterwards NY
131.31	had] 1A; has NY
132.3	clangor] 1A; clammer NY
133.2	furor] 1A; fury NY
133.17	amusements] 1A; amusement NY
133.20	populace] 1A; population NY
133.21	exercise] 1A; extend NY
134.2	instances] 1A; instance NY
134.4	safe] 1A; free NY
134.10	this change] 1A; the change NY
134.13	authors] 1A; author NY
135.14	consequences] 1A; consequence NY
135.21	days] 1A; day NY
137.1	A] 1A; The C
137.1	MAN!] 1A; MAN! From the London Literary Souvenir, for 1827. C
137.9	the] 1A; a C
137.20	ancien] 1A; ancient C
137.20	frizzed] 1A; frizzled C
137.23	an] 1A; a C
137.24	his snuff] 1A; snuff NYA
138.26	had] 1A; now had C
138.35	the shoulder] 1A; each shoulder NYA
138.38	means] MSa; mean 1A
139.39	half] 1A; a half NYA
143.9	stood] 1A; set E
143.41	upon] 1A; on E
147.39	tromp.] 1A; tromp. It is an old Spanish proverb, worthy of all acception, that "where God denies sons the devil sends nephew," and such was the case in the present instance. BH

148.8	lingered] 1A; had lingered E
148.8	but] 1A; but that E
148.10–11	the infinite... rider.] 1A; his infinite astonishment and discomfiture. E
149.2	plying] 1A; playing KSB
149.3	grabbing] 1A; grubbing E
149.5	nor] 1A; or BH
149.14	declared] 1A; declared that E, KnM, KSB, BH
149.42	his] 1A; a BH
150.7	that lay] 1A; which lay BH
150.17	a devil] 1A; the devil BH
150.26	metamorphose] 1A; metamorphosis E
150.30	called] 1A; call BH
155.17	as strife] 1A; as of strife E
155.42	afterward] 1A; afterwards BH
159.12	having read in the Bible that] 1A; having the Bible for E
160.13	emigrating] 1A; emigration KSB
161.13	servant] 1A; a servant KSB
161.18	man] 1A; a man KSB
161.40	run-away] 1A; run-aways KSB
165.34	a square] 1A; as quare KSB
165.39	I received] 1A; received KSB
166.7	horses'] KnM, KSB; horse's 1A
169.10	there] 1A; their KSB
169.39	tolerably] 1A; tolerable KSB
170.10	two] 1A; the two KSB, KnM
171.5	have received] 1A; had received KSB
187.24	rendered] 1A; made NY, Ev
187.25	quite boastful] 1A; boastful NY
187.25	his] 1A; this NY, Ev
187.28	and the cattle] 1A; and cattle NY
188.3	clinchng] 1A; clenchng NY, Ev
188.41	an Indian "trail"] 1A; a 'trail,' NY, Ev
189.17	he] 1A; that he NY, Ev
189.25	were] 1A; wsre NY, Ev
191.5	with all] 1A; with NY, Ev
191.6	pointed out] 1A; pointed NY
*194.11	de Créqui] MSa; of Créqui KnM, 1A
210.23	foment] 1A; ferment E
214.1	ISLAND.] 1A; Island; Or, The Adelantado of the Seven Cities. By Washington Irving R
214.14	There] 1A; Introduction. There R

216.1–2   THE . . . BRANDAN]   1A; Chapter I. R.
220.13–14   Never, *never,* NEVER!]   1A; —never—never— R
220.17   those]   1A; these R
222.14   Pass on."]   1A; On entering the harbour they rowed
               close along an armed galley, of the most ancient form.
               Soldiers with cross-bows were stationed on the deck.
               "Who goes there?" was again demanded. "The Adelan-
               tado of the Seven Cities.' "He is welcome. Pass on.' R
230.1   RECOLLECTIONS OF THE ALHAMBRA]   1A; The
               Abencerrage; Or, Recollections of the Alhambra by
               Washington Irving Chapter I R
230.9   surrounded]   1A; round R
232.8–9   magical . . . chant,]   1A; effect to her magical chant, R
232.30   magnanimous]   1A; noble R
239.19   her honor]   1A; honor R
240.7   wronging]   1A; robbing E

LIST OF COMPOUND WORDS
HYPHENATED
AT END OF LINE

List I includes all compound and possible compound words that are hyphenated at the end of the line in the copy-text. In deciding whether to retain the hyphen or to print the word as a single-word compound (without the hyphen) or as two words without the hyphen, the editor has made her decision first on the use of each compound word elsewhere in the copy-text; or second, when the word does not appear elsewhere in the copy-text, on Irving's practice in other writings of the period; or finally, if the word does not appear elsewhere in the writings, on contemporary American usage. Each word is listed in its editorially accepted form after the page and line numbers of its appearance in the T text.

List II presents all compounds, or possible compounds, that are hyphenated or separated as two words at the end of the line in the T text. They are listed in the form in which they would have appeared in the T text had they come in midline.

LIST I

3.32	battle-axes	128.39	Pont Royal
4.33	ploughman	129.7	nobleman
7.30	hard-headed	133.5	good-humoured
9.4	whirl-wind	135.1	out-breaks
11.9	stout-hearted	137.32	gentleman
17.18	sunrise	143.19–20	well-scoured
18.17	landscape	144.22–23	flower-gardens
19.37	skylark	145.29–30	wood-cuts
19.40	overcome	145.31–32	New-Year's
21.6	firelock	147.20	Hell-gate
26.1	old-fashioned	147.36	true-hearted
44.13	rose-coloured	148.28	overboard
45.11	rose-coloured	149.19	foul-weather
60.11	ill-digested	150.16	grizzly-headed
63.2	forecastle	151.20	look-out
64.16	Sea-Venture	154.28	Gibbet-Island
75.41	court-yard	154.30	freebooter's
122.4–5	by-the-by	122.29	ear-locks

157.28	house-keeper	176.25–26	backwoodsmen
159.21	half-uncle	179.28	forehead
162.11	mad-headed	180.4	fearless
166.17	woodcraft	180.11	beardless
166.21	stock-tracks	180.9	egg-shell
167.5	backwoodsman	190.25–26	neighborhood
167.7	nicknamed	192.37	Commander-in-chief
168.21	spell-bound	199.7	thirty-two
169.32–33	hunting-shirt	220.42	sixteen
170.15–16	cane-brakes	222.23	old-fashioned
174.12	four-and-twenty	225.34–35	casement
174.20	well-meaning	228.8	shipwrecked

LIST II

3.4–5	New-York	85.22–23	drawcansir
3.7–8	old-fashioned	85.42–43	himself
4.12–13	medicine-man	86.8–9	overbearing
7.18–19	head-quarters	91.11–12	something
10.42–43	bush-fighters	92.23–24	supernatural
11.28–29	New-York	93.15–16	stair-case
23.17–18	forefathers	96.29–30	rail-roads
24.33–34	Frenchmen	98.12–13	maintained
26.2–3	steamboat	98.37–38	semi-aristocratical
29.14–15	whenever	99.22–23	himself
29.30–31	Blue-Beard	100.36–37	reckless
35.30–31	household	104.6–7	court-yard
45.36–37	straight-forward	112.18–19	bank-bills
46.27–28	however	118.21–22	bank-notes
49.21–22	somehow	119.12–13	stock-market
54.37–38	all-important	120.35–36	without
60.11–12	ill-digested	120.36–37	bedroom
63.3–4	quarter-deck	122.22–23	petticoat
63.5–6	moonlight	122.24–25	easy-chair
65.16–17	wigwams	124.1–2	overshadow
67.38–39	cedar-built	124.42–43	gentleman
69.16–17	therefore	125.8–9	casements
69.19–20	moreover	127.2–3	whatever
71.10–11	shipwreck	129.20–21	nestling-places
75.15–16	without	139.37–38	goodhumoured
75.18–19	throughout	140.28–29	foregoing
76.38–39	whirlwind	141.2–3	withheld
79.15–16	grayheaded	143.13–14	Broeken-Meer
82.39–83.1	supernatural	143.19–20	well-scoured

144.22–23	flower-gardens	169.41–42	hunting-dresses
145.29–30	wood-cuts	170.15–16	cane-brakes
145.31–32	New-Year's	175.23–24	knee-buckles
148.36–37	blicksem!	175.42–176.1	small-clothes
148.43–149.1	sea-urchin	176.25–26	backwoodsman
151.36–37	gunpowder	193.36–36	grandfather
155.20–21	bed-clothes	193.41–42	wholesome
155.26–27	threshold	201.8–9	death-blow
158.40–41	out-building	203.9–10	outrages
161.21–22	pocket-handkerchief	225.34–35	casement
163.27–28	underwood	232.21–22	warlike
166.23–24	buffalo-tracks	232.32–33	well-mounted
169.32–33	hunting-shirt		

OWNERSHIP OR
LOCATION OF EXTANT
WOLFERT'S ROOST *MANUSCRIPT*

In the chart below, these symbols will be used to indicate the location or ownership of various portions of the *Wolfert's Roost* manuscript:

F	The Folger Shakespeare Library, Washington, D.C.
H	Henry E. Huntington Art Museum and Library
K	Knox College Library, Galesburg, Illinois
Nb	The New York Public Library, Berg Collection
Nm	The New York Public Library, Manuscript Division
R	Redwood Library and Athenaeum, Newport, Rhode Island
V	University of Virginia, Barret Collection
Y	Yale University, Beinecke Library

The number to the left represents the portion of the Twayne text for which there is extant manuscript. The letter(s) in brackets to the right represents the location of that portion of the manuscript.

29.1	("*MOUNTJOY*")—44.22 ("music:")	Nm
56.5	("sticking")—60.1 ("they")	Nm
62.1	("*THE BERMUDAS*")—71.13 ("event.")	F
82.1	("*THE KNIGHT*")—94.26 ("fiction.")	Nb
125.37	("ENGLISH")—130.29 ("arm.")	V
132.26	("PARIS")—136.6 ("etc.")	V
137.1	("*A CONTENTED*")—140.13 ("escaped")	V
142.1	("*BROEK*")—142.27 ("ten;")	V
151.43	("The mystery")—156.3 ("Island")	V
182.1	("*THE SEMINOLES*")—184.36 ("tribes")	H
186.27	("THE CONSPIRACY")—191.17–18 ("Government.")	H
192.1	("*THE COUNT*")—196.16 ("crime.")	Nm
197.12	("To give")—197.24 ("be")	Nm
197.24	("irrestible")—197.37 ("manner")	V
198.9–10	("of the caprices")—198.25 ("appointed")	K
198.25	("four")—198.37 ("that the")	Y
198.37	("infamous")—199.9 ("Regent,")	R
210.1	("*LEGEND*")—213.42 ("longer.")	Nb

PARTS OF PRINTED
EDITIONS USED AS
COPY-TEXT

For the following segments of the Twayne *Wolfert's Roost,* no manuscript has been found; consequently, the editions closest to the missing manuscript serve as copy-text. In the chart below, these symbols, which appear at the end of each line, will be used to indicate the location of various portions of the periodical or first edition used as copy-text:

KnM   *Knickerbocker Magazine,* ed. Lewis Gaylord Clark (April 1839–March 1841).

1A   First American Edition of *Wolfert's Roost.* G. P. Putnam's Sons, 1855

Mag   *The Magnolia,* ed. Monson Bancroft. New York, 1837

LS   *The Literary Souvenir,* ed. A. A. Watts. London: Longman, Rees, Orme, Brown & Green, 1827.

3.1	("*WOLFERT'S*")—12.14 ("judgment.")	KnM
12.15	("CHRONICLE")—16.3 ("wall")	1A
17.1	("*THE BIRDS*")—21.26 ("Crayon")	KnM
22.1	("*THE CREOLE*")—28.10 ("village!")	Mag
44.23	("indeed")—56.5 ("danger")	KnM
60.1	("have")—60.33 ("people")	KnM
72.1	("*THE WIDOW'S*")—81.4 ("widows.")	Mag
95.1	("*A TIME*")—119.32 ("France.")	KnM
120.1	("*SKETCHES*")—125.36 ("it.")	KnM
130.30	("THE FIELD")—132.25 ("honor!")	KnM
140.13	("them;")—141.10 ("man.")	LS
142.27	("a shrewd")—146.23 ("Zion-ward.")	KnM
147.1	("*GUESTS*")—151.42 ("visitation")	KnM
157.1	("*THE EARLY*")—181.24 ("Run.")	KnM
184.37	("ORIGIN")—186.26 ("Indians.")	KnM
191.19	("Note.")—191.20 ("Ringwood).")	KnM
196.17	("Another")—197.10–11 ("insult")	KnM
197.37	("Certain")—198.9 ("one")	KnM
199.9	("I")—201.31 (*"brother"*)	KnM
202.1	("*DON*")—209.9 (*"place!"*)	KnM
214.1	("*THE*")—240.28 ("Montemayor")	KnM